THE STRUCTURE OF MATTER

STRUCTURE OF MATTER SERIES

MARIA GOEPPERT MAYER
Advisory Editor

THE STRUCTURE OF MATTER
Francis Owen Rice and Edward Teller

THE
STRUCTURE
OF
MATTER

FRANCIS OWEN RICE
Professor of Chemistry
The Catholic University of America

EDWARD TELLER
Professor of Physics
The University of Chicago

New York · JOHN WILEY & SONS, Inc.
London · CHAPMAN & HALL, Ltd.
1949

"Nature doth not that by many things which may be done by few."

GALILEO

PREFACE

The discovery and systematic formulation of quantum mechanics have opened up the possibility of understanding the microstructure of matter. The years that followed the formulation of the basic laws of atomic physics have brought the explanation of the known regularities of spectroscopy, chemical-bond formation and metallic conductivity, to mention only some of the more important examples. Even in fields as new and remote as nuclear physics and stellar structure, quantum theory proved to be the prerequisite to progress and understanding.

The purpose of this book is to acquaint the reader with the scope of the phenomena that can be explained with the help of quantum mechanics. We have tried to accomplish this with a minimum use of mathematics. Not even the Schroedinger equation was permitted to enter the following pages. Nor did we try to reproduce the important and beautiful discussions which revolve about the meaning of such words as causality and probability or particles and waves. We have instead emphasized the qualitative and the practical consequences of atomic theory. If in this way we lose in rigor and in depth, we at least can offer a broad informal review which will be useful to the chemist and may serve the physicist as a summary of topics which used to be in the forefront of his discipline only one or two decades ago.

The bulk of this book was written before the summer of 1941. The completion of the manuscript has been greatly delayed by the following troubled years which have given the adjective "atomic" a completely new meaning. It is significant that the spectacular accomplishments of these years produced no change in the basic theory or in the important applications described in the following pages. Quantum theory and its application to the structure of matter enabled scientists to construct the atomic bomb and to predict its behavior. This development is not essentially different from the applications of Maxwellian theory in electrical engineering or from the development of internal-combustion engines on the basis of thermodynamics. In no case did these practical applications introduce a major change in the fundamental scientific concepts.

In the last year physics is taking a new turn. The latest discoveries in the field of cosmic rays and artificially produced high energy particles will carry us far beyond the investigation of what we usually call mat-

ter.   To a future physicist the contents of this book may look as com-
monplace as the simplest facts of Newtonian mechanics seem to us
now.   We hope, however, that the main points will not appear obsolete
to him.

The purpose of this book is to serve as an introduction and not as a
work of reference.   We have not quoted the original literature and have
used names of scientists only where these names had been justly or un-
justly attached to a well-known method or concept.

We are indebted to Dr. John A. H. Duffie for help in reading the manuscript, to Dr. Virginia Griffing, Dr. Lawrence B. Robinson, and Ben-
jamin Sussholz for reviewing the proof, and to Dr. C. Beck for preparing
Figure 11.11(2).   We also wish to acknowledge permission received from
the Office of Alien Property under license JA-1217 to publish Figures
8.4(2), 8.5(2), 8.7(2), 8.8(1), 8.10(1), and 8.10(2), all of which are taken
from *Strukturbericht*, published by Akademische Verlagsgesellschaft,
Leipzig.   Finally, we wish to thank the Very Reverend James Marshall
Campbell, professor of Greek in the Catholic University, without whose
help this book could not have been ended.

Francis Owen Rice
Edward Teller

CONTENTS

1. INTRODUCTION

1.1 USE OF MATHEMATICS At present, atomic physical theory in principle enables us to calculate all of the chemical and most of the physical properties of matter and thus makes the science of experimental chemistry superfluous. If, however, we consider things from an economic point of view, the human labor that must go into such calculations is far greater than that which would be required to make the experimental study. The situation at present is this: To calculate the properties of the hydrogen atom is quite easy, in fact, much easier than to investigate the hydrogen atom experimentally. For the hydrogen molecule and the helium atom, the theoretical attack becomes more difficult and is perhaps about as difficult as the experiments; for atoms and molecules containing more than two electrons, exact calculations become so rapidly more and more difficult with increasing numbers of electrons that we cannot hope that the mathematical problems involved will ever be rigorously solved for more than a few, if any, examples.

Of course, semiempirical calculations may prove to be useful, but as a general rule we feel that, since such calculations are from a mathematical point of view rather unsatisfactory, it is best if they contain a high percentage of empiricism and a low percentage of calculation. Thus we must be satisfied with a roughly approximate treatment which serves as a series of pictures that go along with experimental science, and it would be too much to say that they serve even as a guide.

In the following pages we summarize those conclusions of atomic theory which are frequently used in quantum chemistry; no detailed proofs, either experimental or mathematical, are given, but only the general arguments are indicated.

1.2 NUCLEAR ATOM The fact that matter is practically transparent if bombarded with alpha particles led Rutherford to his nuclear atom; this model has since been substantiated in all its main features.

According to Rutherford's model, an atom consists of a nucleus and one or more electrons. The nucleus carries most of the mass of the atom; it is positively charged, its charge being a multiple of the quantum of charge, 4.80×10^{-10} E.S.U.* Nuclei of different atomic species carry different charges; nuclei of isotopes have the same charge but differ in their mass. The radius of the nuclei is of the order of 10^{-12} cm.; that is, it is 10,000 times smaller than the average atomic radius.

In contrast to the different kinds of nuclei, all electrons obtained from any atom or any other form of matter have identical basic properties. The mass of an electron is very small, 1/1840 times the mass of the hydrogen atom. The electron carries a negative charge of the magnitude of the quantum of electricity, 4.80×10^{-10} E.S.U. The number of electrons in an atom is characteristic of the atomic species and is equal to the number of positive charges carried by the nucleus, so that the atom is electrically neutral. Even a slight variation of this electrical balance in the atom would give rise to noticeable macroscopic electrical effects, and we therefore know that this electrical balance—and probably also the values of the individual electrical charges—must be maintained with extremely high accuracy.

The intrinsic size and even the meaning of the radius of an electron are still much under debate; a value frequently given is 2.8×10^{-13} cm. It is certain, however, that for the purpose of chemical processes we can treat both the electrons and the nuclei as mathematical points.

1.3 QUANTUM THEORY In the early atomic picture of Rutherford, the electrons were supposed to rotate around the nucleus in a way analogous to the motion of the planets around the sun. This picture has now been abandoned, because it led to two difficulties. The first arose from the fact that the electrons rotating around the nucleus would continuously emit electromagnetic waves (either ultraviolet light or X rays) and would thus lose energy, finally falling into the nucleus. The other arose from the fact that equipartition of kinetic energy among all degrees of freedom of a mechanical system would require that the electrons contribute to the observed specific heats, which, for instance for a monatomic gas, is evidently not the case.

These difficulties led to the formulation of the quantum theory. The first step toward the new theory of atomic structure was made by Bohr, who postulated that atoms exist in stable states with definite energy. Transitions between these states may occur, accompanied by emission or absorption of light, the frequency of radiation being connected with the energy difference between the two states by the relation $E_1 - E_2 = h\nu$. Here h is a universal constant whose magnitude is 6.626×10^{-27} g.-cm.^{2}-sec.$^{-1}$ It was introduced into physics by Planck

* Electrostatic units.

in 1900 in the course of a study of the laws of black-body radiation, or, as we may say, in connection with the specific heat of a vacuum.

One immediate verification of Bohr's postulate is the sharpness of spectral lines emitted or absorbed by atoms, corresponding to the sharply defined energy values which atoms possess.

The lowest state of any atom is called the fundamental state; all others are excited states. Excitation—that is, a transition to an excited state—may occur through a violent impact, as well as through absorption of light of appropriate frequency. As a rule, the energy difference between the fundamental state and the lowest or first excited state of an atom is about 100 times greater than the temperature energy kT, so that in temperature equilibrium one atom in every e^{100}, or 10^{43} will be excited; thus the electronic contribution to specific heat is negligible. For a very large class of phenomena, we shall be dealing with atoms in the fundamental state.

1.4 QUANTUM MECHANICS The postulates of Bohr and the empirical laws of spectroscopy and atomic physics were finally, about 1926, welded (de Broglie, Heisenberg, Schroedinger, and Dirac) into a finished discipline called quantum mechanics. The most striking demonstration of quantum mechanics is the electron-interference experiment first performed by Davisson and Germer. Electrons deflected from crystals give rise to interference patterns similar to those obtained in X-ray crystal analysis; this indicates that electrons—like X rays—must have wave properties. However, it is impossible to relinquish the idea that electrons are particles.

Interference experiments have also been performed using protons, that is, nuclei of hydrogen atoms, helium atoms, and hydrogen molecules. There is no doubt that only practical difficulties prevent us from demonstrating the wave nature of bigger particles. It becomes necessary to reconcile the particle and the wave picture as describing one and the same thing. This is done by quantum mechanics.

According to quantum mechanics, an electron is described by a function called the wave function which is capable of having both positive and negative values (sometimes even complex values must be introduced); the square of the absolute value of the wave function integrated over a certain part of space gives the probability of finding the electron within that part of space. The wave function of a free electron moving with a definite momentum p is a simple sine or cosine function (or, more accurately, $e^{i2\pi x/\lambda}$). The wavelength λ and the momentum are connected by de Broglie's relation $p = h/\lambda$, where h is Planck's constant.

The momentum is perpendicular to the wave front; we see that a small wavelength corresponds to a great value of the momentum.

An electron inside an atom will be described by a wave function, the square of which at a definite point is proportional to the probability of finding the electron at that point. Thus the original picture of electron orbits within the atom is replaced by a more uniform structure in space which can be considered as filling the whole atomic volume, in spite of the fact that the electron, when considered as a particle, is small compared with the atom.

1.5 UNCERTAINTY PRINCIPLE We have seen that by use of the wave function describing an atom we can make statements about the probability of the positions of an electron. It is also possible to fix the position with any desired accuracy. The electron would actually have a sharply defined position after a measurement had been carried out designed to find the position. But such a state will not correspond to the lowest or fundamental state of the atom. Even if we start from the fundamental state and carry out a determination of the position of the electron, the measurement itself will perturb the system to be measured, and at the end of the experiment we will have an electron with a definite position but with an energy much greater than that of the fundamental state.

In general, any physical quantity such as position, momentum, or energy can be measured according to quantum mechanics with an arbitrary accuracy, but, when one such quantity has been measured, frequently only probability statements can be made about the simultaneous magnitude of another quantity. This is the essential content of the uncertainty principle. The uncertainty principle is not due to an incompleteness of the theory; in fact, interference experiments show that an electron is not a particle, but a wave; scintillation or Wilson chamber experiments show that the electron is not a wave, but a particle; this direct contradiction can be avoided only if it is supposed that the physical quantities involved cannot all be measured simultaneously with an arbitrary accuracy, but an uncertainty exists which prevents us from following the processes into their minute details.

The method of quantum mechanics is to use both particle and wave pictures in describing one and the same physical entity, for example the electron; to limit the applicability of these pictures with the help of the uncertainty principle; and to correlate by probability statements the results of mathematical theory with experiment. The relation between particle picture and wave picture, both necessary in some cases yet mutually exclusive, is called complementarity.

The simplest formulation of the uncertainty principle is as follows: if the x co-ordinate of a particle is measured with an accuracy Δx, and if the x component of the momentum of this particle p_x is measured at the same time with an accuracy Δp_x, then the product of these two uncertainties cannot be smaller than $h/2\pi$. We cannot localize an electron without giving to it, with a certain probability, a rather high momentum. This can be seen in a qualitative way. If an electron is localized and if, therefore, its wave function becomes zero outside of a small region, its properties will become analogous to those of a wave of short wavelength, and therefore, according to de Broglie's relation $p = h/\lambda$, a high momentum will be obtained.

1.6 CORRESPONDENCE PRINCIPLE It is undoubtedly true that no theory can provide us with exact information simultaneously about all the quantities of classical physics, since that would lead us into the wave–particle contradiction. One may be tempted, however, to discard both the wave and the particle picture and try to construct an atomic theory which permits exact determination of all quantities appearing in it. Such a plan would be all the more hopeful of attainment since the mathematical apparatus of quantum mechanics is complete and, of course, free from contradictions. However, an atomic theory of this nature would start from concepts having no immediate equivalent in our everyday experience; it would seem that in trying to explain the meaning of such an abstract theory one would run into all the difficulties avoided by formulating it. In addition, such a representation would fail to emphasize properly an important part of quantum mechanics, the correspondence principle. This principle states that for certain limiting cases the laws of quantum theory converge toward and finally become identical with the laws of classical mechanics.

In a loose way, this principle may be stated by saying that classical laws will be approached for the limiting case of high quantum numbers. A more rigorous formulation can be obtained in the following way. As a general rule, quantum transitions take place between states with different physical properties. This constitutes a difference between classical and quantum theory, since a transition in quantum theory corresponds to a process in classical theory, and a process in classical theory is connected with one definite set and not with two sets of physical conditions. Now, if we are in a region in which, for all transitions occurring with a considerable probability, the per cent change of physical properties between the initial and final states is small, the laws of quantum mechanics approach, according to the correspondence principle, the laws of classical mechanics.

For the limiting case thus obtained the quantum and classical laws must show a one-to-one correspondence; hence the name correspondence principle. Historically, this principle was postulated by Bohr, and used by him most successfully to obtain the quantum laws for the high-quantum number region and to extrapolate them into the low-quantum number region.

Even now, though the quantum laws are represented by a finished formalism, the correspondence principle may be used to understand and visualize the laws that otherwise appear to be a mere set of formal statements. Any attempt to divorce quantum theory from the classical picture of particles and waves would destroy the significance of the correspondence principle and thus lead us into a field where one is not allowed to use the words in which our everyday thinking and experience is expressed. We do not believe that a theory is possible which in its final analysis is not based on these words and, therefore, on classical physics and common sense.

2. THE HYDROGEN ATOM

2.1 THE FUNDAMENTAL STATE   One immediate use to which we may put the uncertainty principle is to estimate the binding energy of the electron in the hydrogen atom.   The energy of the electron can be written

$$E = E_{\text{pot}} + E_{\text{kin}} = -\frac{e^2}{r} + \frac{p^2}{2m} \qquad 2.1(1)$$

where e is the charge on the proton, r is the distance of the electron from the proton, p is the momentum of the electron, and m is its mass.   Evidently, the lowest total energy will be obtained if we substitute for both r and p as small values as possible; according to the uncertainty relation, however, one has $\Delta r \Delta p \sim h/2\pi$, and of course the average values of the distance from the nucleus $\bar{r}$ and the magnitude of the momentum $\bar{p}$ cannot be smaller than Δr and Δp, respectively.   Therefore, we have for the smallest possible average value, $\bar{r} \times \bar{p} \sim h/2\pi$.   Eliminating $\bar{p}$ and substituting in the expression for the energy, we have

$$E = -\frac{e^2}{\bar{r}} + \frac{h^2}{8\pi^2 m \bar{r}^2} \qquad 2.1(2)$$

If we differentiate the right-hand side, we obtain an expression which vanishes at a value of $\bar{r} = \bar{r}_{\text{min}}$ for which E assumes its minimum.

$$\bar{r}_{\text{min}} = \frac{h^2}{4\pi^2 m e^2} = 0.53 \times 10^{-8} \text{ cm.} = 0.53 \text{ Å.} \qquad 2.1(3)$$

and we obtain

$$E_{\text{min}} = -\frac{2\pi^2 m e^4}{h^2} = -13.5 \text{ electron volts} \qquad 2.1(4)$$

The latter value agrees with the ionization energy of the hydrogen atom.

7

The actual wave function or proper function of the fundamental state of the hydrogen atom is given by

$$\psi = Ce^{-\frac{r}{\bar{r}_{\min}}}$$ 2.1(5)

where $\bar{r}_{\min}$ is the quantity defined in equation 2.1(3), and the constant C, called the normalization factor, must be adjusted in such a manner that the integral of ψ^2 over the whole of space is equal to unity. This must be so since $\psi^2\, d\omega$ is the probability of finding the electron within the volume element $d\omega$, and $\int \psi^2\, d\omega$ integrated over the whole space signifies the probability that the electron is anywhere in space. It may also be seen that $\bar{r}_{\min}$ gives a measure of the extension of the wave function around the nucleus.

It will be noticed that the wave function for the fundamental state of the hydrogen atom depends only on the distance between the electron and the nucleus—that is, the hydrogen atom in its fundamental state is spherically symmetrical; such spherically symmetrical wave functions are called s functions, and for such cases it is said that an electron is in an s state; s functions have a considerable importance in chemical physics. The wave function of an electron in the state of lowest energy is always an s function; it is frequently denoted by the symbol ($1s$).

2.2 FIRST EXCITED STATE   The energy of the first excited state of the hydrogen atom is

$$-\frac{1}{4}\frac{2\pi^2 m e^4}{h^2}$$ 2.2(1)

that is, one quarter of the energy of the fundamental state. Four different wave functions belong to this energy. In other words, we have in reality four states of the hydrogen atom which happen to have the same energy. The four wave functions are

$$xe^{-\frac{r}{2\bar{r}_{\min}}};\quad ye^{-\frac{r}{2\bar{r}_{\min}}};\quad ze^{-\frac{r}{2\bar{r}_{\min}}};\quad \left(\frac{r}{\bar{r}_{\min}}-2\right)e^{-\frac{r}{2\bar{r}_{\min}}}$$ 2.2(2)

Here x, y, and z are the x, y, and z components of the vector drawn from the nucleus to the electron. These four wave functions should be multiplied by normalization factors, making the integral of the square equal to unity. We shall refer to the functions 2.2(2) occasionally as ($2x$), ($2y$), ($2z$), and ($2s$), the last function being spherically symmetrical and therefore an s function.

2.3 DEGENERATE STATES. SUPERPOSITION OF WAVE FUNCTIONS If more than one wave function belongs to one energy, we talk about a degenerate state, and each of the wave functions is called degenerate. According to one of the fundamental rules of quantum mechanics any number of new wave functions can be constructed with the help of a set of degenerate functions. In fact, we may multiply the wave functions by arbitrary constants and add them, and a new correct wave function is obtained.* One may also say that the wave functions have been superposed with arbitrary amplitudes. It must be kept in mind, however, that, for the kind of wave functions with which we are dealing here, superposition is permissible only if the wave functions belong to states of equal energy.

It is of interest to perform this superposition for one special case. Let us suppose that we have a direction in space which includes the angles α, β, γ, with the three co-ordinates used in equation 2.2(2), and let us call the co-ordinate measured along this new direction ξ. We now multiply the first three functions of 2.2(2) by $\cos \alpha$, $\cos \beta$, $\cos \gamma$, respectively, add, and obtain

$$(x \cos \alpha + y \cos \beta + z \cos \gamma)e^{-\frac{r}{2r_{\min}}} = \xi e^{-\frac{r}{2r_{\min}}} \qquad 2.3(1)$$

This removes one objection which could have been raised against the original wave functions which we have given for the first excited state. There it seemed that preference had been given to the x, y, and z co-ordinates, a preference about which nature must be ignorant. We now see that by superposition a new function can be obtained in which the co-ordinate measured along an arbitrary direction has the same significance as the original x, y, or z co-ordinates. It may appear unjustified at this stage that we have given four wave functions for the first excited state of hydrogen, while an indefinite number exist. This indefinite number can, however, be obtained from the original four with the help of superposition, whereas these four functions are independent, since none of them can be written as a superposition of the other three. We say, therefore, that the first excited state of hydrogen is fourfold degenerate.

2.4 ORTHOGONALITY If we have a set of degenerate functions, it will be a question of practical importance to find out whether they are independent of each other, or whether one of them can be obtained from

---

* This new function should be multiplied by an appropriate normalization constant in order to make the integral of its square equal to unity. The procedure of normalization may, however, be omitted if one is not interested in the absolute values of the probabilities of finding electrons in different volume elements.

the others by superposition. The criterion frequently used to verify the independence of the functions is called orthogonality. Two functions ψ_i and ψ_k are called orthogonal if they satisfy the relation,*

$$\int \psi_i \psi_k \, d\omega = 0 \qquad\qquad 2.4(1)$$

where the integration is extended over the whole of space. It can be shown that a set of wave functions is independent if they are all mutually orthogonal. The four wave functions, 2.2(2), have actually been chosen so as to fulfill this requirement. The concept of orthogonality gains in importance particularly since quantum mechanics shows that two wave functions belonging to two states of different energies are always orthogonal; thus it can be verified that any of the four wave functions of the first excited state, when multiplied by the wave function of the normal state and integrated, gives zero. This fact can be utilized to get roughly qualitative information about proper functions, even where the mathematical problem of calculating them is practically insoluble.

2.5 NECESSARY AND ACCIDENTAL DEGENERACY The four proper functions belonging to the first excited state of the hydrogen atom may be subdivided into two groups: $(2x)$, $(2y)$, and $(2z)$ belong to the first group, and $(2s)$ belongs to the second group. The last proper function is spherically symmetrical just as is the proper function of the fundamental state.

The three proper functions of the first group on the other hand are not spherically symmetrical; if rotations are performed, they will not remain unchanged but will rather transform into superpositions of each other. It may be seen immediately for a rotation which brings the x axis into the new position ξ, that the function $xe^{-\frac{r}{2\bar{r}\text{min}}}$ will transform into $\xi e^{-\frac{r}{2\bar{r}\text{min}}}$ which, as has been shown, is a superposition of the three functions of the first group. Evidently wave functions which differ from each other by a mere rotation cannot differ in the energy belonging to them. Therefore, the degeneracy of these three states will be called necessary, arising as it does from the spherical symmetry of our problem. The degeneracy between the wave functions of the first group (that is, $(2x)$, $(2y)$, and $(2z)$) and the wave function of the second group, $(2s)$, is on the other hand called an accidental degeneracy since no rota-

---

* For complex functions the orthogonality relation is $\int \psi_i^* \psi_k \, d\omega = 0$ where ψ_i^* is the conjugate complex of ψ_i.

tion or symmetry operation can be devised which transforms the first kind of wave function into the second.

Accidental degeneracy is a misnomer to the extent that there is a very good reason for that degeneracy in the mathematical properties of the coulomb potential acting between the electron and the nucleus. The word accidental simply signifies that the degeneracy is not a consequence of the symmetry of our problem. The difference between the two kinds of degeneracy may become clear if we modify the force acting between the electron and the nucleus as far as its dependence on the distance is concerned while still assuming that the forces are radial and spherically symmetrical. Then the degeneracy of the three proper functions of the first group would be maintained while the s function of the second group would now have an energy different from that of the other three.

2.6 THE p STATE The first group consisting of the three necessarily degenerate functions is an example of what is called the p proper functions or the p state. The p state is characterized by the behavior of the proper functions with regard to rotations. It may be remembered that an s proper function does not change if rotations are performed. The three p proper functions change if one performs a rotation in the same way in which the x, y, and z components of a vector change if the vector is subjected to a rotation. Thus the proper function,

$$\xi e^{-\frac{r}{2\bar{r}_{min}}} \qquad \qquad 2.6(1)$$

is expressed by the three proper functions,

$$\xi e^{-\frac{r}{2\bar{r}_{min}}} = xe^{-\frac{r}{2\bar{r}_{min}}}\cos\alpha + ye^{-\frac{r}{2\bar{r}_{min}}}\cos\beta + ze^{-\frac{r}{2\bar{r}_{min}}}\cos\gamma \quad 2.6(2)$$

in the same way in which the unit vector pointing in the ξ direction ξ_u is expressed by the three unit vectors, x_u, y_u and z_u

$$\xi_u = x_u\cos\alpha + y_u\cos\beta + z_u\cos\gamma \qquad \qquad 2.6(3)$$

The p functions as well as the s functions have a great importance in chemical physics. The common notation for the three wave functions $(2x)$, $(2y)$, and $(2z)$ is $(2p)$. The notation $(2p)$ may stand for any of the three functions or for any superposition of them.

2.7 HIGHER EXCITED STATES The energies of the higher excited states of the hydrogen atom can be summarized in the formula,

$$E_n = -\frac{1}{n^2}\frac{2\pi^2 me^4}{h^2} \qquad \qquad 2.7(1)$$

For $n = 1$, one obtains the energy of the fundamental state; for $n = 2$, the energy of the first excited state; for $n = 3$, and so on, the energies of the higher excited states. Subtracting such energies from each other and dividing by h gives the frequencies observed in the hydrogen spectrum.

The second excited state $(n = 3)$ is ninefold degenerate. Of the nine proper functions belonging to it, one will be spherically symmetrical and will be an s state. Three of them will be p proper functions having similar angular dependence and transforming under rotation in a way similar to that of the p functions of the first excited state. The remaining five will form a further group; they belong to a d state. The three proper functions of the p state are necessarily degenerate; the same holds for the five proper functions of the d state. However the degeneracy among the s, p, and d groups of states is accidental. The notations used for these proper functions are $(3s)$, $(3p)$, and $(3d)$.

The states belonging to $n = 4$ are 16-fold degenerate, being subdivided into a spherically symmetrical s function, three p functions, five d functions, and seven f functions.

In general, the degeneracy of the nth state is n^2-fold and is subdivided into groups of necessarily degenerate states starting with one s, three p, and five d states.

2.8   THE ANGULAR MOMENTUM   The angular dependence of a $1s$, an appropriate $2p$, an appropriate $3d$, and an appropriate $4f$ function are pictured in Figure 2.8(1) which indicates the behavior of the respective wave functions in a plane. In the areas shaded vertically, the wave function is positive; in the areas shaded horizontally, it is negative; and, on the lines passing through the center, the wave function vanishes. We shall consider a path around the center as indicated in the figure by the circle and the arrow. The length of the path indicated by the circle will be $2\pi r$, r being the radius of the circle. In following the path along the circle we will find changes of the wave function similar to those in a plane wave. In the s function there is no change at all; this means that the wavelength along the circle may be considered infinite, and there is no momentum along the circumference; thus the angular momentum is zero. In the p state one maximum and one minimum will be found in completing a circuit. Therefore $2\pi r$ will be the wavelength, $h/2\pi r$ the momentum (section 1.4), and $r\dfrac{h}{2\pi r} = \dfrac{h}{2\pi}$ the angular momentum. In the d state two crests and two troughs of the wave are found in completing the circle so that the wavelength is $2\pi r/2$, the momentum $2h/2\pi r$, and the angular momentum $2h/2\pi$. In a similar way we find three waves on the circumference for the f function and $3h/2\pi$ for the corresponding angular momentum.

The reason for the p, d, and f degeneracies as well as for the spherical symmetry of the s function is the spherical symmetry of the field in which the electron is moving. On the other hand we see that the quantity in classical physics characteristic of the s, p, d, etc., orbits is

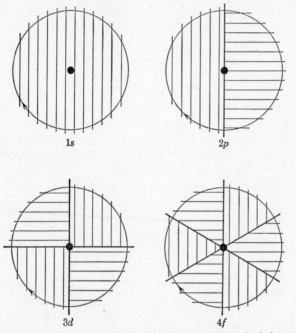

1s   2p

3d   4f

FIG. 2.8(1). Angular dependence of wave functions. Areas shaded vertically indicate positive values of the wave function, and horizontal shading corresponds to negative values. The magnitude of the wave function is not indicated.

the angular momentum; the angular momentum of a particle remains constant during its motion only as long as the field has spherical symmetry, and only in such cases is it of particular * usefulness in classical physics.

2.9 GRAPHICAL REPRESENTATIONS OF H STATES Figures 2.9(1) and 2.9(2) show the wave functions of the hydrogen atom belonging to the three lowest energy levels. As in the previous figure, the amplitude of the wave function is not indicated. Horizontal shad-

* Part of this usefulness is retained in fields of cylindrical symmetry. This is discussed in connection with diatomic molecules.

ing again corresponds to negative values of the wave function and vertical shading to positive values. Full lines and circles show the position of nodes in the actual three-dimensional model; nodes correspond to surfaces on which the ψ function vanishes. In Figures 2.9(1) and 2.9(2)

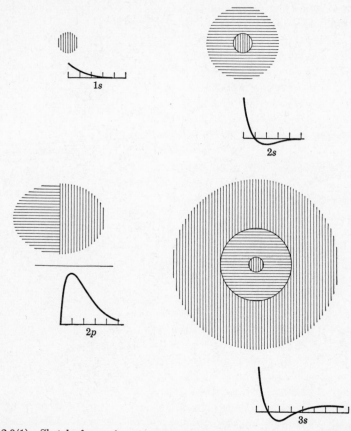

FIG. 2.9(1). Sketch of wave functions of the hydrogen atom. Vertical and horizontal shading correspond to positive and negative values of the wave function. The amplitudes of the wave functions are not indicated. On the bottom of each sketch the value of the wave function is plotted against the distance from the nucleus.

the intersection of these surfaces with the plane of the drawing is shown.

The three-dimensional model of the 1s, 2s, and 3s functions can be readily visualized with the help of the drawing since these functions are spherically symmetrical. The nodes that appear as circles in the drawings for 2s and 3s are of course spherical. They correspond to momenta perpendicular to the spheres, that is, to a radial motion. It is more difficult to visualize the other functions in space. Of the three $2p$ functions, only one has been drawn, which has a plane node perpendicular to the plane of the figure. The spatial dependence may be easily visualized since the wave function has cylindrical symmetry around an axis passing through the nucleus and perpendicular to the node.

A second $2p$ function could be obtained by rotating the figure in the plane of the paper by 90°; the third $2p$ function would have its node in the plane of the paper and cannot therefore be shown.

The $2p$ functions with nodes perpendicular to the plane of the paper correspond to rotations of the electron parallel to the plane of the paper. That there are two such functions corresponds to the two possibilities of clockwise and counterclockwise motion.* The $2p$ function with the node in the plane of the paper represents a rotation of the electron perpendicular to the plane of the paper.

Of the three $3p$ wave functions, again only one is represented in the drawing. The other two can be obtained similarly as with the $2p$ wave functions. The main difference between the $2p$ and $3p$ wave functions is that in the latter a spherical node is present which appears in the drawing as a circle.

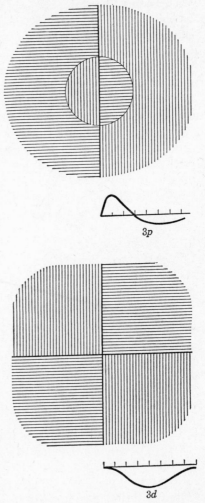

3p

3d

Fig. 2.9(2). Sketch of wave functions of the hydrogen atom. Vertical and horizontal shading correspond to positive and negative values of the wave function. The amplitudes of the wave functions are not indicated. On the bottom of each sketch the value of the wave function is plotted against the distance from the nucleus.

* The wave function that would correspond to the clockwise motion may be obtained by multiplying one of the two wave functions with i and adding it to the other. The counterclockwise motion is represented by a similar sum using $-i$. Complex wave functions are always necessary if the direction of motion is to be represented.

Of the five $3d$ functions only one has been drawn, the nodes of which are perpendicular to the plane of the paper. A second $3d$ function may be obtained by rotating the drawing in the plane of the paper by $45°$. These two wave functions correspond to rotation of the electron (clockwise and counterclockwise) parallel to the plane of the paper. The remaining three $3d$ functions have more complicated nodes some of which form cones around an axis perpendicular to the plane of the paper. The easiest way to visualize the spatial dependence of d functions is with the help of mathematical formulas.

The wave functions describing the state of an electron in a spherically symmetrical field may be written as a product, one factor depending only on the distance of the electron from the center, the second factor depending only on the angles. The first factor, describing the radial dependence, is shown for the wave functions of the hydrogen atom by the curves appearing at the bottom of the figures.

2.10 TIME-DEPENDENT WAVE FUNCTION

The interpretation of the wave functions already given will become more complete if we include the dependence on time. This may be done by multiplying each of the wave functions by $e^{i2\pi\nu_e t}$ where ν_e may be called the electronic frequency and is equal to the energy of the electron in the quantum state under consideration divided by h.

$$\nu_e = \frac{E}{h}$$

Though it is not possible here to give the derivation of the complex factor we have just introduced, we shall point out the main consequences of its inclusion and also its usefulness.

$e^{i2\pi\nu_e t}$ is a periodic function with the frequency ν_e in the same way as $\cos 2\pi\nu_e t$ or $\sin 2\pi\nu_e t$ (in fact $e^{i2\pi\nu_e t} = \cos 2\pi\nu_e t + i \sin 2\pi\nu_e t$). The periodicity of the time factor is important in many ways, as, for instance, in picturing the process of oscillation within the atom and the connected phenomenon of the emission of light. However neither $\cos 2\pi\nu_e t$ nor $\sin 2\pi\nu_e t$ would be an appropriate function, since each vanishes at certain times causing the wave function to become equal to zero simultaneously everywhere at such times; no physical interpretation of such a function could be given, and it has, therefore, to be excluded.

The function $e^{i2\pi\nu_e t}$, on the other hand, has the property that the square of its absolute value (which according to an earlier interpretation gives the probability function for the electron) remains constant and moreover is always equal to unity. Thus multiplying the wave function of a stationary state with this factor will not change the probability distribution at all. This means that the spread of the electron function in a state by no means corresponds to the motion of an electron in that state but merely to the fact that the position of an electron is uncertain if its energy (that is, the energy of the stationary state) is given.

2.11 SUPERPOSITION OF TIME-DEPENDENT FUNCTIONS

We have stated that the original time-independent wave functions can

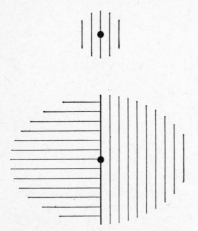

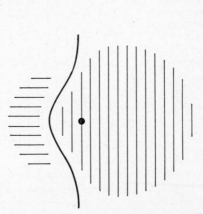

Fig. 2.11(1). Sketch of 1s and 2p wave functions. Vertical and horizontal shadings correspond to positive and negative values of the wave function. The amplitudes of the wave functions are not indicated.

Fig. 2.11(2). Sketch of superposition of 1s and 2p wave functions. (1s) + (2p). Vertical and horizontal shadings correspond to positive and negative values of the wave function. The electron is found with greater probability on the right of the nucleus shown by the solid circle. The probability is low near the node indicated by the solid curve.

be superposed (that is, multiplied by appropriate coefficients and added) only if the wave functions to be superposed belong to the same energy. On the other hand, any two time-dependent functions can be superposed. It will be of interest to investigate the consequences of such superposition in a specific example.

We will consider the function,

$$\psi_1 e^{i2\pi\nu'_e t} + \psi_2 e^{i2\pi\nu''_e t} = \psi_1 e^{\frac{i2\pi E' t}{h}} + \psi_2 e^{\frac{i2\pi E'' t}{h}} \qquad 2.11(1)$$

where E' and E'' are the energies of the fundamental and the first excited states of the hydrogen atom, respectively, and ν'_e and ν''_e are the corresponding frequencies E'/h and E''/h. We take for ψ_1, the wave function of the fundamental state and for ψ_2 the first of the four wave functions of the first excited state, equation 2.2(2). For the time $t = 0$ the complex exponential factors will become one, and the time-dependent function will reduce to $\psi_1 + \psi_2$. If we represent ψ_1 and ψ_2 by drawings [see Figure 2.11(1)] similar to those given in Figure 2.9(1) where vertical and horizontal shading correspond to positive and negative values, then $\psi_1 + \psi_2$ will be represented by Figure 2.11(2). On

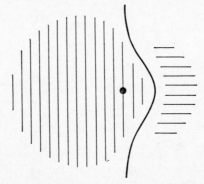

Fig. 2.11(3). Sketch of superposition of $(1s)$ and $(2p)$ wave functions. $(1s) - (2p)$. Vertical and horizontal shadings correspond to positive and negative values of the wave function. The electron is found with greater probability on the left of the nucleus shown by the solid circle. The probability is low near the node indicated by the solid curve.

the right-hand side of the figure the positive values of ψ_1 and ψ_2 have re-enforced each other so that now in this region the function $\psi_1 + \psi_2$ is the biggest. On the left-hand side of the figure ψ_1 and ψ_2 tend to cancel each other, and on this side $\psi_1 + \psi_2$ has small—partly positive and partly negative—values. On this side too is found the line along which the function vanishes, that is, the node.

Let us now consider the original time-dependent function 2.11(1) after the time $t = \dfrac{1}{2}\dfrac{h}{E'' - E'}$ has passed. The wave function can be written

$$\psi_1 e^{\frac{i2\pi E't}{h}} + \psi_2 e^{\frac{i2\pi E''t}{h}} = e^{\frac{i2\pi E't}{h}}\left(\psi_1 + \psi_2 e^{\frac{i2\pi(E''-E')t}{h}}\right)$$

$$= e^{\frac{i2\pi E't}{h}}(\psi_1 + \psi_2 e^{i\pi}) = e^{\frac{i2\pi E't}{h}}(\psi_1 - \psi_2) \quad 2.11(3)$$

where use has been made of the fact that $e^{i\pi} = -1$. Apart from the factor $e^{\frac{i2\pi E't}{h}}$ which does not affect probabilities, the wave function will be pictured as in Figure 2.11(3). It is now on the left-hand side of the picture that ψ_1 and ψ_2 re-enforce each other, and therefore the main probability of finding the electron will be on that side.

It is easy to see that after a further period of $t = \dfrac{1}{2}\dfrac{h}{E'' - E'}$ the wave function and with it the probability distribution will shift back to its original value which it had at $t = 0$; thus the frequencies in the two electronic states produce beats with the total period $\dfrac{h}{E'' - E'}$ or the frequency $\dfrac{E'' - E'}{h}$.

It may be seen that, although an electron does not "move" in a stationary state, motion can be readily produced as soon as an electron is in a superposition of two stationary states. In this case however we can make only probability statements as to the energy of the electron.

It seems very tempting to identify the frequency $\dfrac{E'' - E'}{h}$ of the electronic motion with the frequency of the light emitted or absorbed. But we must not consider emission or absorption of light as a consequence of this electron oscillation, but rather as a phenomenon corresponding to it. Otherwise, we would obtain the result that a hydrogen atom which at the moment is with certainty in the first excited state does not move, does not oscillate, and does not emit light.

3. THE PERIODIC SYSTEM

3.1 ELECTRONS OF THE K SHELL As preparation for treating atoms heavier than hydrogen we will consider a single electron moving around a nucleus, the charge of which is equal to Z times the elementary charge. The total energy of such an electron will then be

$$E = E_{\text{pot}} + E_{\text{kin}} = -\frac{Ze^2}{r} + \frac{p^2}{2m} \qquad 3.1(1)$$

This is the same formula that was obtained for the hydrogen atom with the exception that in the potential energy e^2 has been replaced by Ze^2. A similar reasoning to that used for the hydrogen atom yields

$$\bar{r}_m = \frac{h^2}{4\pi^2 m Z e^2} \qquad 3.1(2)$$

and

$$E_{\text{min}} = -\frac{2\pi^2 m Z^2 e^4}{h^2} \qquad 3.1(3)$$

The last formula shows that with increasing Z the energy necessary to tear the electron away from the nucleus increases rapidly. Thus for fluorine this energy exceeds 1000 volts, and for the heaviest elements it will exceed 100,000 volts. In fact, spectra showing a certain similarity to the hydrogen spectra have been observed for all elements; however, according to the relation $E = h\nu$, the frequencies soon become very great and shift into the X-ray region. Study of the X-ray spectra has proved to be the most reliable method of ascertaining the nuclear charge Z and with it the atomic number.

According to formula 3.1(2), a decrease of the radius of the electron orbit will accompany the increase of binding energy. Thus we might be led to the conclusion that atomic radii decrease as $1/Z$ with increasing nuclear charge Z, whereas actually the atomic radius tends to increase slowly with increasing atomic number.

We might suspect that this disagreement between theory and experience might disappear if the repulsion between electrons is taken into

20

account. It can be shown, however, that the average repulsion between Z unit charges is always considerably outweighed by the attraction of these charges by the Z-fold charge of the nucleus. X-ray spectra moreover show that the electrons which are close to the nucleus are not strongly affected by the other electrons.

3.2 PAULI PRINCIPLE   The difficulties that we have just pointed out prove to be by no means superficial. They reappear in somewhat varied forms whenever two or more electrons get into close interaction. Attempts to resolve the difficulties by application of principles or methods of classical or quantum physics proved unsuccessful.

It was, however, possible to give satisfactory quantitative laws for the motion of more than one electron by introducing a new principle known by the name of Pauli's Exclusion Principle. In its most primitive form this principle states that no two electrons can move in the same orbit or can be described by the same wave functions. Thus only a limited number of electrons will be able to move in orbits close to the nucleus in a heavy atom; additional electrons occupy orbits of smaller binding energy and greater radius. The last electron, and with it the atom as a whole, will require a volume which according to more detailed calculations increases slowly with the atomic number.

The "impenetrability" of matter, as manifested by the small compressibility of liquids and solids, can also be regarded as a consequence of the Pauli principle. In fact, if two atomic nuclei contained in two atoms could approach each other and the electrons around them remain undisturbed, the final result would be that the nuclei would coincide, and more than one electron originally coming from different atoms would be found in the same orbit. The actual repulsion between atoms arises from the increase of energy of the electrons in trying to get out of each other's way when the atoms approach.

For a somewhat more general formulation of the Pauli principle, it is necessary to state when two wave functions will be called different so that two electrons can be allocated to them without violating the exclusion principle. Of course, if two wave functions differed only slightly from each other, that would not suffice to make room for two electrons. The formulation of the Pauli principle as given here implies that a sufficient condition under which two wave functions are to be counted as different is that they belong to different energy levels. As stated in section 2.4, two wave functions belonging to different energy levels are always orthogonal. The orthogonality of two wave functions furthermore has the necessary consequence that the two wave functions should differ strongly from each other. It seems therefore reasonable to use orthogonality as a criterion that two wave functions are sufficiently different to accommodate two electrons. This generalization has actually proved to be the reasonable mathematical formulation of the Pauli principle for the simple case in which a definite wave function can be assigned to each electron. This will be possible if the motion of each electron can be considered as proceeding independently of the rest of the electrons as is described in the next paragraph.

3.3 ELECTRONIC STRUCTURE OF THE LIGHTER ELEMENTS In order to obtain a reasonable approximation for the many electron problems and to apply to it the Pauli principle in a simple form, we assume that the electrons behave to a certain extent independently of each other. By this we do not mean that one electron has no action whatsoever on another. We shall rather assume that each electron will act on another electron with an average force. The independence of the electrons merely means that we neglect the variation from this average force which arises if one considers the force exerted by the first electron in each phase of its motion.

After these simplifying assumptions have been made, it is permissible to consider the behavior of each electron by itself, each electron being pictured as moving in the field of the nucleus and the average field of the other electrons. Each electron will be in a state of its own and will be characterized by a wave function of its own; these wave functions will be similar to the wave function of the hydrogen atom described in the previous chapter. The simplest way in which the Pauli principle might be expected to operate would be to put successively into each of the hydrogen-like orbits one electron. Thus the lowest element, hydrogen, would have in its fundamental state one electron in the lowest, $1s$, state. In the second atom of the periodic system two electrons must be present, the first of which will be in the $1s$ state, the second of which will possess a wave function similar to those of the first excited state of hydrogen; thus the second electron may be either in the $2s$ or a $2p$ state. For the third atom of the periodic system, one electron can be in the $1s$ state and two electrons in $2p$ states or one electron in the $1s$, one electron in the $2s$, and one in the $2p$ state. It may be noticed that more than one electron can be put into $2p$ states, but not more than one electron can be put into the $2s$ state since there are three $2p$ states but only one $2s$ state. Filling up the consecutive states in a similar manner, we will arrive at the fifth element for which the $1s$, $2s$, and three $2p$ states are filled. In the sixth element of the periodic system, in addition to these states, a second excited state of the hydrogen atom must be filled which will be either a $3s$, a $3p$, or a $3d$ state. From the second to the fifth element, new electrons have gone into similar states all corresponding to the first excited state of hydrogen. We are led therefore to the following groups of atoms: Hydrogen corresponding to the $1s$ state stands by itself; helium, lithium, beryllium, and boron form a second group with $2s$ and $2p$ electrons; a third group is started with carbon.

This classification has nothing in common with the classification based on chemical experience. However, chemical facts can be represented if a small change is made in the formulation of the Pauli principle. It has to be assumed that not one but rather two electrons can occupy the same orbit. It may then be seen that the first two elements, hydrogen and helium, will have $1s$ orbits. In the following eight elements from lithium to neon the $2s$ and $2p$ states will be filled up. Thus we see that the periods of the periodic system emerge.

3.4 ELECTRONS OF THE L TO Q SHELLS   After all $1s$, $2s$, and $2p$ orbits are occupied, we would expect that the nine states, $3s$, $3p$, and $3d$ would be filled up next by 18 electrons. Now it is a fact that the periodic table contains periods of 18 elements such as the period from potassium up to krypton, but this period does not follow immediately on neon as it ought to; rather a period of eight elements from sodium to argon is interpolated.

The reason for this disagreement is that our strict adherence to results obtained from hydrogen orbits was an oversimplification. Thus the $2s$ and $2p$ states are degenerate (that is, they have the same energy) only if the electrons move in the coulomb field of the nucleus. Now the average field of the other electrons in a heavier atom will cause a departure from this simple force law. The potential will be particularly low close to the nucleus where its attraction is not shielded by the other electrons. Comparing the probability distribution for $2s$ and $2p$ electrons or those for the $3s$ and $3p$ electrons in Figure 2.9(1), we see that finding an s electron close to the nucleus is more probable than finding the corresponding p electron in the same region. This behavior can be explained by a classical argument: The p electrons having an angular momentum $h/2\pi$ are prevented from coming very close to the attraction center, since at the distance zero from the center their angular momentum would necessarily become zero. The same holds true even to a greater degree for the d electrons, and we can see indeed in Figure 2.9(1) that the $3d$ electrons stay farther away from the nucleus than the $3p$ electrons. Since the $2s$ electrons will be found in the region of particularly low potential energy with a probability greater than that of the $2p$ electrons, we would expect that the $2s$ state will be somewhat lower than the $2p$ state. Therefore the $2s$ state (lithium and beryllium) will be filled first, and the $2p$ states will follow from boron to neon. In a similar way the $3s$ electrons will have a lower energy than the $3p$ electrons, and these again will be lower than the $3d$ electrons. Indeed the difference is so great that the $3d$ electrons have an even higher energy than the $4s$ electrons. Thus, in the row from sodium to argon the $3s$ and $3p$ states will be filled; in the following period from potassium to krypton the $4s$, $3d$, and $4p$ states will be occupied by 18 electrons. From rubidium to xenon 18 more electrons will fill the $5s$, $4d$, and $5p$ states; from caesium to radon 32 electrons will appear in the $6s$, $5d$, $4f$, and $6p$ states.

If several close-lying levels are available for the next electron, it becomes a rather complicated problem to decide what the actual electronic configuration will be. These difficulties are discussed in the following paragraphs.

If for a certain element it is known that, for instance, the $4s$ level lies lower than the $3d$ level, it is by no means certain that the same will hold for the next element in the periodic system. The reason for this is that in the next element the proportion between nuclear charge and the charge of the $1s$, $2s$, and $2p$ electrons will have changed, and the difference caused in the atomic field will affect the $4s$ state not quite in the same way as the $3d$ state. The general tendency is to restore the natural order of a given pair of levels (for instance, $3d$ lower than $4s$) as we proceed toward heavier elements; thus, in the lighter element, potassium, the $4s$ orbit is occupied although all the $3d$ states are empty, whereas in the heavier element, copper, one $4s$ state is still unoccupied although all the $3d$ states are now filled.

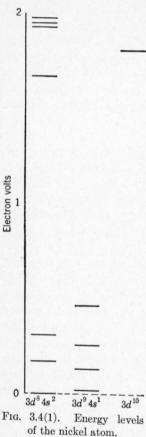

Fig. 3.4(1). Energy levels of the nickel atom.

A further complication arises from the fact that the d states (and also the f states that are being filled up in the rare earth elements) are degenerate. If more than one degenerate electronic state is filled, the interaction between the degenerate electrons may give rise to several atomic levels of different energies which all belong to the same electronic configuration. This, in fact, is not surprising because, for instance, two p electrons will interact in one way if they are in identical orbits and in a somewhat different way if their orbits differ in orientation.

As an example, we may consider the lowest levels of the nickel atom. In Figure 3.4(1) the levels are represented by horizontal lines, the ener-

TABLE 3.4(1)

The Electron Structure of the Atoms

Atomic Number	Element	Number of Electrons in Each Quantum Group										
		1s	2s	2p	3s	3p	3d	4s	4p	4d	4f	5s
1	H	1										
2	He	2										
3	Li	2	1									
4	Be	2	2									
5	B	2	2	1								
6	C	2	2	2								
7	N	2	2	3								
8	O	2	2	4								
9	F	2	2	5								
10	Ne	2	2	6								
11	Na				1							
12	Mg				2							
13	Al		1s to 2p groups filled.		2	1						
14	Si				2	2						
15	P				2	3						
16	S				2	4						
17	Cl				2	5						
18	A				2	6						
19	K							1				
20	Ca							2				
21	Sc						1	2				
22	Ti						2	2				
23	V		1s to 3p groups filled.				3	2				
24	Cr						5	1				
25	Mn						5	2				
26	Fe						6	2				
27	Co						7	2				
28	Ni						8	2				
29	Cu						10	1				
30	Zn											
31	Ga								1			
32	Ge		1s to 4s groups filled.						2			
33	As								3			
34	Se								4			
35	Br								5			
36	Kr								6			
37	Rb											1
38	Sr											2
39	Y									1		2
40	Zr									2		2
41	Cb		1s to 4p groups filled.							4		1
42	Mo									5		1
43	Tc									5		2
44	Ru									7		1
45	Rh									8		1
46	Pd									10		

TABLE 3.4(1) *Continued*

THE ELECTRON STRUCTURE OF THE ATOMS

Atomic Number	Element	Number of Electrons in Each Quantum Group									
		4f	5s	5p	5d	5f	5g	6s	6p	6d	7s
47	Ag		1								
48	Cd		2								
49	In		2	1							
50	Sn		2	2							
51	Sb		2	3							
52	Te		2	4							
53	I		2	5							
54	Xe		2	6							
55	Cs		2	6				1			
56	Ba		2	6				2			
57	La	1s to	2	6	1			2			
58	Ce	4d	2	2	6			2			
59	Pr	groups	3	2	6			2			
60	Nd	filled.	4	2	6			2			
61	Pm		5	2	6			2			
62	Sa		6	2	6			2			
63	Eu		7	2	6			2			
64	Gd		7	2	6	1		2			
65	Tb		9	2	6			2			
66	Dy		10	2	6			2			
67	Ho		11	2	6			2			
68	Er		12	2	6			2			
69	Tm		13	2	6			2			
70	Yb		14	2	6			2			
71	Lu		14	2	6	1		2			
72	Hf				2			2			
73	Ta				3			2			
74	W				4			2			
75	Re	1s to 5p groups filled.			5			2			
76	Os				6			2			
77	Ir				7			2			
78	Pt				9			1			
79	Au				10			1			
80	Hg							2			
81	Tl							2	1		
82	Pb							2	2		
83	Bi							2	3		
84	Po							2	4		
85	At							2	5		
86	Rn							2	6		
87	Fr							2	6		1
88	Ra	1s to 5d groups filled.						2	6		2
89	Ac							2	6	1	2
90	Th							2	6	2	2
91	Pa					2		2	6	1	2
92	U					3		2	6	1	2
93	Np					4		2	6	1	2
94	Pu					5		2	6	1	2
95	Am					7		2	6		2
96	Cm					7		2	6	1	2

gies of which, in electron volts, appear on the scale at the left-hand side. The first column contains the levels which belong to the configuration with eight $3d$ and two $4s$ states filled. The lowest level of the atom belongs to this configuration. However, the levels in the second column which belong to states with nine $3d$ and one $4s$ electrons lie only slightly higher and, in fact, lie lower on the average than the levels in the first column. The level belonging to ten $3d$ and no $4s$ electrons is given in the third column and lies somewhat higher. The flat statement that in nickel eight $3d$ and two $4s$ electrons are present is somewhat insufficient if the electronic configuration of the atom is to serve as the basis of the theory of its chemical properties.

The rather intricate interaction between electrons also accounts for the fact that not all the levels of one kind need necessarily be filled in one atom before some electrons appear in another level. For instance, in the rare-earth elements, there is only one $5d$ electron while the $4f$ levels are gradually being filled up. This would be inconsistent with the simple picture that in each element either the $5d$ or the $4f$ level must be lower, and therefore this lower level must be completely filled before any electron can appear in a higher level.

The main method by which the lowest electron configurations of atoms are found is an investigation of their spectra together with the spectra of their ions. An analysis of the spectra of course yields only the atomic levels and does not lead directly to a statement about the electronic configuration to which these levels belong. However, the grouping of the levels and their behavior in a magnetic field (Zeeman effect) make it possible to find the actual electronic configurations, not only in the fundamental state, but also in the excited states. The electronic configurations of the atoms for the fundamental states are shown in Table 3.4(1).

3.5 INTERACTION OF ELECTRONS IN APPROACHING ATOMS The scheme that has been given for the periodic system suggests that the outermost electrons determine the chemical properties of an atom. Thus in all alkali atoms the outermost electron is an s electron, $2s$, $3s$, $4s$, $5s$, or $6s$, respectively. In fact, it is to be expected that in atomic interactions those electron orbits should be the important ones which touch or may touch the electron orbits of a neighboring atom.

According to the argument given in connection with the Pauli principle, there should be a general tendency of atoms to repel each other since the electrons avoiding each other's orbits have to get into higher states when the atoms approach. If, however, each of the two atoms has, apart from closed shells, only one electron, these outermost electrons of the two atoms need not avoid each other, since, as has been stated, two electrons can be present in any orbit. Thus a repulsion need not appear until an electron orbit of one atom touches the inner and full shell of the other atom. Other effects to be discussed later will cause an attraction as soon as the orbits of the two outermost electrons coalesce; this is the formation of a chemical bond.

In this connection it is interesting to recall a general rule in chemistry. Almost all of the ordinary chemical molecules contain an even number of electrons; in fact, an orbit occupied by only one electron can accommodate a second, which means that the molecule can react easily with its own species and cannot be kept as the monomer.

Even if outside the closed shell there is more than one electron in one or both of the approaching atoms, chemical bonds may be formed; thus the situation, in which more than two electrons occupy the same orbit, may be avoided without expenditure of energy if electrons of the same atom have occupied some but not all levels of a degenerate set of states. In this case the electrons of the atom may be able to avoid the orbits of the electron of the approaching atom by going over into another one of the degenerate set of levels. Even if all such degenerate states are filled, another level with only slightly higher energy may be present; then the energy needed to lift the electron into this higher state may be overcompensated by the energy of bond formation; such is the case when the beryllium atom forms a homopolar bond. Here the $2s$ state is occupied by two electrons, and on the approach of another atom one electron will be lifted into the slightly higher $2p$ state; only if considerable energy is necessary to lift an electron to a higher state will the repulsion outweigh possible bond formation. This is the case for the closed shells of the rare gases.

3.6 HETEROPOLAR BOND We will consider a sodium and a fluorine atom. In the fluorine, one $2p$ orbit is unoccupied; in the sodium atom, in addition to lower orbits a $3s$ orbit is occupied; it might be expected that energy is gained if the $3s$ electron is taken from the sodium and put into the $2p$ orbit of the fluorine. Actually the process just described is endothermic rather than exothermic, but only a little energy is needed to perform the change. The reason why energy is needed rather than evolved is that for purely electrostatic reasons the positive sodium ion attracts an electron at a great distance while the neutral fluorine does not. At closer approach of the electron, however, the fact that in fluorine "a lower orbit" $2p$ will be occupied all but cancels the difference of the long-range attraction.

If now the positive sodium ion and the negative fluoride ion approach each other, electrostatic energy is gained which is greatly in excess of the energy needed to form these ions out of neutral atoms; thus a heteropolar bond is formed.

The same argument seems to lead to a wrong result if other heteropolar bonds, for example, that between sodium and iodine, are considered. Here the first step would involve a transfer of a $3s$ sodium electron into a $5p$ iodine orbit, that is, into a much higher state. However, the corresponding higher nuclear charge of iodine will cause the $5p$ iodine electron to behave rather similarly to the $2p$ fluorine electron, resulting in only a slightly weaker sodium–iodine bond than the sodium–fluorine bond. Conversely the caesium–fluorine bond will be stronger than the sodium–fluorine bond since it is a little easier to remove the $6s$ caesium electron than the $3s$ sodium electron.

In Table 3.6(1) the ionization energies of the gaseous alkali atoms are

TABLE 3.6(1)

IONIZATION ENERGIES OF GASEOUS ALKALI ATOMS

Atom	Li	Na	K	Rb	Cs
Electron Volts	5.4	5.1	4.3	4.2	3.9

shown, that is, the energies necessary to remove the outermost electron, and in Table 3.6(2) the electron affinities of the halogens are given, that

TABLE 3.6(2)

ELECTRON AFFINITIES OF THE HALOGEN ATOMS

Atom	F	Cl	Br	I
Electron Volts	4.1	3.8	3.6	3.2

is, the energies gained if an electron is added to the respective neutral halogen. It may be seen that the electron transfer in itself is exothermic only in the case of caesium fluoride.

The ionization energies of the alkalis are easily determined from their absorption spectra; in fact, below the ionization energy the atom possesses discrete energy levels as described in section 2.7, whereas above the ionization energy the electron that has been torn off may have any energy. Thus at frequencies capable of producing ionization, continuous absorption sets in, and the ionization energy may be obtained with high accuracy by multiplying by h the frequency of the limit of continuous absorption.

On the other hand, the electron affinities are more difficult to determine and are less accurately known. They are found by a study of the number of negative ions formed under suitable conditions at different temperatures.

The arguments discussed in this section are in their essence much older than quantum theory; however, quantum theory provides the possibility of calculating roughly the energies involved and, what is more important, of connecting them with other measurable physical quantities, for instance, frequencies appearing in spectra.

3.7 TRANSITION ELEMENTS

It may be seen in Table 3.4(1) that in certain parts of the periodic system, for example, from scandium to nickel, the $3d$ electrons are filled in after the $4s$ states have been occupied. The elements in question show a remarkable similarity; they constitute the transition elements.

Similar phenomena are observed for the groups, yttrium to palladium, lanthanum to platinum, and more particularly within this group, for the rare earth elements from cerium to lutecium.

The similarity of the transition elements suggests that all the electron orbits which lie outermost in space are similar to each other. Thus it seems that, for instance, in the iron group, the $3d$ orbits which are being filled up lie farther inside the atom than the $4s$ orbits.

This can be understood with the help of a picture taken from classical mechanics. The d orbits have the relatively high angular momentum $2h/2\pi$, and therefore the momentum of a d electron must be at least $\frac{2h}{2\pi}\frac{1}{r}$ if r is its distance from the nucleus. Toward the exterior of the atom the electric potential decreases rapidly, and, since no electron must have energy sufficient to escape from the atom, electrons of high momentum cannot be found in these outside regions.

This reasoning leads to the conclusion that high-angular-momentum electrons cannot be found in the outermost parts of the atom.

We shall repeat this reasoning now in a more quantitative manner.* An average potential distribution in an atom is shown in Figure 3.7(1). This curve has been obtained by a rough calculation which does not show details like the shell structure. The abscissa is the distance from the nucleus multiplied by the cube root of the nuclear charge Z, while the ordinate is the potential divided by the $\frac{4}{3}$ power of the nuclear charge; thus the figure can be used for any atom. However, the approximations that have been made in arriving at the figure are not valid if the potential is small, and therefore application must be limited to the

---

* The following results are derived from a simplified atomic model called the Thomas–Fermi model.

interior of heavy atoms. The treatment of the angular momentum of
electrons in the inner shells is one for which the method is appropriate.
The potential given in Figure 3.7(1), multiplied by the charge, is equal
to the minimum kinetic energy which an electron must possess at that
point in order to escape from the atom; the kinetic energies of the elec-

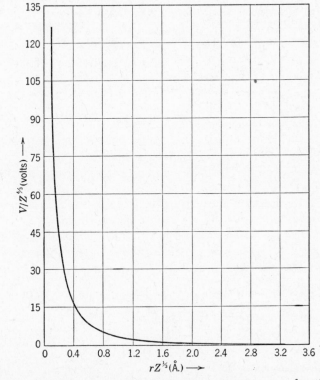

Fig. 3.7(1). Approximate potential distribution in an atom as a function of the
distance r from the nucleus. The curve is roughly valid for all nuclear charges Z
but does not represent the shell structure.

trons must be smaller than that kinetic energy. From this we find a
maximum momentum that an electron can possess at each point.
Multiplying this by r, we obtain the maximum angular momentum that
an electron can have; this maximum angular momentum divided by
$Z^{1/3}$ is plotted in Figure 3.7(2) against $rZ^{1/3}$; the figure may again be used
for any atom. It may be seen that the maximum angular momentum
is found at a position well in the interior of the atom. It also may be
seen that this maximum angular momentum increases with $Z^{1/3}$ so that
higher angular momenta can be expected in heavier atoms. Multiply-

ing the ordinate of the figure by $Z^{1/3}$, we find that the angular momentum $h/2\pi$ becomes possible for the first time with $Z = 1.3$, and therefore helium should be the atom at which the first p electron occurs. Similarly the first d electron (angular momentum $2h/2\pi$) should be found for $Z = 10.6$, that is, for sodium. Finally the first f electron should be found for $Z = 36$, that is for krypton. Comparison with

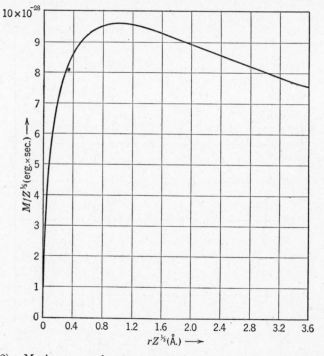

Fig. 3.7(2). Maximum angular momentum that an electron may possess in the ground state of an atom as a function of the distance r from the nucleus.

Table 3.4(1) shows that the first p, d, and f electrons occur respectively in boron, $Z = 5$; scandium, $Z = 21$; and cerium, $Z = 58$. The agreement is not very satisfactory. This is due to the crudely approximate nature of our assumptions. We can show that a better agreement is to be expected if the first appearance of the half-integral values $\dfrac{3}{2}\dfrac{h}{2\pi}$, $\dfrac{5}{2}\dfrac{h}{2\pi}$ and $\dfrac{7}{2}\dfrac{h}{2\pi}$ of the angular momentum in our model is assumed to correspond to the first appearance of a p, d, or f electron in the periodic system. Indeed, according to this assumption, the theoretical values of Z at which p, d, and f electrons make their first appearance are

$Z = 4.5$, $Z = 20.8$ and $Z = 57$, in excellent agreement with experience.

It should be remembered that some of the concepts used here are in direct contradiction to the uncertainty principle. For instance, it is not permissible to talk about the maximum momentum of an electron at a given point; if the electron were localized strictly at a given point, the momentum of the electron must be infinite. The classical argument given here should really apply, not to electrons at a point, but to electrons in a given region of the atom.

3.8 INDEPENDENT MOTION OF ELECTRONS IN WAVE MECHANICS   In formulating the Pauli principle we have supposed that the electrons move independently of each other. We must discuss now to what statement in wave mechanics this statement of classical mechanics will correspond.

We have seen that the wave functions of electrons are closely connected with the probability of finding electrons in certain regions. If we have several electrons that move independently, the probability of finding electrons in a certain configuration will be given by the products of the probabilities as calculated for each electron for its respective position. The same result is obtained from a wave-mechanical description if the wave function of the whole system is the product of the wave functions of the single electrons.

If a classical mechanical picture is made of the atom, the electrons will, of course, not move in a strictly independent way; the corresponding fact in quantum mechanics is that the wave function is not strictly a product of wave functions for single electrons. But, whatever the wave function of the electrons is, we can show that it can always be written as a sum of products. Each term of that sum, if it stood alone, would correspond to a certain distribution of electrons over the different orbits. If several terms appear in the sum, then the electrons may be found with a certain probability in each of the several distributions. As an example, we shall discuss the lowest state of the helium atom; we have pointed out that in this state two electrons are found in the $1s$ state; we can represent that state symbolically by the product of the wave functions of the two electrons, and for each of these wave functions we shall use the symbol $1s$. The complete wave function will therefore be denoted by $(1s)^2$. Another distribution of the electrons would be to put one electron into a $1s$ state, the other into a $2s$ state; that wave function would be $(1s)(2s)$. The real wave function will be approximated better if we take $(1s)^2$ and $(1s)(2s)$, multiply them with appropriate coefficients, and add.

$$C_1(1s)^2 + C_2(1s)(2s)$$

The actual wave function of the fundamental state being rather well represented by the expression $(1s)^2$, C_2 should be small as compared with C_1. The physical significance of C_1 and C_2 is in a way similar to the significance of the ψ function as discussed in the first chapter: the squares of C_1 and C_2 (or more generally the absolute values of their squares) give, respectively, the probabilities of finding both electrons in a $1s$ state and of finding one electron in a $1s$ state and one electron in a $2s$ state. The foregoing consideration is readily generalized for the case where the wave function is represented by the sum of more than two terms. It follows from the physical significance of the constants C_1 and C_2, that the sum of their squares must be equal to unity. Even if it is uncertain in which configuration we shall find the electrons, it is certain that we shall find them in *some* configuration.

By leaving thus a greater latitude in the distribution of electrons among states, a lower total energy may be obtained in a somewhat similar way that a lower energy was obtained for one electron if some latitude was allowed in its position. Actually, using sums containing several terms, we can construct wave functions for which the probability of electrons coming close together will not be so great as it would be if they were moving independently. Greater average distance between electrons decreases their interaction and lowers the total energy. On the other hand, it will not be useful to introduce terms multiplied by a large factor if the corresponding electron distribution has a high energy. That would mean that electrons would be found with great probability in high orbits and therefore in states of high kinetic and high average potential energy. It follows from the general rules of quantum mechanics that the correct wave function for the fundamental state will be found by making the total energy a minimum. This can be done by adjusting the coefficients in the sum in an appropriate manner.

The lowering of energy obtained in this way will be all the greater if two or more possible distributions of electrons each having nearly the same energy are coupled with each other. In this case electrons can avoid each other without being forced into higher orbits. This phenomenon is called "resonance," a name which is intended to recall the greater influence that coupled vibrations exert on each other if their frequencies are nearly the same. The phenomenon of resonance helps to explain a number of curious effects in organic chemistry. In the periodic system resonance for the lowest states occurs in the transition elements and adds to the complexity which we have already encountered in this group.

3.9 THE ELECTRON SPIN It remains to be understood why two electrons rather than one can occupy the same orbit or wave function.

The reason is that electrons have an internal degree of freedom; that is, even after the position and momentum of the electron have been determined as far as possible, the electron may be in one of two states which differ as a rule only very slightly in their energy. The situation can be pictured roughly by assigning a small magnetic dipole or spin to each electron which can have two different orientations. Magnetic effects are usually small, and so the spin will not influence the energy greatly, although data on magnetic susceptibility allow us in some cases to draw conclusions concerning the spin.

Two electrons can be in the same orbit if they differ in the orientation of their spins and are therefore in reality in different states. Only one electron can occupy one state if a state is defined by both the wave function and the spin orientation.

We have seen that the possibility of valence formation is closely connected with the free and occupied states in the outermost shell of electrons. It is therefore evident that the electron spin is of importance for valency, not because spins influence electron energy but rather because they make it possible for two electrons to get into the same orbit.

3.10 GENERALIZED PAULI PRINCIPLE In section 3.2 we have formulated the Pauli principle for the simple case in which each electron can be assigned to a definite orbit and in which the spin of the electrons is disregarded. In the preceding two sections these simplifications have been dropped, and it now becomes necessary to formulate the Pauli principle in a way which is applicable to the more general case.

The wave function in its most general form is one that depends on the co-ordinates and spin orientations of all the electrons. This wave function is connected with the probability of finding the electrons in a certain configuration and at the same time with certain spin orientations. Let us now consider a certain configuration of the electrons and then interchange the position of two electrons and also interchange their spins so that, after the change, electron 1 is in exactly the same situation as electron 2 was, and vice versa. The generalized Pauli principle states that, for the changed configuration, the wave function has -1 times the value which the wave function had assumed for the original configuration. An immediate consequence of this postulate is that the probabilities (which are the squares of the wave functions) are the same for the new and old configurations. It is interesting to notice in this connection that a physical difference between the original and changed configuration would be observable only if the two electrons differed from each other intrinsically, that is, in more than in their names.

In order to understand the preceding postulate it is useful to study its consequences for the case of two electrons that move independently of each other and for which therefore the earlier formulation of the Pauli principle can be applied. The wave function of electron 1 we shall call $\psi(1)$ and the wave function of electron 2 we shall designate by $\varphi(2)$. The total wave function for the independent case is the product $\psi(1)\varphi(2)$; interchanging the two electrons we obtain $\varphi(1)\psi(2)$ which is in general not equal to -1 times the original function; thus the generalized Pauli principle is not satisfied. We can, however, easily construct a function that satisfies our requirement, namely, $\psi(1)\varphi(2) - \varphi(1)\psi(2)$. This can always be done if the functions ψ and φ differ from each other. If these functions happen to be identical, no function exists which conforms to the generalized principle and which is different from zero. This corresponds to the earlier statement that no two electrons can be in the same state.

The product wave functions used in the previous sections are in the strict sense not correct wave functions because they do not satisfy the generalized Pauli principle; they only symbolize the correct functions which should be constructed from them in a manner essentially similar to that shown in the preceding paragraph.

The preceding formulation of the Pauli principle has proved to be in complete agreement with experimental facts. It fits well into the mathematical theory of quantum mechanics for the following reasons. (1) It is applicable to any wave function; (2) if it is postulated for the wave function at any one time, the rules of wave mechanics insure that it will continue to be valid at any future time. Thus the Pauli principle takes on the aspect of an initial condition, behavior at later times being taken care of by the rules at which one has arrived with the help of considerations independent of the Pauli principle. The last statement is valid, however, only as long as there is no intrinsic difference between electrons. If two electrons differed to the slightest extent in their reaction to any outside physical influences, then, according to the rules of wave mechanics, the Pauli principle could not continue to hold. Thus the fact of the Pauli principle is a very strong argument in favor of the identity of all electrons. In more concrete terms the reason for an L electron not falling into the full K shell is not the presence of some force prohibiting that process but the fact that the same physical action that would throw an electron from an L into the K shell will always lift an electron from the K into the L shell, so that no observable effect takes place. The slightest difference between the properties of the two electrons would upset this balance.

4. MOTION AND POSITION OF NUCLEI IN MOLECULES

4.1 SEPARATION OF MOTIONS OF NUCLEI AND ELECTRONS

The structure of atoms and that of molecules differ essentially in one respect: In the atom the electrons move in the field of one nucleus; in the molecule they move in the field of several nuclei. For atoms, nuclear motion will essentially manifest itself as a translational motion of the whole atom. In the molecule, nuclei can move with regard to each other causing important changes in the electronic structure. Owing to the much greater weight of the nuclei as compared to that of the electrons, the following picture can be applied. We first consider the nuclei at rest in an arbitrary position and then investigate the motion of the electrons in the field of the nuclei.

Subsequently the slow motion of the nuclei has to be discussed. For that purpose, however, only the interaction of the nuclei and the average force exerted by the electrons on the nuclei are important. The rapid changes of the forces exerted by electrons owing to their motion around the nuclei may be neglected. The heavy nuclei will react on these forces by a vibration of the electronic frequency but of very small amplitude.

The corresponding statement in wave mechanics is as follows: The total wave function describing electrons and nuclei can be written as a product of two factors. The first factor describes the state of the electrons in the field of the fixed nuclei; this factor contains, of course, the nuclear co-ordinates as parameters. The second factor describes the motion of the nuclei in a potential arising from their interaction and from the average potential of the electrons.

It may be noticed that, for a fixed set of positions of the nuclei, different electronic states are possible: that is, a fundamental state which will be our main concern in chemistry, and excited states which in most cases have so much energy that they cannot be excited in a thermal way; the latter will, however, be of importance in photochemistry. For the different electronic states the electronic distribution and with it the average potential of the electrons will be different. Thus the electronic motion will depend on the state, fundamental or excited, of the electrons.

37

4.2 CLASSICAL MOTION OF THE NUCLEI According to the correspondence principle, quantum laws will approach classical laws in the limiting case of "high quantum numbers." Owing to their greater mass, the nuclei move with smaller frequencies than the electrons, and the energy, $E = h\nu$, necessary for their excitation is less. For heavy nuclei, room temperature is as a general rule sufficient to lift them into high quantum states so that the motion of such nuclei can be described by classical mechanics. At low temperatures all nuclei depart from the rules of classical mechanics, as shown by specific heats which fall below the value given by application of the principle of the equipartition of kinetic energy. For light nuclei, particularly those of hydrogen, even room temperature must be counted as low temperature, and classical behavior is attained only at several thousand degrees.

Nevertheless, in discussing chemical reactions it has sufficed up to now to consider the motion of the nuclei as purely classical. The reasons are twofold: (1) In the reactions which do not proceed with too great a rate, large activation energies are involved which can be overcome only by those atoms which have an excess energy and therefore approach in their behavior the laws of classical mechanics; (2) for the great potential differences involved, and for the shapes of potential curves that occur, the classical and quantum laws do not deviate significantly from each other. In fact, the laws of quantum mechanics may easily cause a change of a factor two in the rate of a reaction, but no case is known in which a reaction that, owing to a high activation energy, ought not to proceed according to classical mechanics will proceed because of the quantum laws.

There is one effect, namely the tunnel effect, which, according to the views of some, causes an important quantum deviation in reaction velocities. The effect consists in a particle penetrating through a barrier, even if its energy is too small to do so in classical physics. The ultimate reason for this effect is the impossibility of localizing a particle in quantum mechanics without giving it high kinetic energy.

The behavior of the proper function of the hydrogen atom in its fundamental state is closely related to the tunnel effect. Though the electron does not have enough energy to escape the nucleus, its wave function and, with it, its probability distribution extends toward infinity, of course in an exponentially decreasing way. In chemical reactions the penetration of nuclei through barriers is not of practical importance because of the greater mass of the nuclei. The wave function of a nucleus will penetrate much less deeply into a region where, according to classical mechanics, the nucleus should not be found. Among nuclei, the proton having the smallest mass will have the greatest chance of penetrating through a potential barrier.

It is undoubtedly true that for an appropriate shape of the potential, the tunnel effect would become important; a very narrow and high barrier would be a case in point. There is, however, not a single chemical reaction where the importance of the tunnel effect has been demonstrated with any certainty.

4.3 NUCLEAR VIBRATIONS In stable molecules, the nuclear motion is usually confined to a narrow region around the equilibrium positions of the nuclei. The vibrational amplitudes are in the range 0.1–0.01 Å., and thus are small as compared to atomic and molecular radii. For these small amplitudes, Hooke's law will hold, and the nuclei will perform, therefore, harmonic vibrations. Even at low temperatures the nuclei will not be localized strictly to their equilibrium positions; the lowest vibrational quantum level lies $\frac{1}{2}h\nu$ higher than the minimum of the potential energy. This residual energy or zero-point energy is again due to the fact that the nucleus cannot be strictly localized at the point where the potential energy is a minimum without its being given a high momentum and a high kinetic energy.

The frequencies with which the nuclei can vibrate in a molecule can be found with the help of infrared spectra, the Raman effect, specific heats, and also absorption and fluorescence spectra. These methods complement each other and frequently all must be used in order to get a complete picture of the vibrations of a polyatomic molecule, although for a diatomic molecule any one of the methods may serve the purpose.

Nuclear vibrations will not be simple for polyatomic molecules; in most vibrations all atoms of the molecule participate to a greater or less extent, although some of the vibrations may be restricted in the main to one group, serving as a practical spectroscopic indication of the presence of that group in the molecule. Careful analysis is needed to obtain the restoring forces acting on the nuclei from the observed frequencies; these restoring forces are a qualitative measure of the energy with which that nucleus or atom is bound in the molecule; a great restoring force will in general correspond to a strong binding.

4.4 THE ISOTOPE EFFECT If we consider the motion of the electrons in the field of the nuclei at rest, no difference will be obtained when a nucleus is replaced by one of its isotopes. Thus, the electronic states will remain the same after isotopic substitution, and the average forces which the electrons exert on the nuclei will not change either. It follows that isotopic substitution will not change the potential field in which the nuclei are moving.

According to classical statistical mechanics, the kinetic energy follows the equipartition law, and the distribution of the nuclei in space is given by the Boltzmann law. The potentials being the same for isotopes, no difference should therefore arise for statistical equilibrium among isotopes.

Differences do arise, however, particularly apparent in the case of the hydrogen isotopes. Such differences are pure quantum phenomena. That they arise primarily for hydrogen is explained by the great percentage difference in the masses of these isotopes and also by the small mass of the hydrogen atom so that quantum effects become particularly noticeable.

The simplest and most important quantum effect of this kind is the zero-point energy. The potentials, and therefore restoring forces, being the same for hydrogen and deuterium, their vibrational frequencies will differ by a factor $\sqrt{2}$. Thus the zero-point energies $\frac{1}{2}h\nu$ will be different, giving rise to differences in heats of reaction which amount as a rule to several hundred calories. The arguments just given are oversimplified because in many vibrations hydrogen atoms will not be the only ones that are moving; however, it gives a good qualitative and sometimes even quantitative idea of the chemical differences between the isotopes.

At high temperatures the difference in chemical equilibrium will tend towards zero since the motion of the nuclei will approach that prescribed by the classical laws.

Reaction velocities will remain different, however, owing to the smaller average velocity of deuterium atoms at a given temperature. Apart from this classical difference, quantum differences in reaction velocity may be expected for the isotopes. In fact, comparison of reaction velocities of isotopes might become very helpful in detecting differences due to quantum theory and in particular in detecting the tunnel effect. However, the differences occurring for the equilibria for final and intermediate products frequently complicate the picture to such an extent that the elementary reaction-velocity differences cannot be isolated.

In general, however, even hydrogen and deuterium do not differ greatly in any chemical reactions. This is the most direct experimental justification for neglecting quantum effects of the nuclear motion in a qualitative survey of chemical equilibria and chemical reactions.

4.5 NUCLEAR POSITIONS Although nuclear vibrations frequently have an amplitude of as much as 0.1 Å., the vibrations do not deviate much from the purely harmonic law. Thus the mean distances of the nuclei will correspond closely to the equilibrium distances. These average distances can be measured by two main methods: The one is the diffraction of electrons or X rays, the other is investigation of molecular rotation in the spectra.

The X-ray diffraction method is based on the fact that X rays, scattered by different atoms in a molecule or in a crystal, interfere with each other and that the interference depends on the distance between the atoms. The fact that electrons (and other particles) have wave properties makes it possible to use electrons instead of X rays. It can be shown that, if a train of waves falls on a crystal, there will be in general no direction in which the scattering of all lattice cells gives rise to constructive interference; one can find for every region in the crystal lattice another region such that the scattering by the two regions cancels. Thus, in general, no scattering takes place, and the original beam remains undisturbed except for processes which involve energy losses. If, however, the wavelength and direction of the incident beam satisfy certain relations, there will exist a direction in which the wave can be scattered by all the crystal cells so that the scattered radiations re-enforce rather than cancel each other. Thus sharp interference maxima occur. From their positions one can derive the size and the microscopic symmetry of the crystal cells. Sometimes this is sufficient for the determination of the position of the nuclei. This is the case if all nuclei lie in centers of symmetry, in intersections of symmetry axes, or in other points defined uniquely by the crystal symmetry. If this is not the case, the position of the atoms might still be obtained by a rather laborious process from the intensities of the interference maxima.

The diffraction method can also be applied to molecules in the gaseous phase. Interference of the radiation scattered by the various atoms in the molecule gives rise to scattering in all directions with varying intensity. The sharpness of the interference maxima in crystals is due to the regularity of the crystal lattice and to its theoretically infinite extension. A finite assembly of scattering centers on the other hand always produces continuous scattering rather than discrete maxima. The angular distribution of the intensity of the scattered radiation depends on the orientation of the molecule. To obtain the experimental intensity distribution one has to average over-all molecular orientations. In simple molecules it is possible to calculate from the observed broad interference maxima the interatomic distances.

Both electron and X-ray interferences have been used in diffraction experiments on crystals and molecules. But for molecules it is much easier to work with electrons since they are scattered more strongly and necessitate only short exposures, whereas molecular diffraction experiments with X rays are difficult on account of the small intensity. For crystal analysis the use of X rays is perhaps preferable. Because of the smaller scattering of the X rays, they penetrate deeper into the crystal and give a truer picture of the body of the crystal. Electrons are apt to be deflected nearer to the surface, particularly if their velocity is relatively low. Thus electron diffraction may be used to explore surface effects. X rays are scattered mainly by electrons rather than by nuclei; however, near any heavy nucleus there is a region of higher electron density; thus X rays scattered from these electrons will give a good indication of the nuclear position.

In electron diffraction the electrons will have a perturbing influence, but the greatest amount of scattering is due to the strong coulomb field of the nucleus.

Neither of these two methods can fix the position of hydrogen atoms with any accuracy; the electron density does not increase sufficiently in the neighborhood of the proton, and the hydrogen nucleus will also not deflect an incoming electron much more strongly than any one of the electrons in the molecule.

Scattering due directly to nuclei can be obtained by using neutron beams rather than X rays or electrons. Practical results have been reached using directed beams of high intensity. Such beams can be obtained from piles producing atomic energy. When such a pile is working, a great density of neutrons is present in its interior. By use of appropriate shields and slits an intense neutron beam can be obtained. The neutrons must be slowed down by an appropriate number of collisions before they pass through the slits. This is necessary because only slow neutrons have long enough wavelength to be useful in crystal interference experiments. With the help of neutron diffraction one may hope to determine the positions of the hydrogen nuclei in crystals and molecules.

Nuclear positions may also be obtained by investigating molecular rotation. The investigation of rotational structures leads to a determination of moments of inertia; these depend primarily on the nuclei rather than on the electrons. There is, moreover, no particular difficulty in obtaining the position of hydrogen atoms; thus rotational structures give as a general rule more accurate, more reliable, and in a way, more general results than diffraction experiments. However, the rotational structure can be investigated only in the gaseous state, and even there the method is practicable only for rather simple molecules. This method is discussed in greater detail in Chapter 10.

With the help of the methods mentioned, it is, as a general rule, easy to determine the (average) nuclear positions with an accuracy of 0.01 Å.

A careful study of the vibrational spectra of molecules may lead to conclusions about the symmetry and the shape, but not the size of a molecule. Qualitative results may be obtained from the classical methods of stereochemistry which in the last decades have been supplemented by the study of dipole moments.

5. ATOMS AND MOLECULES IN ELECTRIC FIELDS

5.1 ATOMIC FIELDS AND MACROSCOPIC FIELDS The electric charges of the constituents of matter give rise to strong electric fields which cause the chemical forces. The only reason why chemical laws are not simply reduced to electrostatics is that the electrons behave under the influence of these electric forces, not according to classical mechanics but according to quantum mechanics, and that they furthermore show that peculiar behavior which we have described under the name of the Pauli principle. In explaining chemical forces, it must be borne in mind that both the particles that produce the electric field and the particles on which the electric field acts behave according to quantum laws. A simpler application of the electrical structure of molecules will be treated in this chapter, namely, the interaction of atoms and molecules with macroscopic electric fields, that is, with electric fields produced by the usual electrical apparatus rather than with the exceedingly strong fields of individual atoms and molecules.

5.2 ATOMS IN HOMOGENEOUS FIELDS We will consider a molecule in an electric field with the nuclei in their equilibrium positions; the effect of their vibration may be neglected. A definite orientation of the molecule with regard to the electric field will be assumed.

The interaction energy between molecule and electric field can then be obtained as follows: The value of the electric potential at the position of each nucleus will be multiplied by the positive charge of that nucleus, and the sum will be taken. The contribution of the electrons is obtained by spreading out the electrons according to their probability distribution as given by the absolute square of the wave function; the interaction of this continuous charge-density with the external field is to be taken.

This prescription does not mean that the electrons are actually spread out into a continuous cloud of negative charge. It only means that for the interaction of electrons and field the weighted average has to be taken as calculated with the help of the probabilities of distinct positions which the electron may occupy.

44

For the purpose of this calculation the electron distribution will be taken to be the same as that valid for the molecule in the absence of the electric field; this of course means that we disregard the distortion of the electronic structure; that is, we neglect polarizability. The effects due to polarizability are discussed later.

If the electric field acting on the molecule is homogeneous, a particularly simple picture will be obtained. We will first consider an isolated neutral atom. In this case the interaction energy is zero; the reason for this is that the probability of finding the electrons at points removed from the nucleus by the vector r and the vector $-r$ [see Figure 5.2(1)] is always the same. Now the mean value of the interaction of the electron and the homogeneous field at the points r and $-r$ is the same as the interaction which would be obtained if the electron were at the same position as the nucleus. Thus the electronic charge effectively neutralizes the nuclear charge. A similar argument holds if many electrons

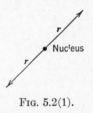

FIG. 5.2(1).

have to be considered; in the corresponding argument all vectors drawn from the nucleus to the electrons have to be inverted, that is, replaced by $-r$, simultaneously. Again the probabilities of these inverted configurations will be the same, and their mean action is equivalent to all electrons being concentrated in the nucleus.

An example of the zero interaction between an atom and the field will be furnished by the fundamental state of the hydrogen atom, where the electron is in an s state, and its charge distribution has spherical symmetry. Even if an electron is in a p state, its interaction will remain zero, since the square of the ψ function (giving the probability distribution) will be symmetrical to the inversion as previously described. The only kind of exception that occurs is illustrated by Figure 2.11(2) where the main electronic charge is found to the right, or in Figure 2.11(3) where the main electronic charge is found to the left of the nucleus and can no longer be replaced by a charge at the same position as the nucleus. This occurs, however, only if excited states are taken into account or if there is an accidental degeneracy between an s and a p state or between further states. There is no known example of such degeneracy in the fundamental state of an atom. Therefore the interaction between a homogeneous electric field and an undistorted atom in its lowest state is zero.

5.3 PERMANENT DIPOLES The interaction between a homogeneous field and an undistorted molecule will vanish if the molecule has a sufficiently high symmetry. One can give as examples CS_2, CCl_4,

C_6H_6, and C_2H_6. In other molecules, however, such as HCl, H_2O, C_6H_5Cl, and C_3H_8, the effects of positive and negative charges will not cancel, and a finite interaction with the field will be obtained. It can be shown that such an interaction depends in the following way on the orientation of the molecule: It has a maximum value for a certain orientation of the molecule with regard to the electric field; this maximum interaction will remain unchanged if the molecule is rotated through any angle around an axis parallel to the electric field. If the molecule is rotated through an angle θ around any axis perpendicular to the electric field, then the interaction is multiplied by $\cos \theta$. For $\theta = 180°$, the interaction will have changed sign.

This behavior can be represented by rigidly attaching to the molecule an imaginary vector called its dipole moment; the length of this vector is given by the maximum interaction the molecule can have with a unit electric field. The orientation of the vector has to be fixed in the molecule in such a way that the maximum interaction with the field is obtained when the vector is parallel to the field.

The physical significance of the dipole moment is that it is a measure of the separation of the center of the positive charges from the center of the negative charges in the molecule. The easiest way to represent it is to locate an appropriate positive charge e and the corresponding negative charge $-e$ at the distance l from each other; it is easy to verify that such a charge distribution will have just the required interaction with the homogeneous field. It represents a dipole of the magnitude $el = d$; dE is equal to the maximum interaction energy between the dipole and an electric field E. The direction of the dipole moment is given by the line pointing from the negative towards the positive charge. In general, the interaction between the electric field and the dipole is $-dE \cos \theta$, where θ is the angle between the directions of the dipole and the electric field. The minus sign is due to the fact that the energy of the dipole is a minimum when it points in the direction of the electric field.

There still remains an arbitrariness, since the magnitude of the dipole moment determines only el, and not e and l separately. It is customary to define a pure dipole as the special case where e tends to ∞ and l tends to zero, so that their product remains constant.

To represent the charge distribution in a molecule by the simple picture of a dipole is permissible only as long as an interaction with a homogeneous electric field is considered. For atomic dimensions every macroscopic field may be considered to be homogeneous, but the electric field originating in a neighboring molecule will in general be strongly inhomogeneous. In order to obtain the interaction with such molecular fields, the dipole moment of the molecule is not sufficient, but a rather more detailed description of the charge distribution in the molecule is needed. Unfortunately, it is very difficult to obtain exact information about the detailed charge distribution, the dipole moment being the only well-defined quantity which can be determined by direct experiment.

5.4 ORIENTATION OF DIPOLES IN AN OUTSIDE FIELD

The most direct manifestation of dipole moments is their effect on the dielectric constants of materials, due to the orienting effect of an electric field on the dipoles. We shall consider a volume of 1 cc. containing an assembly of dipoles in an electric field. The electric field will try to orient all the dipoles, while the temperature motion will tend to introduce a random orientation of the dipoles. According to the Boltzmann law, the relative number of molecules possessing potential energy V is $e^{-V/kT}$, where k is the Boltzmann constant and has the value 1.38×10^{-16} erg per degree. If we are interested in the relative number of dipoles at different angles to the direction of an electric field E, we have to introduce for V the expression $-Ed \cos \theta$ so that we obtain $e^{Ed \cos \theta/kT}$. It is easily verified that for conditions obtainable in laboratories the exponent is small * compared with unity. We can therefore write

$$e^{Ed \cos \theta/kT} = 1 + Ed \cos \theta/kT \qquad 5.4(1)$$

We see that under experimental conditions there are only slightly more dipoles pointing toward the direction of the electric field ($\cos \theta$ positive) than pointing away from the electric field ($\cos \theta$ negative). The slight preponderance of dipoles pointing in the direction of the electric field will cause, in the assembly of molecules, a net dipole moment parallel to the electric field. This net dipole moment can be calculated by multiplying the contribution of each dipole at orientation θ (which is $d \cos \theta$) by the number of molecules having that orientation and by averaging over-all orientations. One obtains

$$\text{Net dipole} = \overline{Nd \cos \theta[1 + Ed \cos \theta/kT]}$$
$$= \overline{Nd \cos \theta} + \overline{NEd^2 \cos^2 \theta/kT} \qquad 5.4(2)$$

Here N is the total number of molecules in the unit volume considered.

* Even if we substitute for E the high value of 10^5 volts per centimeter, that is, $\frac{1}{3} \times 10^3$ E.S.U., for T, the value of 300° K., and for d the value 10^{-17} E.S.U. (corresponding to the rather large dipole moment produced by approximately two electronic charges at a distance of 1 Å. from two corresponding positive charges), we obtain $Ed/kT = 0.08$.

The horizontal lines above the symbols indicate the averaging process. In evaluating the average, all orientations in space have to be given equal weight since the fact that more molecules point in the direction of the field than in the opposite direction has been already taken into account by the factor $1 + Ed \cos \theta / kT$. In averaging over the first term, $Nd \cos \theta$, we obtain zero; this is due to the perfectly random orientation of the molecules in the absence of an electric field. In the second term the average over $\cos^2 \theta$ gives $\frac{1}{3}$, so that we obtain for the net polarization (that is, net dipole per cubic centimeter) $\frac{1}{3} NEd^2 / kT$. The expression just obtained can be written in the form $N\bar{d}$ where the average contribution of one molecule toward the net dipole moment is

$$\bar{d} = \frac{Ed^2}{3kT} \qquad\qquad 5.4(3)$$

The expression for the average dipole $\bar{d}$ can be easily understood since it has to be proportional to the potential energy Ed of one dipole parallel to the electric field, to the contribution d towards the net dipole moment of one parallel dipole, and also inversely proportional to the temperature T tending to introduce random orientation.

5.5   DIELECTRIC MEDIA   The fact that electric fields cause a net dipole within media gives rise to what is called their properties as dielectrics. These properties are characterized by the dielectric constant K which we will now define.

In measuring the electric field within a dielectric medium the detailed interaction of a test charge with the dipoles of the medium is of importance. Two simple cases may be distinguished. First, we shall make in the dielectric medium a cavity of oblong shape parallel to the direction of the electric force and measure the electric field in this cavity. The result of this measurement, when the length of the cavity is made great as compared to its two other dimensions, is called the electric field E in the dielectric. Second, we consider a flat cavity with its two dimensions perpendicular to the electric field great as compared to its thickness parallel to the electric field. The electric field measured in such a cavity is called the electric displacement D of the dielectric. The dielectric constant K is then given by the ratio D/E.

The reason for the difference between D and E is that, whenever a dielectric medium has a boundary perpendicular to the electric field, a surface charge will be present on that boundary. In the case of the flat cavity, these surface charges are close to the test charge within the cavity, whereas in the oblong cavity they are far away. Figure 5.5(1) shows a dielectric (shaded) with a field in the direction of the arrow and a flat cavity having two parallel surfaces of area S. We can find the surface density of the charge by considering a volume below the cavity of the same cross section S and thickness L. In that volume LS there will be a total dipole equal to the net dipole per cubic centimeter, called the polarization P, times LS. Some of the dipoles oriented * by the field are shown in Figure 5.5(1). The dipoles close to the surface will give rise to an uncompensated average charge on the surface. In order to get a net dipole PLS, we might take a positive-charge distribution

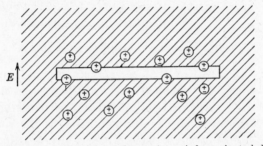

FIG. 5.5(1). Dielectric, with field and flat cavity. A few oriented dipole molecules are shown.

LSP/l and a negative-charge distribution of the same size and displace them by a distance l from each other. A fraction l/L of the positive charge then will remain uncompensated on the lower surface of the cavity shown in Figure 5.5(1); that is, we will have the total surface charge $l/L \cdot PLS/l = PS$. Dividing by the surface we find that the surface density is P; that is, the surface density is equal to the net dipole induced within the material per cubic centimeter. In a similar manner we find that on the upper surface of the cavity there is a negative sur-face charge of density P. The positive test charge in the cavity will be repelled by the lower surface and attracted by the upper surface so that it will experience a stronger force than in an oblong cavity parallel to the field in which the surface charges are not effective. Thus we find in general $D > E$ and $K > 1$.

In order to calculate the increase of field strength in the flat cavity due to the surface charges, we represent the electric field by lines of force. The lines of force are drawn parallel to the direction of the

---

* For the purpose of the present argument, it makes no difference whether the dipoles are completely oriented as shown in the figure or whether there are a greater number of dipoles with a slight preference of orientation in the field direction as described in the previous section.

force and their number per square centimeter gives the strength of the electric force. They are convenient, because, as can be shown, they are continuous lines having no beginning and no end except in regions where charges are present; therefore, these lines will give an immediate picture not only of the electric forces but also of the charge distributions, the regions of positive charge being their source and the regions of negative charge their termination. A simple example is the field

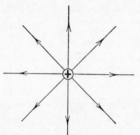

e/r^2 produced by one positive charge e. The lines of force emanating from this charge are shown in Figure 5.5(2). The number of lines of force crossing any sphere of radius r drawn around the charge as center is $\dfrac{e}{r^2} 4\pi r^2 = 4\pi e$, so that no sources for the lines need be assumed except at the position of the charge. We can generalize this result and say that any positive charge e is the source of $4\pi e$ force lines, whereas any negative charge $-e$ is the termination of the same number of force lines.

FIG. 5.5(2). Field produced by one positive charge. The field is represented by lines of force.

In Figure 5.5(3) the flat cavity perpendicular to the direction of the field is shown again with the negative surface charges on the top of the cavity and the positive surface charges at the bottom. The additional field which these surface charges cause is represented by the force lines

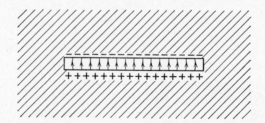

FIG. 5.5(3). Flat cavity in electric field. The electric field produced by the surface charges is represented by lines of force.

drawn from the positive to the negative charges. These force lines will be a set of parallel lines across the cavity having a more complicated form near the edges. Since the surface density is equal to P, the number of force lines per square centimeter will be $4\pi P$, and the added electric field due to the surface charges is $4\pi P$. This added field represents the difference between D and E, and we have therefore

$$D - E = 4\pi P \qquad\qquad 5.5(1)$$

and $$K = \frac{D}{E} = 1 + \frac{4\pi P}{E} \qquad\qquad 5.5(2)$$

5.6 MEASUREMENT OF DIELECTRIC CONSTANTS The
customary procedure for measuring the dielectric constant is to introduce a dielectric medium between the plates of a capacitor and to measure to what extent capacitance of the capacitor is changed. In Figure 5.6(1) a capacitor is shown with its positive plate p^+ and its negative
plate p^-. If the surface density of electricity of the plate is ρ, then in
the absence of a dielectric medium in the capacitor, an electric field
$E = 4\pi\rho$ is produced between the plates. The capacitance of the
capacitor is the charge on its plates ρS (S = surface area of capacitor)
divided by the potential, that is, by the work necessary to carry a unit
positive charge from the negative
plate to the positive plate. This work
is the thickness of the capacitor L,
times the electric field $4\pi\rho$, so that
we get for the capacitance $\rho S/4\pi\rho L$
$= S/4\pi L$.

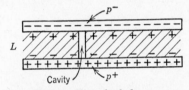

Fig. 5.6(1). The shaded area represents a dielectric medium. The
charge density on the plates of the
capacitor is partly compensated by
smaller charge densities of opposite
sign on the adjacent surfaces of the
dielectric.

If we now introduce a dielectric
medium M [shown in Figure 5.6(1)
by shading] into the capacitor, a
negative surface charge of density
$4\pi P$ will appear opposite the positive plate and a positive surface
charge of the same density opposite the negative plate. In order to
measure the potential across a capacitor, we have to move a charge
along a cavity as shown in Figure 5.6(1). This cavity being parallel to
the direction of the electric field, the force acting on the electric charge
is E in the dielectric. E is caused by the charge densities both on the
capacitor plates and on the surface of the dielectric and therefore is
$E = 4\pi\rho - 4\pi P$. Now, according to equation 5.5(1), $(K - 1)E =$
$4\pi P$; adding these two relations, we obtain $KE = 4\pi\rho$. The potential
across the capacitor is therefore $LE = L\dfrac{4\pi\rho}{K}$, and the capacitance of
the capacitor $\rho S/\dfrac{4\pi\rho L}{K} = K\dfrac{S}{4\pi L}$. We see therefore that the capacitance has become K times as great by the introduction of a medium of

dielectric constant K between its plates, and that the dielectric constant can be obtained by measuring the ratio of the capacitances.

5.7 DETERMINATION OF DIPOLE MOMENTS If the dielectric properties of a medium are caused by permanent dipoles, we shall have, according to the discussion in section 5.4, for the polarization $P = N\bar{d} = \dfrac{N}{3}\dfrac{Ed^2}{kT}$, and, for the dielectric constant,

$$\frac{1}{4\pi}(K - 1) = \frac{P}{E} = \frac{N}{3}\frac{d^2}{kT} \qquad 5.7(1)$$

This formula for the dielectric constant will have to be corrected later since it does not take account of the fact that the dielectric constants of nondipole substances with $d = 0$ have dielectric constants K differing from unity. Moreover, it is not true that the dielectric constants of dipole substances approach unity at very high temperatures, as would be indicated by our formula. The reason for these discrepancies is that we have considered the electronic structure of the molecules as rigid, thus neglecting their polarizability. The polarizability will give rise to a temperature-independent term in the dielectric-constant formula. Equation 5.7(1), therefore, represents the temperature dependence of the dielectric constant correctly. It may be added that the contribution of the permanent dipoles to the dielectric constant is at room temperature greater than the contribution of the polarizability except, of course, for substances for which the dipole moment is rather small ($\ll 10^{-18}$ electrostatic unit).

The temperature dependence of the dielectric constant of gases can be used to determine the dipole moment of the molecules in the gas. If one plots the dielectric constant against the reciprocal of the temperature, a straight line is obtained, the slope of which, as can be seen from Equation 5.7(1), is $\dfrac{4\pi N}{3}\dfrac{d^2}{k}$, so that d can be calculated readily. It may be seen that, although this formula may give accurate values for rather large dipole moments, it is difficult to get a good determination of a small dipole moment or even to distinguish a small dipole moment from zero. If we compare, for instance, the rather large dipole moments 2×10^{-18} E.S.U. and 2.1×10^{-18} E.S.U., the d^2 values differ by 0.41×10^{-36}; on the other hand, if we compare $d = 0$ and $d = 0.1 \times 10^{-18}$ E.S.U., a difference of only 0.01×10^{-36} will be obtained for the d^2 values.

The determination of molecular dipole moments by measurements on gases is of course limited to substances with sufficiently high vapor pressures; no determination can be carried out in the liquid phase since the strong interaction of dipoles of neighboring molecules of the liquid will lead to more or less well-defined molecular complexes, and measurements of dielectric constants will give some average value of the dipole moments of these complexes rather than the dipole moments of the molecules themselves. It is more feasible to obtain dipole moments by investigating the dielectric properties of dilute solutions. It is important that the solvent should have no permanent dipole moment.

Even in the dilute solutions, the interaction of the solute molecules with those of the solvent affects the results. The solvent may be considered as a dielectric, and, as we have seen, the forces that act on charges in a dielectric depend on the shape of the cavity in which we place the charges. The shape of the cavity, however, will depend on the shape of the molecule. Moreover, the orientation of the molecule with regard to the electric field causes the cavity for the same molecule to resemble sometimes the oblong cavity and sometimes the flat cavity. The simplest and most frequently adopted method is to take the averaging effect of the orientations on the type of cavity into account by using a spherical cavity. It can be shown that the field in a spherical cavity is $\frac{2}{3}E + \frac{1}{3}D$; then, analogously to equation 5.7(1), the polarization P_d due to the dissolved dipoles will be

$$P_d = \left(\frac{2}{3}E + \frac{1}{3}D\right)\frac{Nd^2}{3kT} \qquad 5.7(2)$$

where N is the number of dipoles per cubic centimeter. The polarizability of the dissolved molecules has again been neglected. We can [see equation 5.7(1)] set in sufficient approximation for the polarization P_s of the pure solvent,

$$P_s = \frac{E(K_0 - 1)}{4\pi} \qquad 5.7(3)$$

where K_0 is the dielectric constant of the pure solvent. Introducing the total polarization $P = P_s + P_d$,

$$P = \frac{E(K - 1)}{4\pi}$$

$$\frac{E(K - 1)}{4\pi} = \left(\frac{2}{3}E + \frac{1}{3}KE\right)\frac{Nd^2}{3kT} + \frac{E(K_0 - 1)}{4\pi} \qquad 5.7(4)$$

which simplifies to

$$\frac{3(K - 1)}{4\pi(K + 2)} = \frac{Nd^2}{3kT} + \frac{3(K_0 - 1)}{4\pi(K + 2)} \qquad 5.7(5)$$

or

$$\frac{3(K - K_0)}{4\pi(K + 2)} = \frac{Nd^2}{3kT} \qquad 5.7(6)$$

If the polarizability of the solute molecules had been taken into account, a temperature-independent term would appear on the right-hand side of equation 5.7(5). It is again possible to determine d by plotting $\dfrac{K - K_0}{K + 2}$ against $1/T$.

Table 5.7(1) gives the dipole moments of chlorobenzene in different

TABLE 5.7(1)

DIPOLE MOMENTS OF CHLOROBENZENE, ACETONE, AND HYDROCHLORIC ACID

	Gas	C_6H_{14}	C_6H_6	CCl_4	CS_2	Cyclo-hexane
C_6H_5Cl		1.6	1.56	1.56	1.49	1.59
CH_3COCH_3	2.84	2.71	2.71	2.82		
HCl	1.03		1.28	1.32		1.32

solvents as obtained by the method just described. The apparent agreement of the dipole moments determined in different solvents helps to justify the method. A similarly good agreement is found for acetone in the same table, and these values also agree with the dipole moment as obtained from measurements in the gas. But for hydrochloric acid the dipole moment as obtained from measurements in the gas does not agree with the values obtained from solutions. This is not too surprising, since the theory of determination of dipole moments in dilute solutions involves rather crude approximations such as treating the solvent as a continuous medium and neglecting the influence of the shape of the solute molecule. Thus steric effects between the solute and solvent molecules are not taken into account, and dipole-moment determinations are strictly speaking exact only if carried out in the gaseous state. As the case of HCl shows, even agreement between values obtained with different solvents is no guarantee for the correctness of the values.

Another method of measuring dipole moments makes use of molecular beams. The deflection of a molecular beam in a strongly inhomogeneous electric field is studied. The reason for using an inhomogeneous electric field is that a homogeneous field does not deflect any uncharged molecule, since the repulsion and attraction acting on the positive and negative charges, respectively, cancel. In an inhomogeneous electric field, however, the molecule will be deflected if it possesses a dipole, since the positive and negative charges of the molecule will be under the influence of somewhat different electric-field intensities.

Determinations of dipole moments by molecular-beam methods have the great advantage of being free from any uncertainty due to interaction between molecules. A more refined molecular-beam technique makes use of resonance between rotation (or precession) of dipoles and an oscillating electromagnetic field. This method is capable of great precision. Up to the present it has been chiefly used to determine magnetic dipoles. But it eventually may become the best way to obtain information about electric dipole moments.

5.8 VALUES OF DIPOLE MOMENTS   Measurements have confirmed the expectation that atoms have no permanent dipole moments. Likewise the dipole moments of diatomic molecules containing two atoms of the same kind are zero. This holds, even if the two atoms are different isotopes, as would be expected (see section 4.4). Diatomic molecules containing two different atoms have dipole moments, although in the case of such "non-polar molecules" as CO and NO the moments are not easily distinguishable from the moment zero. Dipole moments of some polar molecules are contained in Table 5.8(1).

TABLE 5.8(1)

DIPOLE MOMENTS OF DIATOMIC MOLECULES IN THE GASEOUS STATE

E.S.U. ($\mu \times 10^{18}$)

HCl	1.03
HBr	0.78
HI	0.38
NaI	4.9
KCl	6.3
KI	6.8

It may be seen that halogen hydrides have comparatively small dipoles which decrease with increasing atomic weight of the halogen. The dipole moment is much smaller than we would obtain by attaching a positive electronic charge to the hydrogen and a similar negative charge to the halogen. The small dipoles are to be actually expected, since the hydrogen ion which is a bare atomic nucleus is imbedded in the charged cloud of the negative ion and attracts the negative charge of the strongly polarizable halogen ion. The alkali halides are more polar since the alkali ion retains inner shells of electrons and, according to the Pauli principle, cannot penetrate into the halogen ion. Nevertheless the polarizability of the ions reduces the dipole moments. Even for the least polarizable of the molecules investigated (KCl) the dipole moment is only about half the value obtained if positive and negative electronic charges are attached to the alkali and the halogen.

In triatomic molecules, dipole moments are important because they are used to obtain information about the shape of the molecule. Thus the absence of a dipole moment in CO_2 and CS_2 confirms the idea of a symmetrical linear molecule. On the other hand, the dipole moments of H_2O, H_2S, SO_2, and N_2O show that these molecules are either non-symmetrical or nonlinear [see Table 5.8(2)]. In a similar way the dipole moments of ammonia, phosphine, and arsine show that these molecules cannot have a plane symmetrical configuration. Table 5.8(2) gives the dipole moments of some simpler polyatomic molecules.

TABLE 5.8(2)

DIPOLE MOMENTS OF SOME SIMPLER POLYATOMIC MOLECULES

E.S.U. ($\mu \times 10^{18}$)		E.S.U. ($\mu \times 10^{18}$)	
N_2O	0.14	PH_3	0.55
HCN	2.6	AsH_3	0.15
H_2O	1.79	CH_3Cl	1.97
H_2S	0.93	CH_2Cl_2	1.59
SO_2	1.61	$CHCl_3$	0.95
NH_3	1.46		

5.9 VECTOR ADDITIVITY OF DIPOLES The dipole moments of more complicated molecules can be measured as a general rule only in the liquid state. A study of these moments has shown that in many cases the net dipole moment of the molecule can be obtained as a vector sum of dipoles attached to certain bonds within the molecule. The best examples of the operation of this rule are the disubstituted benzenes. If for instance the two substituents are in the para position, the dipole moment should be equal to the difference of dipole moments of the corresponding monosubstituted products. Thus p-chlornitrobenzene has a dipole moment 2.36×10^{-18} E.S.U., while nitrobenzene and chlorobenzene have dipole moments 3.8×10^{-18} and 1.55×10^{-18}, giving a difference 2.25×10^{-18} E.S.U. If the two substituents are the same, the para compound has, of course, a zero moment but the meta compound should have the same dipole moment as the monosubstituted product since the sum of two vectors of equal magnitude at an angle of 120° has the same magnitude as either of the vectors. Table 5.9(1)

TABLE 5.9(1)

DIPOLE MOMENTS OF MONOSUBSTITUTED AND METADISUBSTITUTED BENZENE DERIVATIVES IN ELECTROSTATIC UNITS. EACH META DERIVATIVE CONTAINS ONLY ONE TYPE OF SUBSTITUENT

	Mono	Meta
Chlor	1.55×10^{-18}	1.48×10^{-18}
Brom	1.52×10^{-18}	1.50×10^{-18}
Iodo	1.30×10^{-18}	1.27×10^{-18}
Nitro	3.8×10^{-18}	3.9×10^{-18}

gives the comparison between the meta and mono compounds. In the case of the ortho compounds vector addition gives a dipole moment $\sqrt{3}$ times as great as for the monosubstituted product. Table 5.9(2)

TABLE 5.9(2)

WEIGHTED DIPOLE MOMENTS OF MONOSUBSTITUTED AND ORTHOSUBSTITUTED BENZENE DERIVATIVES IN ELECTROSTATIC UNITS. EACH ORTHO DERIVATIVE CONTAINS ONLY ONE TYPE OF SUBSTITUENT

	$\sqrt{3}$ Mono	Ortho
Fluor	2.42×10^{-18}	2.38×10^{-18}
Chlor	2.68×10^{-18}	2.25×10^{-18}
Brom	2.63×10^{-18}	2.00×10^{-18}
Iodo	2.25×10^{-18}	1.69×10^{-18}
Nitro	6.75×10^{-18}	6.00×10^{-18}

shows this comparison. It may be seen that values for the ortho substances are smaller than one would expect. Apparently the closeness of the substituents caused a considerable perturbation of the charge distribution. The vector-addition rule for dipole moments is significant because it shows to what extent physical properties of parts of molecules are independent of the other parts. It will be seen later that, in molecules containing systems of conjugated double bonds, relatively distant parts can influence each other, and thus it is surprising that even approximate additivity obtains.

Another consequence of a rigorous rule of additivity would be that the dipole moments of all saturated hydrocarbons would be equal to zero. It follows from the tetrahedral direction of carbon valencies that the CH_3 group has the same dipole as the C–H bond and this together with the zero dipole of the C–C bond shows that substitution of an H by CH_3 will not change the dipole moment. By such substitutions all hydrocarbons can be obtained from methane which has of course a zero dipole moment. That nearly all hydrocarbons actually have dipole moments too small to be measured need not be considered as a striking confirmation of the additivity of dipoles. The absence of dipole moments may be rather a consequence of a small polarity of the C–H bond.

5.10 ELECTRONIC POLARIZABILITY We shall now investigate the influence of external electric fields on the motion of electrons; that is, we shall discuss the electronic polarizability. If an atom or a molecule is placed in an electric field, the electrons will be repelled by the electric field, and there will be a greater electron density on the side opposite the direction of the electric field. This effect is, however, rather small as long as the perturbing electric field is small compared to the electric fields of electrons and nuclei within the molecule. There exists a close analogy between this situation and the orientation of dipoles in a weak field. In the latter example it was the temperature energy (kT) that prevented all dipoles from lining up in the direction of the field. In the case of the electronic polarizability it is the kinetic energy of the electrons that takes over the role of the temperature energy.

It may be recalled that electrons do not fall into the nuclei because a localization of the electron position near the nucleus would lead to an excessive kinetic energy. The actual distribution of electrons in atoms or molecules is a compromise between the tendency of the potential energy which favors localization of the electrons and the tendency of kinetic energy which favors small values of the momentum and, therefore, according to the uncertainty principle works against localization. This compromise between strong forces and high kinetic energies cannot be greatly disturbed by weak external forces. The actual electronic dipole moment d_e, induced in the molecule by the electric field E can be written in a form similar to the one we have obtained for the average value $\bar{d}$ [see equation 5.4(3)] in weak fields. To obtain d_e we must replace in the formula, $\bar{d} = \dfrac{1}{3}\dfrac{Ed^2}{kT}$, the permanent dipole moment d by the dipole moment which the electron and the nucleus would have at a distance of approximately one atomic radius a. We also replace kT by the average kinetic energy of the electrons which is roughly of the same magnitude as the ionization energy V of the molecule. Since these considerations are only approximate, numerical coefficients will be omitted, and we obtain

$$d_e \cong \frac{Ee^2a^2}{V} \qquad\qquad 5.10(1)$$

The induced dipole moment of the molecule divided by the electric field E that caused it is called the polarizability α of the molecule. We thus obtain

$$\alpha = \frac{d_e}{E} \cong \frac{e^2a^2}{V} \qquad\qquad 5.10(2)$$

In the formula for the net dipole moment per cubic centimeter P, we now must add the contribution of the polarizability to the contribution of the dipole moments,

$$P = NE\alpha + \frac{N}{3}\frac{Ed^2}{kT} \qquad\qquad 5.10(3)$$

Thus we obtain, for the dielectric constant,

$$\frac{1}{4\pi} (K - 1) = \frac{P}{E} = N\alpha + \frac{N}{3} \frac{d^2}{kT} \qquad 5.10(4)$$

Since α is a positive quantity, the dielectric constant will be greater than unity even for nondipole substances and also for dipole substances at very high temperatures.

5.11   ANISOTROPIC POLARIZABILITY   The rare gases and many metallic vapors consist of atoms, the electronic structure of which has spherical symmetry.   For such atoms one may expect that the induced dipole moment will be parallel to the inducing electric field and that its magnitude will depend only on the strength of the electric field and not on its orientation.

Molecules have a structure that is not spherically symmetrical so that one may expect different polarizabilities according to the orientation of the electric field relative to the molecule.   Moreover, the induced dipole moment is not always parallel to the inducing electric field but will tend to include the smallest angle with the direction of greatest polarizability. But it still is true that the induced dipole moment is a linear function of the inducing field and that it vanishes if the inducing field is zero.   We may express this fact in terms of the components of the dipole moment d_e and the electric field E along the co-ordinate axes, x, y, and z.

$$d_x = \alpha_{xx}E_x + \alpha_{xy}E_y + \alpha_{xz}E_z$$
$$d_y = \alpha_{yx}E_x + \alpha_{yy}E_y + \alpha_{yz}E_z \qquad 5.11(1)$$
$$d_z = \alpha_{zx}E_x + \alpha_{zy}E_y + \alpha_{zz}E_z$$

Here α_{xx}, α_{yy}, etc., are constants which take the place of the simple polarizability α.   For the components of d_e we write d_x, d_y, d_z, and for the components of the electric field E_x, E_y, E_z.

This representation, of course, changes in form if a new set of co-ordinate axes is used.   In the new co-ordinate system both the components of the vectors and the values of the coefficients α_{xx}, etc., have new values, but the new values of the coefficients α_{xx}, etc., are uniquely determined by the values of the coefficients in the original system and by the rotation of the co-ordinate axes.   One considers the nine coefficients as components of one quantity, the polarizability α, just as the three numbers d_x, d_y, and d_z are components of d, the induced dipole moment.   We may write in a symbolical way for the system of equations 5.11(1),

$$d = \alpha E \qquad 5.11(2)$$

In this equation d and E are vectors, and α is a quantity with nine components, the characteristic property of which is that they establish linear relationships among the components of two vectors. Quantities of this kind are called tensors.

In the specific case of the polarizability tensor, all tensor components α_{xx}, etc., are not independent. The relations,

$$\alpha_{xy} = \alpha_{yx}$$

$$\alpha_{yz} = \alpha_{zy} \qquad 5.11(3)$$

$$\alpha_{zx} = \alpha_{xz}$$

exist as can be shown to follow from the idea that a molecule in an electric field possesses a definite electrostatic energy and a definite energy associated with the distortion of the electronic structure in the electric field. We can also show that, if the relations 5.11(3) hold for one co-ordinate system, they must hold for all co-ordinate systems. Thus these relations do not represent an accidental property of the tensor components but correspond to a property of the tensor itself. Tensors with this property are called symmetrical tensors because the quadratic scheme, or, as it is called, matrix, of their components is symmetrical with regard to the main diagonal, shown in the matrix as a dotted line [see 5.11(4)].

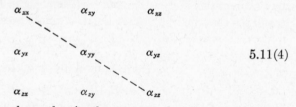

$$5.11(4)$$

Symmetrical tensors have the simple property that if we choose a set of co-ordinates ξ, η, ζ in an appropriate way, then only the diagonal components $\alpha_{\xi\xi}$, $\alpha_{\eta\eta}$, $\alpha_{\zeta\zeta}$ are different from zero while the nondiagonal components $\alpha_{\xi\eta}$, $\alpha_{\eta\zeta}$, $\alpha_{\zeta\xi}$ vanish. The equations 5.11(1) assume in this particular co-ordinate system the simple form:

$$d_\xi = \alpha_{\xi\xi}E_\xi$$

$$d_\eta = \alpha_{\eta\eta}E_\eta \qquad 5.11(5)$$

$$d_\zeta = \alpha_{\zeta\zeta}E_\zeta$$

The physical significance of these equations is that there are three orthogonal directions, ξ, η, ζ, fixed in the molecule, along which the induced moments are parallel to the inducing fields. The three axes are called the principal axes of polarizability. Polarizability is conventionally represented by a triaxial ellipsoid with semiaxis values $\alpha_{\xi\xi}$, $\alpha_{\eta\eta}$, $\alpha_{\zeta\zeta}$ along the three principal axes.

It may be seen that, if two of these axes, for example $\alpha_{\xi\xi}$ and $\alpha_{\eta\eta}$, are equal, the ellipsoid reduces to an ellipsoid of revolution, in the example around the ζ axis. In this case any orthogonal axis perpendicular to ζ may be chosen as principal axis, and an electric field perpendicular to ζ will always induce an electric moment parallel to itself. The polarizabilities of diatomic molecules are as a rule ellipsoids of revolution. This holds also for molecules of lesser symmetry such as benzene; in fact, it is clear that if an ellipsoid is to have hexagonal symmetry it must be an ellipsoid of revolution.

If all three principal axes, $\alpha_{\xi\xi}$, $\alpha_{\eta\eta}$, $\alpha_{\zeta\zeta}$, are equal, the polarizability ellipsoid reduces to a sphere; then any direction can be considered as a principal axis. The induced dipole moment is always parallel to the inducing field, and the polarizability in every direction is the same. Not only atoms possess spherical polarizability; in molecules with tetrahedral or octahedral symmetry, the polarizability must also possess tetrahedral or octahedral symmetry, and the only ellipsoid of that symmetry is a sphere. Spherical polarizability is called isotropic, whereas the polarizability is called anisotropic if at least two of the principal axes are different.

For the general case of an anisotropic polarizability the dielectric constant K can be obtained in a rough way by assuming that one third of the molecules are oriented with their ξ axes parallel to the electric field, one third with their η axes and one third with their ζ axes parallel to this direction. Then the contribution to the polarization will be

$$\frac{N}{3}E\alpha_{\xi\xi}, \quad \frac{N}{3}E\alpha_{\eta\eta}, \quad \frac{N}{3}E\alpha_{\zeta\zeta} \qquad 5.11(6)$$

respectively, and we obtain,

$$P = \frac{N}{3}E\alpha_{\xi\xi} + \frac{N}{3}E\alpha_{\eta\eta} + \frac{N}{3}E\alpha_{\zeta\zeta} + \frac{Nd^2E}{3kT} \qquad 5.11(7)$$

and finally

$$\frac{1}{4\pi}(K-1) = \frac{P}{E} = N\bar{\alpha} + \frac{N}{3}\frac{d^2}{kT} \qquad 5.11(8)$$

with

$$\bar{\alpha} = \frac{\alpha_{\xi\xi} + \alpha_{\eta\eta} + \alpha_{\zeta\zeta}}{3} \qquad 5.11(9)$$

It may be seen that equation 5.11(8) is the same as equation 5.10(4) if α in the latter equation is replaced by the mean polarizability $\bar{\alpha}$. A more rigorous argument shows that equation 5.11(8) is correct in spite of the rough assumptions made. By measuring the dielectric constant of a gas we have a method of finding $\bar{\alpha}$ for the molecules. The same holds for a liquid except that in a liquid the polarizabilities of neighboring molecules influence each other. From measurements on a crystal in which the molecules are oriented, we may get more detailed information about the separate components of the polarizability (though again the effect of neighboring molecules on each other complicates the picture to some extent). In a crystal of sufficiently low symmetry it is not at all unusual to find very different dielectric constants along different directions.

For isolated molecules, that is, for a gas, direct experiments do not give us information beyond the value of $\bar{\alpha}$. A more complicated approach using scattering of light and other methods in optics discussed in Chapter 10 will give us information on the anisotropy of the polarizability. But even without further experiments, statements about the polarizability ellipsoid can be made using only symmetry properties of the molecule. Thus we have encountered ellipsoids of revolution for diatomic molecules and for benzene; another example would be ammonia. In molecules of lower symmetry such as H_2O the polarizability ellipsoid will have three different axes, the directions of which are perpendicular to the molecular plane, parallel to the line joining the two hydrogen atoms and along the line bisecting the H–O–H angle. In fact, any axis of symmetry is a principal axis of the polarizability ellipsoid, and any plane of symmetry contains two axes of the ellipsoid. Thus, even for molecules of rather low symmetry, information on the orientation of the polarizability ellipsoid within the molecule can be obtained from very general arguments.

6. VAN DER WAALS ATTRACTION FORCES

6.1 VAN DER WAALS FORCES According to general physical chemical evidence, two atoms or molecules weakly attract each other at distances of a few angstroms; at smaller distances when the atoms "touch," chemical-bond formation may occur; in the case of saturated molecules, however, repulsion will result.

The weak attraction at great distances is called van der Waals attraction, and the strong repulsion at small distances, the van der Waals repulsion. We have gained a roughly qualitative insight into the latter by pointing out its connection with the Pauli principle; in both its nature and magnitude it is similar to the forces of chemical-bond formation. Therefore, the van der Waals repulsion will conveniently be treated together with the chemical bond.

The van der Waals attraction on the other hand is primarily an electrostatic phenomenon due to the dipole moment and polarizability of molecules.

6.2 INTERACTION BETWEEN MOLECULES DUE TO DIPOLES AND POLARIZABILITIES. Dipole molecules produce strong electric fields which act on other molecules in the neighborhood; the molecular electric fields are not homogeneous, and therefore their interaction with another molecule will depend on the detailed charge distribution in the second molecule. Moreover, electric fields may emanate from a molecule even if its net dipole moment is zero. But for somewhat greater distances the orienting effect of the field produced by the one dipole on the second dipole will be the strongest reason for interaction between the two molecules.

If the second molecule has no dipole moment or even if it is an atom and has a spherical charge distribution, it will, because of its polarizability, interact with the field emanating from the first molecule. We can go still further and consider two molecules without dipoles or even two atoms with spherical charge distribution from which no electric fields should emanate. We shall see that even in these cases polarizability causes an interaction between the molecules. These effects of atomic fields mainly due to dipoles and polarizabilities cause the van der Waals attraction forces.

Of these forces, the strongest ones are due, as a general rule, to the interactions between dipoles. Molecular polarizability usually produces smaller effects.

6.3 DIPOLE–DIPOLE INTERACTION A dipole of magnitude $e \times l = d$ produces at a distance r an electric field of the approximate magnitude d/r^3. From this the interaction between two dipoles is readily obtained; the first dipole d_1 produces a field $E_1 \propto \dfrac{d_1}{r^3}$, r being the distance between the two dipoles. The interaction of the second dipole d_2 with this field gives rise to the interaction energy $d_2 E_1 \propto \dfrac{d_1 d_2}{r^3}$. This is actually the correct figure for the interaction of two dipoles alongside each other. For the two dipoles in a straight line the interaction will be doubled. Using for the dipole moments d_1 and d_2 the rather high values of 2×10^{-18} E.S.U. and for the distance the rather small value 3 Å., we obtain for the interaction energy of two dipoles alongside each other, 1.5×10^{-13} erg, which corresponds to 2.1 kcal. per mole; if the two dipoles are in a straight line, we obtain 4.2 kcal. for the interaction energy per mole. This is the right order of magnitude for the stronger kind of van der Waals forces.

6.4 EFFECT OF TEMPERATURE The dipole–dipole interaction, as just described, is frequently smaller than the temperature energy kT; for weak dipoles this will be the case for all possible distances of approach. For the strongest dipoles it will also be so as soon as the distance becomes as much as about two molecular diameters. It is then no longer permissible to consider the second dipole occupying the most favorable position in the field of the first dipole and giving rise to an interaction energy $d_2 E_1 = d_1 d_2 / r^3$. The temperature will in first approximation give rise to uniform distribution of orientations for each dipole leading to an average interaction of zero between the two dipoles.

The field $E_1 = d_1 / r^3$ causes (see section 5.4), however, a preferential orientation of the second dipole d_2 and gives rise to an average dipole moment d_2 parallel to E_1 and having the magnitude,

$$\bar{d}_2 = \frac{1}{3} \frac{E_1 d_2{}^2}{kT} \qquad\qquad 6.4(1)$$

The interaction of this average dipole moment with the field E_1 will be

$$E_1 \bar{d}_2 = \frac{1}{3} \frac{E_1{}^2 d_2{}^2}{kT} = \frac{1}{3} \frac{d_1{}^2 d_2{}^2}{kT r^6} \qquad 6.4(2)$$

Thus we see that, although the dipole–dipole van der Waals energy decreases as $(1/r^3)$ in strong fields, it decreases much more rapidly [as $(1/r^6)$] in weak fields. The individual molecules still have interaction energies proportional to $\pm d_1 d_2 / r^3$, according to the relative orientation of the interacting dipoles. It is, however, the average interaction energy $\frac{1}{3} \frac{d_1{}^2 d_2{}^2}{kT r^6}$ which will be of importance in weak fields.

6.5 POLARIZABILITY–POLARIZABILITY INTERACTION
In discussing the electronic polarizability (section 5.10), we have seen that the dipole due to the polarizability is analogous to the average dipole due to the orientation of a dipole molecule. Whereas in the latter case the temperature motion opposes the orientation of the molecules, in the former case the kinetic energy of the electrons within the molecule prevents the nucleus–electron dipole from lining up with the electric field.

Amplifying this analogy, the electronic polarizability will give rise to interactions between molecules similar to those obtained for dipole–dipole interaction in the case of weak fields. The analogy of the strong-field case does not arise since the interactions of the electronic dipoles of two different molecules are smaller than the zero-point energy of the electrons within the separate molecules, which replaces the kT of our previous consideration. To obtain the formula for the interaction of two molecules not possessing permanent dipole moments we have to replace in $\frac{1}{3} \frac{d_1{}^2 d_2{}^2}{kT r^6}$, d_1 by $a_1 e$, d_2 by $a_2 e$ (a_1 and a_2 are the radii of the two atoms) and kT by $\frac{1}{2}(V_1 + V_2)$, the mean of the zero-point energies or ionization energies of the two molecules. Omitting again numerical coefficients, we obtain, for the interaction,

$$\frac{(ea_1 ea_2)^2}{(V_1 + V_2) r^6} \qquad 6.5(1)$$

Since in this formula a_1 and a_2 are not readily accessible to experiment, we express them with the help of the polarizabilities from formula 5.10(2) and obtain

$$\frac{\alpha_1 \alpha_2 V_1 V_2}{(V_1 + V_2) r^6} \qquad 6.5(2)$$

A more careful calculation on the basis of quantum mechanics shows that this formula for interaction should be multiplied by a factor of $\frac{3}{2}$ but even so, this coefficient is based on a roughly approximate atomic model, and its exact value would vary from case to case and is very difficult to determine.

We see that the interaction potential due to the polarizability of two molecules will again decrease with $(1/r^6)$. The reason for this interaction is that the electrons have a weak tendency to prefer configurations in the two molecules which make their interaction energy as low as possible.*

6.6 DIPOLE–POLARIZABILITY INTERACTION The interaction of the polarizabilities of two molecules has to be taken into account, whether or not the interacting molecules have dipoles. If, however, at least one of the interacting molecules has a permanent dipole, an additional term arises from the interaction of this permanent dipole with the polarizability of the other molecule. If both interacting molecules have permanent dipoles, this interaction has to be taken into account both ways.

According to the definition of polarizability, an electric field E induces the electronic dipole moment,

$$d_e = \alpha E \qquad 6.6(1)$$

in the molecule. The interaction energy of the polarizability with the electric field is $\alpha E^2/2$. The reason we get this expression rather than $E d_e = \alpha E^2$ is that the electronic dipole d_e has been created by the electric field E and has been increasing along with it as the field E has been increased. Therefore, the interaction between electric field and polarizability will be obtained by multiplying E by $d_e/2$, the latter being the mean value of the electronic dipole during its gradual increase from the initial value 0 to the final value d_e.

The permanent dipole d_1 of the first molecule causes an electric field $E = d_1/r^3$ at a distance r in a direction perpendicular to the dipole; if at this distance there is located a second molecule of polarizability α_2, there will be an interaction energy,

$$\frac{\alpha_2}{2} E^2 = \frac{\alpha_2 d_1{}^2}{2r^6} \qquad 6.6(2)$$

If the second molecule is located at a distance r along the line of the dipole, then it will be under the influence of an electric field $2d_1/r^3$, and the dipole–polarizability interaction of the two molecules is $2\alpha_2 d_1{}^2/r^6$.

* The forces discussed above were first investigated by F. London. The expression "London forces" is often used to describe this interaction.

It can be shown that the average value of all dipole–polarizability interactions at the distance r over all orientations of the dipole with regard to the line joining the two molecules is given by

$$\text{Average dipole–polarizability interaction} = \frac{\alpha_2 d_1{}^2}{r^6} \qquad 6.6(3)$$

If the second molecule possesses a permanent dipole moment d_2 in its turn, we shall have the further addition $\alpha_1 d_2{}^2/r^6$ to the interaction energy.

6.7 INTERACTION AT SMALL DISTANCES All the formulas which have been given in this chapter are idealizations which can be used only as long as the molecules are sufficiently far apart. If they approach to a distance of one or two molecular diameters, it ceases to be permissible to replace the distribution of electricity in a molecule by a simple dipole; it then also becomes questionable whether the changes of electronic motion can be adequately described by the simple idea of polarizability.

Thus, for instance, carbon dioxide has no dipole moment but has probably a strong quadrupole moment with more positive charge near the carbon and more negative charge near the oxygens. Two carbon dioxide molecules may interact at small distances as strongly as two dipole molecules. This interaction will, however, decrease rapidly with increasing distance.

For calculating interactions of big molecules at close approach, it is frequently of great advantage not to consider dipole moments or polarizabilities of the molecules as a whole, but rather to take into account dipole moments, polarizabilities, and possibly charges attached to the different atoms, groups, or regions of the molecule. Thus for the interaction of a nitrobenzene and an aniline molecule it would be a great mistake to ignore the localization of dipole moments in the NO_2 and NH_2 groups on the periphery of the molecules. Dipole moments, charges, and great polarizabilities on the periphery facilitate close approach of these effective regions and give rise to particularly strong and directed van der Waals forces.

One well-known example of strong and directed van der Waals forces is the so-called hydrogen bond. A hydrogen atom lying on the periphery of a molecule is apt to carry an excess positive charge, particularly if the hydrogen belongs to an OH or NH group. This positive charge may strongly interact with a negatively charged region of another molecule or even with a negatively charged end of the same molecule bent back into the vicinity of the hydrogen atom. The negatively charged end being rich in electronic charge is apt to have a considerable polarizability, and the interaction of the positive charge near the surface and the approaching polarizable region further increases the attraction. The interaction may become as great as 10 Kcal. per mole. The type of interaction is not intrinsically connected with hydrogen atoms except for the fact that there are few other atoms, particularly in organic molecules, that are apt to lie on the surface of the molecule and carry a positive charge.

Unfortunately, only the polarizability and dipole moment of the molecule as a whole are susceptible to direct measurement. A more detailed picture of the localization of these quantities in the molecule can be obtained only by indirect methods, particularly by comparing dipole moments and polarizabilities of different molecules, and by assuming that the dipole moment and polarizability can be obtained by adding up characteristic dipole moments and polarizabilities of groups or atoms. This kind of reasoning can give, of course, only limited precision. Furthermore, the localization of the dipole moment, the distribution of charge, and the replacement of polarizability by a more detailed picture become essential even for the separate groups in the molecule if accurate prediction of the interaction potentials at close approach is to be made. There is, however, no general method of finding out these properties of separate groups, so that predictions about van der Waals interaction for the most important case of close approach, for instance, liquids, are strictly qualitative.

If we add to this picture the uncertainties and difficulties connected with the van der Waals repulsion which determines the distances of closest approach, it becomes evident that a theory of van der Waals forces can be used only as a method to correlate experimental results, rather than to predict these forces.

6.8   ION INTERACTIONS   Interaction of ions with each other and with neutral molecules is usually not included in van der Waals forces; however, we shall add some remarks about them, since the electric nature of the forces involved makes the forces and potentials very similar to those already discussed.

The energy of interaction between two ions of charges e_1 and e_2 at the distance r, is $e_1 e_2/r$. The interaction energy of a charge e_1 with a dipole d_2 is $(e_1/r^2)d_2$, the factor e_1/r^2 being the field produced by the charge e_1 at the position of the dipole. This charge–dipole interaction represents the average interaction correctly only if it is big compared to the temperature energy kT. Otherwise, it has to be replaced by $\dfrac{1}{3}\dfrac{e_1^2 d_2^2}{kTr^4}$.

The interaction energy between an electric charge e_1 and a molecule of polarizability α_2 is $\dfrac{1}{2} \dfrac{e_1^2 \alpha_2}{r^4}$.

The chemist deals with ions mostly when they are in solution. Their interaction energy with the solvent is known as the energy of solvation, a quantity which is of importance in calculating ionic equilibria. Treating the solvent as a dielectric medium, we obtain for this energy

$$\left(1 - \frac{1}{K}\right)\frac{e^2}{2r} \qquad\qquad 6.8(1)$$

where e is the charge on the ion and r is the distance of the solvent molecule. This formula can be understood by considering the electric energies necessary to concentrate an ionic charge e on the surface of a sphere of radius r_0 in vacuum and in a medium of dielectric constant K. The difference between these two energies is the amount by which the electric energy changes if the ion is brought into solution. An ion of the charge e may be built up by increasing its charge continuously from zero to e; if at one instant the charge is ϵ, then on the surface of the ion the potential is ϵ/r_0, and it will require the work $\epsilon d\epsilon/r_0$ to increase the charge by the amount $d\epsilon$. If ϵ is increased from 0 to e, the total electrical work is $e^2/2r_0$. In a dielectric medium of dielectric constant K the infinitesimal work is $\epsilon d\epsilon/Kr_0$, and the total electrical work $e^2/2Kr$.

These energies, of course, depend on the ionic radius r, whereas in the difference of energies, equation 6.8(1), we have used for r the minimum distance between an ion and a solvent molecule. We have done this since at distances smaller than r from the ion the influence of the solvent molecules on the electric energy is not fully developed. It is simplest to assume that the contribution to the electric energy at distances smaller than r is the same for vacuum and for the dielectric.

Formula 6.8(1) has to be corrected for several reasons. First, if the ion is not spherical, the distance of closest approach is different in different directions, and an appropriate average value has to be used. Second, if the solvent molecules are large, it will be preferable to use for r the closest distance of approach of the nearest atom in the solvent molecule, although this method too may be misleading if the polarizability or dipole moment, and with it the main contribution of the solvent molecule to the dielectric constant, is located in a part of the solvent molecule which cannot make close contact with the ion. This brings us to the final and most important objection. In the immediate neighborhood of the ion, it is, as a general rule, not permissible to simplify the interaction between solvent and ion by simply taking into account the dielectric constant. This procedure assumes that the dipoles of the solvent behave in the same manner in the immediate neighborhood of the ion as they do under the influence of an external (macroscopic) field. In reality, very close to an ion the fields are strong and will cause in many cases a complete orientation of the dipoles which practically never happens if an external field is applied. It is, therefore, best to take the interaction of the ion and the neighboring molecules individually into account whereby attention has to be paid to the shape of the solvent molecules and the ion, to the distribution of electrons and polarizability in the solvent molecules, and to the interaction of the solvent molecules with each other. After the ion has been surrounded by a monomolecular layer, it is, as a general rule, safe to take the interaction with the more distant solvent ions into account by using the formula $\left(1 - \dfrac{1}{K}\right)\dfrac{e^2}{2r}$ wherein for r will be substituted the radius of closest approach of an outside solvent molecule to the center of the complex consisting of the ion and the monomolecular layer.

This more complex method of calculation gives, for dipole solvents, smaller heats of solvation than would follow from the straightforward application of formula 6.8(1). In fact, formula 6.8(1) would give the right result if the average ion–dipole interaction were everywhere given by $\dfrac{1}{3}\dfrac{e_1{}^2 d_2{}^2}{kTr^4}$. However, this interaction has to be replaced by $e_1 d_2/r^2$ wherever this latter expression is smaller than the former, that is, near the ions. Thus the straightforward application of the formula $\left(1 - \dfrac{1}{K}\right)\dfrac{e^2}{2r}$ tends to overestimate the interaction of the ion with the neighboring dipoles.

The effect of the solvent on the interaction of two distant ions can be again taken into account by using the dielectric constant. The interaction energy is $e_1 e_2/rK$. Having taken the dielectric constant into account, we have of course included the change of interaction between ions and solvent molecules due to the approach of the two ions. At very close distances of two ions where no solvent molecules intervene, this formula becomes, of course, inapplicable, and a detailed study of the interaction of ions and surrounding molecules has to be made. The interaction can be simplified by using dielectric constants only at great distances, that is, if many solvent molecules lie between the interacting ions.

7. THE CHEMICAL BOND

7.1 NECESSARY APPROXIMATIONS Chemical-bond formation means an essential rearrangement of the electronic structure. The problem of the behavior of many electrons all strongly interacting with each other and with the nuclei is so complicated that only very drastic simplifications will make a discussion and a calculation possible.

As soon as a really good and simple approximation could be found, it would not be difficult, by a method of successive approximations, to improve it further; however, the method of successive approximations has this characteristic property: If the first approximation is good, the following approximation will be much better, and the next approximation will be excellent. If the first approximation is bad, no further approximation means an improvement or is worth the labor. It is by no means certain that any of the general methods as yet proposed warrants a calculation of further approximation, except in specific cases. Nor is it very probable that the "valence problem" will be solved by finding approximations which are both simple and good; the most we can hope for is that the specific cases for which good calculations can be obtained may become somewhat more numerous.

In the following, we shall give an outline of the chief simplifications that have been proposed.

7.2 THE ATOMIC-FUNCTION METHOD The atomic-function approximation was the first attempt at a theory of valence. It was first applied by Heitler and London, whose names are frequently used to designate this method. According to this procedure, a molecule is represented in first approximation by the unperturbed atomic functions with the atoms placed at appropriate distances from each other. For the inner electrons, such as the electrons of the K shell in carbon, this undoubtedly is a satisfactory procedure, since the energy of bond formation is too small to perturb these inner electrons. For the outer electrons, however, the approximation seems to be far from justified, since the energy of bond formation and with it the interaction of electrons belonging to different molecules is of the same order of magnitude as the energies of the electrons within an atom. Thus the neglected quantities are not small compared to the quantities which have been taken into account. This criticism must not, however, be taken as specific; it attaches to all methods so far proposed.

The atomic-function method seems particularly apt for the calculation of incipient reactions, that is, for the calculation of the case where the atoms are still far apart and are just starting to interact chemically. For these large distances the interaction energy is still small and may justly be treated as a perturbation.

Even for large distances, however, the following difficulties are encountered: (1) The electronic structures of the interacting atoms are frequently not known with high accuracy, and so the interaction cannot be calculated quantitatively. In a few exceptional cases, namely for the hydrogen atom, for the helium atom, and to a lesser extent for the alkali atoms, the proper functions of the atoms are known, and quantitative predictions for interactions at large distances are possible. (2) In most of the interesting cases, one of the interacting partners is itself a molecule. The only molecule for which we have a reasonably accurate proper function is the hydrogen molecule. Therefore, incipient electronic rearrangements at great distances—and with it the calculation of activation energies according to the atomic function method—seem to have a very limited applicability.

7.3 VAN DER WAALS REPULSION The Heitler–London method has led, nevertheless, to an understanding of some very important properties of interacting atoms, molecules, and radicals. Frequently the first effect owing to the overlapping of the electron distributions will be a repulsion. We have mentioned earlier that this repulsion is due to the Pauli principle which makes it necessary for the electrons of two approaching atoms to get out of each other's way. The resulting force is the van der Waals repulsion. This repulsion will be the only strong force occurring if both reacting partners are nondegenerate, or if one reacting partner is nondegenerate and the other has a degeneracy owing to spin.

The shape of the repulsion can be obtained for great distances. We have seen that in quantum mechanics electrons have a chance to get away from the atom, radical, or molecule to which they belong, the only limiting factor being that the greater the distance, the smaller the wave function, and also the smaller the chance that the electron is found at that distance. These extensions of the wave functions towards great radii cause the first overlapping of wave functions, and the first effects of van der Waals repulsion.

An example for the wave function of one electron extending to great distances has been given for the hydrogen atom. The expression given there, equation 2.1(5), can be written with the help of equation 2.1(3).

$$\psi = Ce^{-\frac{4\pi^2 me^2}{h^2}r} \qquad 7.3(1)$$

This formula remains valid for systems other than hydrogen if one introduces a change taking into account the difference in the difficulty of extracting an electron from the atom, radical, or molecule. The energy needed to extract an electron from the hydrogen atom is, according to equation 2.1(4), $2\pi^2 me^4/h^2$. If this energy is denoted as the ionization energy, V, equation 7.3(1) can be rewritten

$$\psi = Ce^{-\frac{\sqrt{8\pi^2 mV}}{h}r} \qquad 7.3(2)$$

which is a reasonable approximation to ψ at large r values for all atoms, molecules, and ions, if the appropriate value for the ionization energy is used. Of course, although for hydrogen V and the constant C can be easily calculated, V has to be determined in the general case experimentally whereas C can be obtained only from calculations which are either difficult or crude. In fact, in the general case C is strictly speaking not a constant but a function which varies slowly compared to the exponential factor.

The expression 7.3(2) is valid only as an asymptotic expression for great distances r. Its particular weakness is that except for atoms it seems difficult to define accurately from which point r has to be measured. A simple statement that we can make is that r may be taken as the distance from the nearest nucleus in the molecule. Sometimes it may be better to use the distance from the nucleus of the most electronegative atom.

Owing to the spread of electronic proper functions, two effects appear as atoms or molecules approach. First, when the wave functions of the two molecules overlap, an electron of one molecule might get within the electronic cloud of the other molecule and into the attractive region of the nucleus of the second molecule. This is represented in the calculations by the "coulomb integral." The second effect which is another consequence of the overlapping is due to the operation of the Pauli principle. It is represented in the calculation by the exchange integral. The coulomb integral causes attraction; the exchange integral for the case of nondegenerate interacting systems or for the case of spin degeneracy of only one partner causes repulsion. This repulsion outweighs the coulomb attraction.

All the interactions mentioned will be proportional to the probability for the electron which is most easily ionized to penetrate into the structure of the second reactant. This probability is

$$\psi^2 = C^2 e^{-2 \frac{\sqrt{8\pi^2 m V}}{h} r} \qquad 7.3(3)$$

Here we have to substitute for V the ionization energy of the most easily ionized molecule. In fact, the wave function of the molecule with the smallest ionization energy extends farthest and determines at large distances the overlapping of the wave functions. The expression 7.3(3) shows that the van der Waals repulsion changes exponentially with the distance. If the minimum ionization energy is comparatively small, the van der Waals repulsion has a large range. As to its absolute magnitude, only rough estimates are possible; it seems to be preferable to determine it experimentally from the equilibrium distances of atoms or molecules, that is, from the point where van der Waals attraction and repulsion forces balance. Again, as in the case of van der Waals attraction, the approximate formula which we are able to give for the van der Waals repulsion retains no more than a qualitative significance in the most interesting region of close approach.

7.4 ATTRACTION IN THE HEITLER–LONDON MODEL If both the interacting groups have a spin degeneracy, or if at least one of them has a degeneracy depending on the orbital motion of the electrons, then, as the two groups approach, the degeneracy will at least partly be removed. By this, we mean that, instead of several states having the same energy, at least some of them will now have a different energy. In such cases we say that the degenerate levels are split. As a general rule, at least one of the new levels obtained will have a lower energy than it had originally. That means attraction will result for this particular state.

As a special example, we shall cite the interaction of two hydrogen atoms. This example has played a particularly important role in the development and discussion of the atomic-function method. The electrons in the hydrogen atom have a twofold degeneracy because of their spins. These spins can orient themselves in opposite directions, giving rise to a nondegenerate (singlet) state; on the other hand, they may line up in the same direction, giving rise to a threefold degenerate (triplet) state.* Heitler and London have shown that the former state leads to

* Nondegenerate, twofold degenerate, threefold degenerate, etc., states are called singlet, doublet, triplet states if the degeneracy is due to the electronic spin (see Section 11.4).

attraction, the latter to repulsion. Moreover, the attraction has the right order of magnitude, though, according to their rough calculations, it is not in quantitative agreement with the energy of formation of the hydrogen molecule.

They furthermore showed that, if any two atoms have only spin degeneracy, the lowest state which one obtains, that is, the one corresponding to the strongest attraction, will as a general rule be the one where the spins of the two atoms are oriented in opposite directions.

One seeming objection that can be raised against the atomic-function theory is that it predicts repulsion between some atoms which, according to chemical ideas, possess valences and actually form compounds. Thus the atoms of the alkaline-earth metals are nondegenerate in their fundamental state and should therefore repel each other. But not much energy is necessary to reach a higher excited state of an alkaline-earth atom. If we forget about this relatively small excitation energy, we obtain a degenerate state which is capable, according to Heitler and London, of giving rise to attractions. If, then, the work done by this attraction becomes greater than the excitation energy which we have originally neglected, we shall have arrived at an actually stable state. This can occur only at comparatively small distances where the work of attraction has become great. At large distances the repulsion due to the original nondegenerate state must predominate. This gives an explanation for activation energies which in its general features we believe to be correct. If, however, for the actual bond formation more than the fundamental state of the reacting atoms must be taken into account, as has been the case in the example cited previously, the simplicity and with it the usefulness of the atomic function picture suffers.

7.5 H + H₂ REACTION An interesting application of the method here discussed is the treatment of the reaction $H_2 + H \rightarrow H + H_2$. The occurrence of such a reaction can be experimentally followed by the use of isotopes or by following the ortho–para hydrogen conversion under appropriate conditions.

In the initial state, two hydrogen atoms form a molecule with the electron spins pointing in opposite directions and making up a singlet state; the third hydrogen atom is at a greater distance. In the final state, the second and third hydrogen atoms form the molecule in the singlet state, and the first hydrogen atom is far away.

In the course of the reaction, a state or reaction complex has to be formed in which all three hydrogen atoms are close together. Of all such possibilities the one with the lowest energy has to be selected. It has been shown that the lowest energy occurs when the three hydrogen atoms are on a straight line:

$$\leftarrow \bullet \qquad \bullet \qquad \leftarrow \bullet$$
$$1 \qquad\qquad 2 \qquad\qquad 3$$

When the third hydrogen atom approaches the second, the first will be pushed away.

Both rough calculations and experiments show that the activated complex has an energy a few kilocalories higher than the initial or final state. These few kilocalories constitute the activation energy of the reaction.

It is interesting to note that, according to the positive value of this activation energy, a hydrogen atom is repelled if it approaches a hydrogen molecule. In fact, the hydrogen molecule acts initially in the same way as a closed shell, repelling any electronic structure that approaches it. That the hydrogen atom can most easily approach in the direction of the axis of the molecule is due to the fact that in this way the overlapping of the electron clouds between hydrogen atom and hydrogen molecule is the least; in fact, such overlapping takes place primarily between the electron of the third hydrogen and the electron of the second hydrogen with which it is going to form a bond. If the hydrogen atom were to approach in the symmetry plane between the two atoms of the molecule, it would overlap the electron cloud of the hydrogen molecule at the point where it is densest and, in doing so, would unnecessarily overlap the electron cloud of the first atom.

These calculations have illustrated both the saturation character of valence forces as derived from the atomic-function method, and also the applicability of this method to calculate activation energies. For heavier atoms, however, similar calculations become much more difficult. For practical purposes several of the constants necessary for the calculation may be obtained with the help of analogy considerations and empirical data.

7.6   MOLECULAR-ORBITAL METHOD   In building up the states of atoms by successively adding electrons into certain orbits and obtaining the periodic system, we have assumed that the motion of the electrons can be considered as independent. More exactly, we have assumed that the electrons act on each other only by their average fields, and we furthermore assumed that this average field does not modify the spherical symmetry of the field. The molecular-orbital method proceeds along similar lines. We shall consider first the wave functions of the separate electrons in the field of the nuclei; a correction must be made on the nuclear field because of the presence of the other electrons, and the assumption is made that this changes the quantitative features of the field, but not its symmetry. Finally, we shall have to consider the order of electronic levels and the filling up of closed shells, just as in the atomic case.

The main difference between the atomic and molecular cases is that for molecules we have a much lower symmetry. Thus for diatomic molecules for which the molecular-orbital method has been worked out in greatest detail, instead of the spherical symmetry of the atoms, only cylindrical symmetry appears. The same holds for any linear molecule such as acetylene or hydrogen cyanide. For a nonlinear triatomic molecule only one or two planes of symmetry remain, and for many other molecules no symmetry at all is left.

An important consequence of the lack or lower degree of symmetry is that in the molecular case degeneracy will be absent or, at any rate, of less importance than in atoms. We recall that degeneracy means that several electronic orbits or wave functions belong to the same energy. Unless due to chance, such degeneracy will be caused by the symmetry of the problem, that is, by the fact that several orbits or wave functions, though different in space, can be reduced to each other by reflections or rotations of the molecule and can therefore not be different in energy. Actually, in order to obtain degeneracy, a rather high degree of symmetry is required, such as, for instance, the cylindrical symmetry of a diatomic molecule. Even this cylindrical symmetry is going to cause degeneracy which is not higher than twofold, whereas in the atomic case the p, d, f, etc., electrons have 3, 5, 7, etc.,-fold degeneracy. Filling all orbits of a degenerate set is equivalent to filling a closed shell. The result is that in molecules there is room for fewer electrons in a closed shell, and there are correspondingly more closed shells with smaller energy differences between them. It is, however, just the great difference between the energies of consecutive closed shells on which the applicability of the independent electron picture hinges. It may be remembered that the atomic-orbital method used in constructing the periodic system gave simple and clear-cut results only in those cases where the shell, being filled up, was lying much lower than any other electronic state. If two states of different kind have comparable energies, the more complicated situation of the transition elements is obtained; because of the denser spacing of closed shells, this kind of a complication will be a rule rather than an exception in the molecular-orbital method. A further complication arises from the facts that a new variable, namely, the nuclear distance, is introduced, and that the order of consecutive closed shells might be different for different nuclear separations. These reasons explain the difference in practical use of atomic- and molecular-orbital methods. The former is the generally accepted starting point for the theory of atomic physics, particularly atomic spectra; the latter, though very useful in some cases, can only be considered as *one* of the ways to tackle the problem of molecular structure.

In comparing the molecular-orbital method with the atomic-function method, we find that the former is more adapted to give a description of the molecule in its stable state in which at least some of the electrons are under the influence of both nuclei; in the atomic-function method, on the other hand, the emphasis lies on the formation of the molecule from separate atoms.

Another practical difference between the two methods is the greater flexibility of the molecular-orbital method; this flexibility is obtained by starting from semiempirical wave functions and energy levels instead of using calculations throughout. Thus, information as to the behavior of molecular orbits is frequently obtained by interpolating between the two cases of infinite nuclear separation and zero nuclear separation, these cases being known from atomic spectra. Also the results can be checked and the assumptions corrected by comparison with the spectra of diatomic molecules. The success of the method in the hands of its originators, Hund and Mulliken, was due to constant guidance by empirical data. The spectra of molecules of the first row of the periodic table have been particularly thoroughly discussed.

The molecular-orbital method recognizes and, in fact, overemphasizes the fluctuation of the probability of charge distribution in molecules. In the Heitler–London method each electron belongs to one definite atom; in the Hund–Mulliken method the electrons are in first approximation free to move throughout the molecule. This means that ionic states are used with the same weight in building up molecules as atomic states. Of course, the independence of the motion of the electrons is rather strongly restricted even in the Hund–Mulliken method by the exclusion principle which always guarantees that no more electrons can be present near an atom than the closed shell, which is being filled up in that atom, can hold. Thus, at least for saturated molecules, the atomic-function and molecular-orbital approximations lead to less divergent results than would perhaps be expected.

7.7 THE TUNNEL EFFECT Greater Nuclear Separation.—We first shall have to consider the orbit or rather the wave function of an electron in the field of two similar atomic nuclei: for example, two hydrogen nuclei. This wave function will depend on the distance of the nuclei, and it will be necessary to investigate the effect of this distance.

Let us suppose that the distance is very great compared to the radius of the hydrogen atom, and let us ask then how a system consisting of two such nuclei and one electron will behave. Evidently the electron will be attached to one or the other nucleus, so that we have a hydrogen atom and a hydrogen ion. In Figure 7.7(1)A the electron has been attached to nucleus 1, the proper function being that of the hydrogen atom. In Figure 7.7(1)B, it is similarly attached to nucleus 2.

Now neither of these two states represents, strictly speaking, a stationary state. The wave function in A overlaps the wave function in B. Therefore, the electron may assume positions at which it cannot be

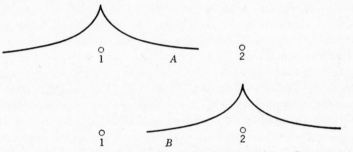

FIG. 7.7(1). Two hydrogen nuclei and the wave function of one electron attached to one of the nuclei.

decided whether it belongs to nucleus 1 or nucleus 2. It can be actually shown that, if we start with the electron in the state shown in A, it will after some time go over into the state B. If the two nuclei 1 and 2 are very far from each other, the statements just made imply a rather surprising result. We start with a hydrogen atom at one point and a hydrogen ion at a point one centimeter away, and later we find that the electron has escaped from the hydrogen atom, leaving a hydrogen ion behind, and has attached itself to the former hydrogen ion, transforming it now into a hydrogen atom. In order to do so, the electron must pass through the region of high potential energy between the nuclei where, according to classical ideas, the electron can never be found. Actually, even according to quantum mechanics, the electron is found between the two nuclei only with a very small probability at any given time. Nevertheless, after sufficient time has passed, the electron will be found with a probability practically equal to unity near the second nucleus. The name for this effect, the tunnel effect, is based on the picture that the electron has leaked through the potential barrier that exists between the two nuclei.

The apparent absurdity of this fact is greatly reduced if some actual numbers are considered. A calculation of the time in which the transition of the electron is completed can be made, using the approximate formula,

$$t = \frac{h^3}{8\pi^3 m e^4} e^{\frac{+2r}{a}} \qquad 7.7(1)$$

where r is the distance of the two nuclei and a (0.53 Å.) is the radius of the hydrogen atom. If the distance of the two atoms is about 1 Å., the time the electron will take to go over to the other nucleus is approximately 10^{-15} sec.; at a distance 10^{-7} cm., the time necessary will be one second; at a distance of 2×10^{-7} cm., the time will be approximately equal to the age of the earth. The time that is necessary for an electron to get to a proton at a distance of one centimeter will be $10^{164,000,000}$ sec. or $10^{164,000,000}$ years, the difference between the two statements being much smaller than the error in the physical constants from which we calculate the exponents.

7.8 MOLECULAR-ORBITAL FUNCTIONS FOR THE H_2^+ ION

The actual proper functions for the stationary states of the H_2^+ ion (for which the probability distribution of the electron does not change

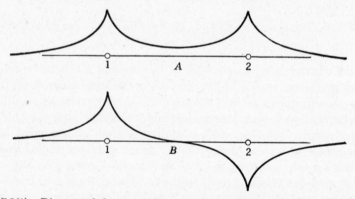

FIG. 7.8(1). Diagram of the proper functions for the lowest bonding state (A) and the lowest antibonding state (B) of the H_2^+ ion.

with time) are obtained by adding and by subtracting the two proper functions, A and B, shown in Figure 7.7(1). Thus we obtain Figures 7.8(1)A and B.

In each of these states the electron is with the probability 0.5 at nucleus 1 and with the probability 0.5 at nucleus 2. If the nuclei are very far apart, the proper function will stay very close to zero over a long distance between the nuclei; however, for the state represented by A in Figure 7.8(1), the proper function never actually becomes zero, whereas, for B in Figure 7.8(1), the proper function vanishes or has a node in the plane of symmetry between the two nuclei. In B only one point of this plane is represented, namely, the point bisecting the distance between nucleus 1 and nucleus 2.

The difference of energy between the states represented by A and B in Figure 7.8(1) becomes very small for great separation of the nuclei. If, however, the nuclei come closer together, the difference in energy will become appreciable; this is so for two reasons acting in the same

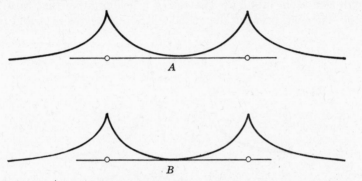

FIG. 7.8(2). H_2^+ ion. Diagram showing the probability of finding the electron at various points on the line joining the two nuclei. The probability vanishes at the mid-point between the nuclei in the antibonding state (B) but does not vanish in the bonding state (A).

direction: (1) In A there is a greater chance for the electron to be between the two nuclei where the potential energy is relatively low; this is illustrated by A and B, Figure 7.8(2), giving the square of the ψ function, that is, the probability of finding the electron at various points along the line joining the two nuclei.   (2) The kinetic energy of the electron will be all the greater, the shorter the wavelength of the wave function.   Now Figure 7.8(1)B with the node in the center of the two nuclei can be represented by a superposition of shorter waves than Figure 7.8(1)A; in fact, if we push the nuclei close enough together in Figure 7.8(1)B, both a short wavelength and an absence of electron density in the region of low potential energies becomes very apparent [see Figure 7.8(3)].   The curve marked ψ shows that the wave function behaves like a short wave while the curve ψ^2 exhibits the low probability of finding the electron in the region of low potential energy lying between the two nuclei.

If we finally bring the two nuclei to coincidence, then we actually obtain a twofold charge which acts on the electron in the same way as the nucleus of the helium atom.   The wave function shown in Figure

7.8(1)A goes over into the wave function $1s$, that is the lowest state of the helium atom. The wave function shown in Figure 7.8(2)B will, however, have a node passing through the helium nucleus; it will be, therefore, a $2p$ function. The energy difference between these two is known to be 40 volts. For actual nuclear distances occurring in molecules, of course, no such great energy differences will be obtained for the states shown in Figure 7.8(1)A and B. It may be said, however, that it is the incipient promotion of a $1s$ electron (fundamental state) of a hydrogen atom into a $2p$ electron of a helium atom that causes the energy difference between the actual states represented in A and B.

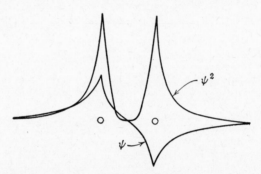

Fig. 7.8(3). Wave function (curve ψ) and probability density (curve ψ^2) for the antibonding state of the $H_2{}^+$ ion with the nuclei close together.

The energy difference of the two wave functions represented in Figure 7.8(1) is closely related to the time necessary for the tunnel effect. The consideration is the same as has been given for the superposition of a $1s$ and $2p$ state of a hydrogen atom. This is explained in the next paragraph.

7.9 ENERGY DIFFERENCE AND TIME IN THE TUNNEL EFFECT　We designate the proper function shown in Figure 7.8(1)A by ψ_a and the corresponding energy by E_a; similarly, the ψ function and energy for Figure 7.8(1)B by ψ_b and E_b. The time-dependent ψ functions will then be

$$\psi_a e^{\frac{2\pi i E_a t}{h}}$$

$$\psi_b e^{\frac{2\pi i E_b t}{h}}$$

According to our general statements, we may superpose these two functions; that is, we may multiply by any constants and add. We choose both constants as unity and obtain

$$\psi_a e^{\frac{2\pi i E_a t}{h}} + \psi_b e^{\frac{2\pi i E_b t}{h}} = e^{\frac{2\pi i E_a t}{h}} \left(\psi_a + \psi_b e^{\frac{2\pi i (E_b - E_a) t}{h}} \right) \qquad 7.9(1)$$

For the time $t = 0$ the expression reduces to $\psi_a + \psi_b$ which, as is seen from Figure 7.8(1), is the function represented in Figure 7.7(1)A; that is, for $t = 0$ the electron will be on the first nucleus.

The superposition of ψ_a and ψ_b has thus concentrated the electrons on the first proton and has effected a localization of the electron into a smaller region than would be obtained by either ψ_a or ψ_b. To that effect, however, both ψ_a and ψ_b have to be used, which means that we can localize the electron more exactly by sacrificing our knowledge of whether it is in the quantum state corresponding to ψ_a or in the quantum state corresponding to ψ_b.

The function 7.9(1) changes with time rapidly, owing to the factor $e^{\frac{2\pi i E_a t}{h}}$, but this does not influence the probability distribution of the electron. The slowly changing factor $e^{\frac{2\pi i (E_b - E_a) t}{h}}$ will influence the probability distribution. At the time $t = \dfrac{h}{2(E_b - E_a)}$ the latter exponent has the value,

$$\frac{2\pi i (E_b - E_a) \dfrac{h}{2(E_b - E_a)}}{h} = \pi i$$

and $e^{\pi i} = -1$. Thus the expression in the bracket in equation 7.9(1) will have changed after a time, $t = \dfrac{h}{2(E_b - E_a)}$, to $\psi_a - \psi_b$ which gives the function shown in Figure 7.7(1)B; that is, $t = \dfrac{h}{2(E_b - E_a)}$ is the time necessary for the electron to get from the first nucleus to the second. It may be seen that in twice that time, $t = \dfrac{h}{E_b - E_a}$, the electron is found again near the first nucleus and that it will continue to oscillate between the two states with that period. This oscillation, however, does not correspond to a stationary state but rather to a transition between the two stationary states with the energies E_a and E_b. Indeed, the frequency which must be radiated in such a transition, $\nu = \dfrac{E_b - E_a}{h}$, is the reciprocal of the period $t = \dfrac{h}{E_b - E_a}$ which we have just calculated. It may be noticed that, if the two hydrogen nuclei are separated, the energy difference $E_b - E_a$ becomes small at the same rate as the time necessary for the tunnel effect increases.

With the help of the expression 7.9(1) it is possible to follow the change of the wave function during the time interval between $t = 0$ and $t = \dfrac{h}{2(E_b - E_a)}$. In this time interval the wave function will be different from zero near both the first and second nuclei. The wave function near nucleus 1, and with it the probability of finding the electron near nucleus 1, decreases steadily. The wave function and

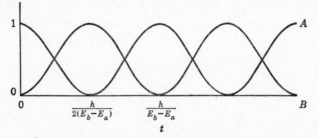

FIG. 7.9(1). H_2^+ ion. Curves A and B show the probabilities of finding the electron on the first and second nucleus, respectively, as a function of time.

probability at the second nucleus increase correspondingly. In the following time interval from $t = \dfrac{h}{2(E_b - E_a)}$ to $t = \dfrac{h}{E_b - E_a}$ the process is reversed. The probabilities of finding the electron on the first and second nuclei are illustrated in Figure 7.9(1).

If the two nuclei are far apart, the probability of finding the electron at the one or the other nucleus adds up at all times to almost exactly unity. The probability of finding the electron for instance midway between the two nuclei becomes very small though not exactly equal to zero. Thus we cannot say that the electron moved from one nucleus to the other on anything like an orbit, but rather we will have to picture the probability function of the electron as leaking from one nucleus over to the other through a region in which the probability density is small. The smaller the probability density in the intervening region, the slower will be the leakage.

7.10 HYDROGEN MOLECULE We now proceed to consider the hydrogen molecule, consisting of two nuclei and two electrons. The lowest state will be obtained if both electrons are put into the symmetrical ψ_a function shown in Figure 7.8(1)A. The energy of such a state will be lower than that of two separate hydrogen atoms, because the energy of the smooth ψ_a function is lower than that of the atomic proper functions. A quantitative calculation of the binding energy remains very laborious, however, particularly because of the interaction of the two electrons.

Since we have put two electrons into the same state, we must assume that their spins are opposite and that we have a singlet state. This agrees with the statement made in connection with the atomic-function method.

There exists, however, an important difference between the two methods. In the atomic-function method each atom had one electron to start with, and the fact that each of these electrons can get over to the neighboring atom has been treated as a perturbation. In the molecular-orbital method each electron can move in first approximation freely within the molecule. The fact that the electrons repel each other and therefore try to avoid being at the same atom may be taken into account later as a perturbation.

For small distances and probably for the equilibrium distance of hydrogen the molecular-orbital method is the better approximation; for great distances, however, the atomic-function method is better, being adapted specially for this case. If the molecular-orbital method were applied to distant atoms, we would be led to the result that the probability of the presence of an electron near a nucleus is independent of the question whether an electron is already there; thus we include in the description of the two hydrogen atoms the ionic case where both electrons are on the same hydrogen; for great distances this is evidently a very poor approximation to the lowest state.

7.11 He$_2$$^+$ We consider two helium nuclei and three electrons, that is, a system carrying, as a whole, one positive charge. Two of the electrons can be put into the same low states which have been filled in the hydrogen molecule. The third electron will have to be put into the state shown in Figure 7.8(1)B, for which there is a node in the symmetry plane between the two nuclei. The two first electrons cause an attraction; the energy of the last electron, however, will be raised when the two nuclei approach so that it will cause a repulsion. The first two electrons are, therefore, called bonding electrons, and the third an antibonding electron. He$_2$$^+$ is known in spectroscopy and is a stable molecule, though its binding energy seems to be smaller than that of the hydrogen molecule. The equilibrium distance is 1.09 Å. which is greater than the distance of the protons in H$_2$ (0.75 Å.). The greater equilibrium distance and the smaller binding energy are due to the presence of the antibonding electron.

7.12 THE He_2 MOLECULE In the He_2 molecule, consisting of two nuclei and four electrons, two electrons can be put into the bonding state and two into the antibonding state. Without more detailed calculations we cannot say whether attraction or repulsion will result. The atomic-function method, however, shows the presence of repulsion at large distances, and general empirical evidence excludes the existence of a He_2 molecule.*

We have here the first example of a general empirical rule. If the number of bonding electrons is equal to or smaller than the number of antibonding electrons, repulsion will be obtained, whereas attraction is expected if the number of bonding electrons is greater.

With the four electrons in He_2 we have completely filled the two states, represented in Figures 7.8(1)A and B, which have been derived from the $1s$ atomic orbits. Because of this circumstance it may be seen that for the He_2 molecule the molecular-orbital method will give a reasonable electron distribution even for a great interatomic distance. In fact, for great distances no electron can be in a state other than $1s$ near one of the nuclei, these being the only atomic orbits that have been used to make up the molecular orbits. On the other hand, a consequent quantum-mechanical treatment of the Pauli principle prevents, in any one of the approximations used, the appearance of more than two electrons in the same state. Therefore, the only state at which we can arrive for great interatomic distances is a state with two $1s$ electrons near each of the helium atoms. This is a great convenience for the following discussion. If we pass to heavier atoms containing more electrons, it will make no difference whether we treat the $1s$ electrons by the molecular-orbital method or simply distribute them into the K shells of the nuclei; in fact, for heavy atoms the interatomic distance will always be great compared to the radius of the K shell, so that for the $1s$ electrons we are practically always in the case of great interatomic distances, all approximations leading to the same result: complete K shells with practically no interaction.

7.13 Li_2 AND Be_2 We have seen that in the periodic system the $2s$ electrons are being filled in after the $1s$ electrons. From the $2s$ atomic orbits we can construct bonding and antibonding states in the same way as from the $1s$ orbits for hydrogen and helium. The only difference is that in the case of the $2s$ electron there is a spherical node around the nucleus which is absent for the $1s$ electron. This, however, does not affect the ways in which the wave functions of the two atoms can be

* He_2 molecules in the gas are merely bound by very weak van der Waals forces owing to the interaction of polarizabilities as discussed in Chapter 6.

combined nor the type of binding or repelling forces that result. Thus the Li_2 molecule may be described in a similar way to the H_2 molecule. There is one difference in a quantitative respect. The wave function of lithium is spread out over a greater distance than that of hydrogen; therefore, the average potential energies will be smaller for the $2s$ electron of lithium than for the $1s$ electron of hydrogen. Because of the greater wavelength and smaller momentum involved, the same holds for the average kinetic energies. Thus, for Li_2 a greater equilibrium distance and a smaller binding will be found than for H_2.

For Be_2 repulsion has to be expected because of the analogy with He_2. Because of the possible influence of the $2p$ state which does not lie much higher than the $2s$ state, it might, however, happen that at smaller distances attraction and formation of a stable molecule will occur.

Experimentally the Li_2 molecule has a binding energy of 1.14 electron volts which is indeed smaller than the 4.45 electron-volt binding of H_2. The distance, 2.67 Å., of the Li nuclei in Li_2 is quite great compared to the 0.75 Å. distance of the protons in H_2. A Be_2 molecule has so far not been observed.

7.14   MOLECULAR ORBITS OBTAINED FROM p ELECTRONS

After beryllium, the p states of the atoms are filled up in the periodic system. There are three degenerate p states, each of which has a plane node passing through the nucleus.

Out of each one of these p states we can obtain two molecular states by taking two corresponding p states in two neighboring atoms and adding or subtracting them. Thus we may take a p function in both nuclei with nodes perpendicular to the molecular axis and take the sum or the difference. The resulting wave functions will have cylindrical symmetry around the axis. If the nuclei are brought closer together, the position of the nodes will change; thus the $2p$ nodes will cease to be plane and will no longer pass exactly through the nuclei, but the wave function will retain its cylindrical symmetry, and, if by subtracting the two states (antibonding state) we have produced a node in the plane of symmetry, this node will remain in this plane of symmetry. Wave functions with cylindrical symmetry are called σ functions. In a σ state the electron has no angular momentum around the molecular axis. This statement is analogous to that made earlier about s states in which the electron did not have an angular momentum around any axis. All states that have been discussed for H_2, He_2, Li_2, and Be_2 were σ states; in fact, states built from s states are necessarily σ states, whereas, if we combine p states, which themselves possess an angular momentum, we may get σ states only if the angular momentum has no component around the molecular axis.

Out of a p state we may also obtain states called π states having an angular momentum equal to $h/2\pi$ around the molecular axis. These π states are obtained by taking p states of the two atoms with a node passing through both nuclei. These p states can then be added or subtracted, giving bonding or antibonding states. The bonding π states will have one node through the two nuclei; the antibonding π states will have in addition a second node in the plane of symmetry between the nuclei. For any π state there are two independent degenerate possibilities; one degenerate function transforms into the other by rotating its node, which passes through the nuclei, by 90° around the molecular axis. A similar situation has been discussed for p states where three independent possibilities have been found, each of which has a node passing through the nucleus.

The reason for the presence of two degenerate π states may be described in an alternate way: The electron may rotate clockwise or counterclockwise around the molecular axis.

7.15 B, C, N, O, F, Ne We have constructed six molecular states out of the three p states, a bonding σ state, an antibonding σ state, two degenerate bonding p states, and two degenerate antibonding p states. Each of these states can hold two electrons, and these 12 electrons are filled in, in sequence from B_2 to Ne_2, inclusive. We shall expect that the first six electrons will go into the three bonding states bringing about an increasingly strong binding. Thus, the molecules B_2 and C_2 should be stable and are indeed observed spectroscopically. That they are not common molecules is probably due to the fact that these elements have very stable solid forms. The most stable molecule in the series should be N_2 with three pairs of bonding electrons. Its stability is borne out by its high binding energy, small internuclear distance, high vibrational frequency, and general chemical behavior. In fact, the electrons in its structure occupy low lying states and can be excited only by relatively high energy quanta. Thus the behavior of the electron cloud will be similar to that of a rare gas. C_2 and B_2 having fewer bonding electrons have smaller binding energies, greater nuclear distances, and smaller vibrational frequencies. From nitrogen to neon, antibonding electrons are added; in the sequence O_2, F_2, Ne_2, the binding energies and vibrational frequencies decrease, and the interatomic distances increase in a regular manner. In fact, for Ne_2 the binding energy has become zero and the distance infinite, further supporting the rule that no binding results if the number of bonding and antibonding electrons is equal.

In Table 7.15(1) the known binding energies, interatomic distances, and vibrational frequencies are given for the molecules B_2 to F_2 and for some of the positive molecular ions. In the last column the difference of the number of bonding and antibonding electrons is given.

The role of the antibonding electrons can be illustrated nicely by considering the O_2 ion. Ordinarily the positive ion of a diatomic molecule has a smaller binding and greater internuclear distance than the neutral molecule; thus, in the case of N_2 and N_2^+, the internuclear

TABLE 7.15(1)

Molecule	Binding Energy in Electron Volts	Interatomic Distance in Å. Units	Vibrational Frequency in Sec.$^{-1}$	Difference Between Number of Bonding and Antibonding Electrons
B_2	3.6 *	1.59	3.15×10^{13}	2
C_2	5.5 *	1.31	4.92×10^{13}	4
N_2^+	6.35	1.11	6.62×10^{13}	5
N_2	7.38	1.09	7.08×10^{13}	6
O_2^+	6.48	1.14	5.63×10^{13}	5
O_2	5.082	1.20	4.74×10^{13}	4
F_2	3 *	1.3 *	$3.4* \times 10^{13}$	2

* Uncertain

distances are 1.09 Å. and 1.11 Å., respectively. On the other hand, in the case of O_2 and O_2^+, the internuclear distances are 1.2 Å. and 1.14 Å., respectively. The explanation, of course, is that O_2^+ is bound more firmly because it has fewer antibonding electrons.

More detailed investigation shows that in the series from N_2 to Ne_2 the antibonding π electrons were filled in first; there are two antibonding π states capable of holding four electrons; in oxygen only two of these are filled in. The fact that only two out of four equivalent states are full accounts for some particular properties of oxygen. Thus if the Heitler–London method is applied to reaction partners, one of which is O_2, the latter may react like an unsaturated atom since there are free places in its outer shell. The paramagnetism of oxygen can be traced to the same cause.

7.16 DIATOMIC MOLECULES WITH DIFFERENT ATOMS

If in a diatomic molecule the nuclei have charges differing by one or two units, as for instance in NO or CO, it may be still permissible to describe the molecule in a reasonable approximation with the same electronic-wave functions as are used for a molecule with identical atoms. The difference in nuclear charges will then cause polarity which, however, will be greatly diminished by the distortion of the original electronic-wave functions. In Table 7.16(1) internuclear distances,

TABLE 7.16(1)

Molecule	Binding Energy in Electron Volts	Inter- atomic Distance in Å. Units	Vibrational Frequency in Sec.$^{-1}$	Dipole Moment in Electronic Charge $\times$ Å.	Difference between Numbers of Bonding and Antibonding Electrons
BeO	5.8	1.33	4.46×10^{13}	.....	4
BO	Unknown	1.20	5.66×10^{13}	.....	5
CO$^+$	Unknown	1.11	6.63×10^{13}	.....	5
CO	9.6 (uncertain)	1.13	6.51×10^{13}	0.023	6
NO	5.3	1.15	5.72×10^{13}	0.021	5
CN	6.7	1.17	6.21×10^{13}	.....	5

vibrational frequencies, dissociation energies, and, in two cases, the dipole moments are given for a few of these almost completely homopolar molecules. The smallness of the dipole moments * shows how completely the difference in nuclear charges has been compensated by the distortion of the electronic cloud. The internuclear distances and vibrational frequencies are rather similar to the corresponding constants for molecules or molecular ions, having the same number of electrons but containing two identical nuclei [see Table 7.15(1)]. This shows that the distortion of the electronic cloud previously mentioned does not change the main properties of the electronic orbits. Dissociation energies behave in a less regular manner, but this is easily understood. Although the molecular orbits for the two cases under comparison are analogous, the orbits for the dissociation products are not.

In contrast to these nearly homopolar molecules, the ionic picture will be preferable in those cases in which the energy of the electron is considerably different, according as it is attached to one atom of the other. Then the wave functions for molecular orbits do not correspond to electrons found with equal probability near either one of the two nuclei, but rather to states in which the electron is attached to the one atom and to other states in which the electron is attached to the other atom. According to this picture, lithium fluoride may safely be regarded as Li$^+$F$^-$ in first approximation. The Li$^+$ ion will, of course, attract the electrons of the highly polarizable F$^-$ ions, diminishing the dipole

---

* The dipole moment of HCl is about ten times as great.

moment and causing the electron structure to approach to a slight extent the homopolar character.

Intermediate cases between the heteropolar and homopolar bonds can be represented in the molecular-orbital method by choosing wave functions in which the electron may be found near any one of the two atoms, but the amplitude of the wave function near the one atom is greater than the amplitude near the other, and therefore the probabilities of finding the electron near one or the other atom are different. Thus we see that a continuous transition is possible between the heteropolar and homopolar bond, these being the extreme cases corresponding, respectively, to equal and to completely one-sided density distributions.

7.17 POLYATOMIC MOLECULES The Hund–Mulliken method has been applied to polyatomic molecules. We proceed by constructing electronic-orbital functions for the whole molecule, using a linear combination of the electron proper functions in the single atoms. These orbits are then filled successively with electrons.

It is, as a general rule, simpler to treat polyatomic molecules by the valence-orbital method which we shall discuss in the following section. That holds particularly for saturated molecules; for unsaturated molecules it is often useful to employ a mixed procedure describing the more firmly bound electrons by the valence-orbital method and the more loosely bound (for example, double-bond) electrons by the molecular-orbital method. This corresponds to the chemical intuition that the latter electrons can move with a certain freedom over more extended parts of the molecule or even the whole molecule.

7.18 THE VALENCE-ORBITAL METHOD Both the atomic-function method and the molecular-orbital method take as their starting point a very clear-cut physical idea, namely the motion of the electron, in the atom on one hand, and in the molecule on the other hand. A third possibility is to connect certain atomic orbits directly with the valence bond, that is, with a chemical rather than a physical concept; this method is closely related to the ideas of G. N. Lewis. The method has the advantage of being particularly adapted to chemical language and being thus able to reformulate and generalize the results of chemistry, without the addition of more extraneous material than is necessary for obtaining new results. On the other hand, the method has the obvious disadvantage of postulating rather than proving the existence of the chemical bond.

In the valence-orbital method, a wave function will be co-ordinated to each valence bond; this wave function will then be filled with two electrons of opposite spins (electron pair of Lewis). One qualitative consequence of this picture is a greater stability of molecules with an even number of electrons; in fact, only very few stable molecules are known in which the total number of electrons is odd. The only good example among the more common molecules is NO; the molecules NO_2 and $(C_6H_5)_3C$ have a tendency to associate, and ClO_2 is explosive.*

The simplest case is again the molecule H_2. Here the valence-orbital method is identical with the molecular-orbital method. By adding the atomic proper functions, a σ state is constructed which is now called a valence-orbital function rather than a molecular-orbital function. The essential difference between the two methods becomes apparent only for polyatomic molecules. Thus, in C_2H_6 a valence-orbital function for the C–C bond is obtained by adding proper functions of the two carbons; valence-orbital functions for C–H bonds are constructed from the corresponding carbon and hydrogen wave functions. Thus each valence-orbital function is filled by an electron shared by two neighboring atoms. In the molecular-orbital method, on the other hand, each electronic orbit would extend over the whole molecule. The polarity of a bond may be represented by using the wave function of one atom with a greater coefficient than that of the other, so that the electrons will spend more time near the first atom.

One essential restriction in applying these simple rules is contained in the Pauli principle; if the filling of one valence-orbital function by electrons is not to interfere with the presence of electrons in another valence-orbital function, these proper functions must be orthogonal to each other. Since wave functions of the same atom may be used in making up several different orbital functions (compare C_2H_6), care must be taken that the orbital functions so constructed should fulfill the requirement of orthogonality. It has been shown by Slater and Pauling that in this way the valence-orbital method leads with necessity to the concept of directed valences. These conclusions will be best explained by using a number of examples.

7.19 DIRECTED VALENCE IN H_2O AND NH_3

In the oxygen atom the orbits $1s$ and $2s$ are filled by four electrons. The three $2p$ orbits are approximated by the functions,

$$xe^{-r/a}, \quad ye^{-r/a}, \quad ze^{-r/a}$$

They have been denoted by $(2x)$, $(2y)$, and $(2z)$. The three $2p$ orbits

---

* More exceptions to the rule are found among molecules containing transition elements. The unpaired electron is then in an inner shell and does not affect strongly the behavior of the molecule.

contain altogether four more electrons. Thus, at least one of these functions must hold two atomic electrons (unshared electrons); we shall, for the sake of definiteness, let $(2x)$ be that function. It is no longer available for the formation of a valence-orbital function. The functions $(2y)$ and $(2z)$, however, can be used for the formation of valences. We start with the $(2y)$ function which has maximum probability densities in the $\pm y$ direction and has a node in the $y = 0$ plane. We shall add to that function an atomic-wave function of hydrogen in such a way that the functions should overlap as much as possible. We shall thereby obtain a smooth function with a low kinetic energy having its maximum in the regions of high negative potential energy. To get the greatest overlapping it is best to locate the hydrogen-atomic function and with it the hydrogen atom itself in the $+y$ or the $-y$ direction. The valence-orbital function so arrived at will be filled by one of the oxygen electrons and the hydrogen electron.

Once a hydrogen atom is placed in one of these directions, and the valence-orbital function made up from the hydrogen function, and the $(2y)$ function is filled with two electrons, the $(2y)$ function is no longer available for valence formation. Though other functions can be constructed in which $(2y)$ is strongly represented (for instance one can superpose $(2y)$ and the hydrogen function with opposite signs) such functions will have an antibonding character and lead to repulsion. Thus, a hydrogen approaching from the $-y$ direction will be repelled, since it will overlap strongly a wave function already filled with two electrons. Therefore a second hydrogen can be bound only by interaction with the $(2z)$ function which as yet contains only one oxygen electron. The smoothest valence-orbital function can be formed from the hydrogen-atomic function and from $(2z)$ if the second hydrogen atom is located along the plus or minus z direction. Thus 90° is obtained for the stable H–O–H angle. It is a consequence of the orthogonality of the functions that the two O–H bonds tend to be perpendicular; but the "orthogonality" of functions has nothing to do with the concept of perpendicular lines in space. In fact, it will be shown later that for the carbon valences the orthogonality leads to tetrahedral angles.

The $(2y)$ proper function as well as the function of the hydrogen atom situated on the y axis have cylindrical symmetry around the y axis, that is, around the direction of the valence bond; therefore, one may call this orbital a σ function. However, the influence of the other hydrogen atom will destroy the strict cylindrical symmetry, and the σ notation therefore has to be taken in an approximate sense.

As soon as a σ valence orbital is filled by an electron pair, it acts like a complete shell; in particular, it will repel other filled valence orbitals.

Thus the two O—H bonds will tend to spread, making, as a result, an angle greater than 90°. This tendency is enhanced by the polar character of the O—H bonds since the positive ends of the dipoles repel each other. That the H–O–H angle does not spread out to 180° is due to the fact that the H–O orbital function must be pictured as effectively extending beyond the oxygen atom; for instance, the probability-density of the valence orbital containing the $(2y)$ function has a maximum on the side turned towards the hydrogen atom and a smaller maximum on the opposite side. The observed H–O–H angle is actually 105°.

The valence angles in ammonia can be explained in a similar way. Nitrogen has two electrons in $1s$, two electrons in $2s$, and three electrons in $2p$ states. The three $2p$ states can thus be used for the formation of valence-orbital functions. Arguments exactly analogous to those used for H_2O lead to three mutually perpendicular N—H bonds; the repulsion between bonds and electrostatic action will again increase the angle, the observed angle being 108°. The molecular ion $OH_3{}^+$ which occurs in solutions of acids in water is isoelectronic with NH_3. It is very probable that the electrons fill similar orbits in the two molecules; the only difference between $OH_3{}^+$ and NH_3 is that the central oxygen carries one more charge than the central nitrogen. As a consequence all electronic orbits will be drawn towards the oxygen in $OH_3{}^+$, and a greater average charge will be left near the hydrogen atoms; however, each of the hydrogens will carry the same increased average charge, and none of them can be designated simply as an H^+ ion.

It is difficult to predict which will be greater, the H–O–H angle in $OH_3{}^+$ or the H–N–H angle in NH_3. The stronger charge of the hydrogen in $OH_3{}^+$ would tend to increase the angle. On the other hand, the valence orbits in $OH_3{}^+$ contain the O atomic functions to a greater extent than the NH_3 orbits contain the N functions; the tendency of the valence angles to be perpendicular is due to the contribution of the central-atomic function to the valence-orbital function, and for this reason we would expect more nearly 90° valence angle in $OH_3{}^+$. The two influences mentioned tend to cancel.

There is a special reason for interest in the $OH_3{}^+$ valence angle. If this angle happens to be close to the tetrahedral angle like that of NH_3 and H_2O, then $OH_3{}^+$ would fit easily into the essentially tetrahedral structure of water.

7.20 HYBRIDIZED FUNCTIONS In the examples discussed up to now, an atomic function occupied by one electron in one reaction partner has been combined with an atomic function occupied by one electron in the other reaction partner to form a valence-orbital function. In the following examples, some atomic functions will have to be changed before they can be used for the formation of the valence-orbital functions. The simplest examples where this necessity arises are beryllium compounds. It may be recalled that according to the atomic-function method beryllium is a saturated atom and becomes reactive only if it is excited.

For a theoretical discussion the molecule beryllium hydride will be most suitable. The chemical stability of this molecule is uncertain, and nothing is known experimentally about its shape. Nevertheless, it

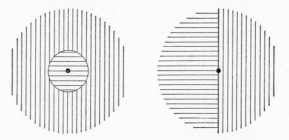

FIG. 7.20(1). Diagrammatic representation of 2s and 2p wave functions. Vertical and horizontal shading indicates positive and negative values of the wave function.

will be useful for the sake of illustration, to predict its shape with the help of the model here discussed. The conclusions at which we are going to arrive may be at once generalized to cover the beryllium halides.

Beryllium has two electrons in the $1s$ and two in the $2s$ state, thus forming a configuration analogous to that of a closed shell. No electrons are available for the formation of valence orbitals; if, however, an electron is transferred from a $2s$ to a $2p$ state, two electrons become available for the formation of two bonds. Since the excitation energy is small and the binding energy may be considerable, a stable molecule will probably result. For the purpose of valence formation, we must therefore deal with a $2s$ and a $2p$ electron. For instance, we may use the electron in the $(2x)$ orbit. The wave functions are indicated in Figure 7.20(1).

Hydrogen proper functions might be combined with any one of these states. However, a stronger binding can be produced if first new orthogonal combinations, namely, $(2s) + (2x)$, and $(2s) - (2x)$, are introduced. These new functions are illustrated in Figure 7.20(2). The new proper functions have the advantage that each of them extends most strongly in a certain direction (as drawn in the figure, $(2s) + (2x)$ extends farther to the right, $(2s) - (2x)$ extends farther to the left), producing in that direction a particularly high probability density. If the hydrogen function is introduced in that region of highest probability density and added to the respective function, a most strong overlapping, the smoothest valence orbital with the minimum energy, and the maximum binding, is obtained. The two valence directions corresponding to $(2s) + (2x)$ and $(2s) - (2x)$ are in opposite directions, the $+x$ and $-x$ directions. Therefore, it should be expected that the H–Be–H angle will be 180°.

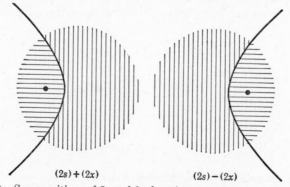

$(2s) + (2x)$ $(2s) - (2x)$

FIG. 7.20(2). Superpositions of $2s$ and $2p$ functions appropriate to the formation of valence orbitals.

It may be noticed that in beryllium we have constructed two wave functions, the one having a strong maximum in the $+x$, the other in the $-x$ direction in contradistinction to the O—H bond where we had one $(2y)$ wave function with equal maxima in the $+y$ and $-y$ directions. Correspondingly, beryllium can form bonds with two hydrogens located along the $+x$ and $-x$, whereas the $2y$ electron of oxygen can bind only one hydrogen located along the $+y$ or the $-y$ axes. In order to construct the valence orbitals in BeH_2, we have superposed the $2p$ and $2s$ wave functions just as though they were degenerate. This is justified, as has been stated, if the original energy difference between the s and p wave functions is small compared with the gain in energy due to the strength of the bond to be formed. The process of superposing the two atomic wave functions of slightly different energies in order to obtain a wave function particularly adapted to strong bond formation is called hybridization.

The radical CH_2 differs essentially from BeH_2 in that two more electrons are present on the central atom. In the carbon atom the orbits $1s$ and $2s$ are filled each by two electrons; the remaining two electrons must be distributed on the $2p$ orbits, $(2x)$, $(2y)$, and $(2z)$. Using the proper functions of the two hydrogen electrons, we can now construct two valence orbits, for instance, one from the wave function of a hydrogen atom situated on the x axis and the function $(2x)$, and the other from the wave function of a hydrogen atom situated on the y axis and the function $(2y)$. Each of these valence orbits may then be filled by two electrons; we thus obtain a molecule constructed in a way that is very similar to H_2O, the only difference being that for the latter molecule two additional (unshared) electrons are found in the $(2z)$ wave function of the oxygen atom.

It is, however, by no means certain that the CH_2 molecule has an angle somewhat greater than $90°$ as the previous discussion would suggest. A different angle is obtained if hybridized functions are used. It is possible that hybridized wave functions composed of s and p wave functions can give a so much greater binding energy as to justify the hybridization. It has been pointed out in connection with beryllium hydride that superposition of the $(2s)$ wave function and the $(2x)$ wave function gives a greater maximum of the wave function in the x direction and with it a stronger binding than would have been obtained with either the $2s$ or the $2x$ orbit. Therefore, it is possible that it is energetically more favorable to build the CH_2 molecule in a way that is analogous to beryllium hydride with two additional (unshared) electrons in the still unused p wave functions $(2y)$ or $(2z)$ of the carbon.

Whereas in CH_2 hybridization was a possibility, in CH_3 it seems to be very probable. If we want to build up CH_3, we cannot start from carbon with only two electrons in $2p$ states; in such a carbon atom only two valence orbits could be formed. In order to form at least one more bond, it will be necessary to promote one of the $2s$ electrons into a $2p$ orbit. It then seems highly probable that an additional hybridization would lower the energy by strengthening the bonds which are going to be formed. It will be most favorable to construct three valence orbits which overlap as little and diverge as greatly as possible. The three orbits,

$$\frac{1}{\sqrt{3}}\,(2s) + \sqrt{\frac{2}{3}}\,(2x); \quad \frac{1}{\sqrt{3}}\,(2s) - \frac{1}{\sqrt{6}}\,(2x) + \frac{1}{\sqrt{2}}\,(2y);$$

$$\frac{1}{\sqrt{3}}\,(2s) - \frac{1}{\sqrt{6}}\,(2x) - \frac{1}{\sqrt{2}}\,(2y)$$

can be shown to satisfy these conditions. All of them have their maxima in the xy plane, the first along the x direction, the second and third including angles of $120°$ with that direction and with each other. They are constructed in such a way that the functions are orthogonal to each other (though of course the directions of valences are not). We can verify this for instance by multiplying the first two functions and integrating.

$$\int \left[\frac{1}{\sqrt{3}}\,(2s) + \sqrt{\frac{2}{3}}\,(2x) \right] \left[\frac{1}{\sqrt{3}}\,(2s) - \frac{1}{\sqrt{6}}\,(2x) + \frac{1}{\sqrt{2}}\,(2y) \right]$$

$$= \int \frac{1}{3}\,(2s)^2 - \int \frac{1}{3}\,(2x)^2 + \int \frac{1}{3\sqrt{2}}\,(2x)(2s) + \int \frac{1}{\sqrt{6}}\,(2y)(2s)$$

$$+ \int \frac{1}{\sqrt{3}}\,(2x)(2y)$$

The last three integrals vanish since the functions $(2x)$, $(2y)$, and $(2s)$ are mutually orthogonal. Owing to normalization,

$$\int (2s)^2 = \int (2x)^2 = 1$$

and thus the foregoing sum of five integrals gives zero, showing that the functions which we have chosen are indeed orthogonal.

We have constructed so far three valence orbits lying in the xy plane and pointing in directions which include 120° angles with each other. The three orbits will hold six electrons of the CH_3 molecule. With two electrons in the K shell ($1s$ orbit), one electron is left over which occupies the p_z orbit. This orbit has a node in the xy plane; that is the electron is either above or below the plane of the three valences but never in the plane itself. Thus a symmetrical plane structure of the CH_3 molecule is likely. An unshared electron will be present; the probability of it being found on either side of the molecular plane is equal.

The only effect that may counteract to some extent the tendency of forming a plane structure is the repulsion between the unshared electron and the electrons which fill the three valence orbits. A slightly bent structure is possible if the last atomic function $(2z)$ participates in the hybridization. This would give rise to a flat pyramid structure which would bring the electrons in the valence orbits closer together and may give rise to slightly weaker overlapping between carbon- and hydrogen-atomic functions. The unshared electron would be found with a greater probability in the direction pointing away from the apex of the flat CH_3 pyramid. Whether the smaller interaction of this electron with the rest of the molecule will stabilize the out-of-plane structure can probably be decided only by spectroscopic evidence.

In the case of methane the valence-orbit method has been used to reinterpret the oldest stereochemical concept, that of the tetrahedral carbon atom. In order for four electrons of the carbon to be available for the four bonds to be formed, the electrons must be in four different states, that is in $(2s)$, $(2x)$, $(2y)$, and $(2z)$. Any set of orthogonal linear combinations may be used instead of these four states, and the most appropriate linear combination will be the one in which the electron orbits avoid each other to the greatest possible extent. Four linear combinations of this kind are:

$$\tfrac{1}{2}[(2s) + (2x) + (2y) + (2z)]$$

$$\tfrac{1}{2}[(2s) + (2x) - (2y) - (2z)]$$

$$\tfrac{1}{2}[(2s) - (2x) + (2y) - (2z)]$$

$$\tfrac{1}{2}[(2s) - (2x) - (2y) + (2z)]$$

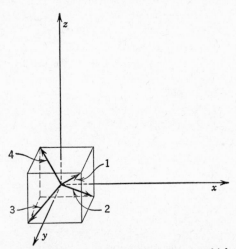

In these four wave functions the electron density is chiefly concentrated along lines in space, pointing towards corners of a tetrahedron as shown in Figure 7.20(3). The most stable configuration will be obtained therefore for methane if the hydrogens are at the corners of a tetrahedron, so that a maximum overlapping of the hydrogen electrons with the corresponding carbon electrons becomes possible. Any C–H dipoles that may be present will further stabilize the tetrahedral configuration.

Fig. 7.20(3). Tetrahedral directions in which the wave functions (1), (2), (3), and (4) of the text assume their maximum values. The figure shows the orientation of these directions with respect to the x, y, and z co-ordinate axes. The cube has been drawn to help in visualizing the directions in space of (1), (2), (3) and (4).

The foregoing considerations on CH_4 may be easily generalized to cover saturated organic molecules, since the second electron in any of these orbits may be furnished by a carbon, oxygen, nitrogen, or similar atom, just as easily as by a hydrogen atom. Similarly, the valence angle on oxygen and nitrogen will remain roughly the same if in H_2O and NH_3 hydrogen is replaced by other substituents. Thus we have interpreted the elements of stereochemistry in terms of electronic orbits within the molecules.

7.21 VALENCE ORBITS IN DOUBLE AND TRIPLE BONDS

The valence-orbital method led to an understanding of valence angles in saturated molecules. In unsaturated molecules it will be necessary to explain both the valence angles and the fact that the double- and triple-bond electrons are bound less strongly than the single-bond electrons.

In the conventional description of the carbon–carbon double bond, the valences participating in the double bond fix a plane in the molecule so that the remaining bonds will have no free rotation. In addition, a strain is introduced, pulling the double-bond valences closer together. Inasmuch as the valence bonds repel each other, and, since more room is available now for the remaining two bonds, it is expected that their angle will be somewhat larger than the tetrahedron angle.

These chemical terms can be formulated in the valence-orbital method by considering in what way two carbon atoms have to be brought together if we want two pairs of electron orbits of the carbons to overlap as strongly as possible. The most favorable position will be one in which the line joining the two carbons will bisect the angle of the two valences on each carbon. The valences to be joined cannot point then towards each other in a straight line. Consequently, the overlapping and the energy per bond will be smaller in the double bond than it would be in the single bond. This decrease of energy has been interpreted in chemistry as due to the strain.

Actually the most convenient linear combinations will be different in the case of the double bond from those which we obtained for methane. To begin with, we may use without introducing any actual change the sum and difference of the proper functions belonging to the valence orbits of the double bond. This in effect is merely a change in representation. This can be seen in the following way. The valence-orbital function representing the first single bond between the two carbons can be denoted by ψ_1; the valence-orbital function for the second bond which differs from the first only in direction we call ψ_2. If we fill up these two orbits with two electrons,* 1 and 2, we obtain, according to the general formulation of the Pauli principle,

$$\psi_1(1)\,\psi_2(2) - \psi_2(1)\,\psi_1(2)$$

Introducing the sum and the difference of the original orbital functions,

---

* Taking spin into account, we should fill the two orbits with two electron pairs. This would merely complicate the following treatment, but it would leave the result unchanged. We shall proceed in the following argument to disregard spin and fill each orbit with one electron.

we have

$$\frac{1}{\sqrt{2}}\,[\psi(1) + \psi(2)] \quad \text{and} \quad \frac{1}{\sqrt{2}}\,[\psi(1) - \psi(2)]$$

The factors $1/\sqrt{2}$ have been introduced to normalize the new function, that is, to insure that the integral of their squares will still give unity. Filling each of the new orbits with an electron and writing the whole function to conform with the Pauli principle, we get

$$\frac{1}{\sqrt{2}}\,[\psi_1(1) - \psi_2(1)]\,\frac{1}{\sqrt{2}}\,[\psi_1(2) + \psi_2(2)]$$

$$- \frac{1}{\sqrt{2}}\,[\psi_1(1) + \psi_2(1)]\,\frac{1}{\sqrt{2}}\,[\psi_1(2) - \psi_2(2)]$$

After performing the multiplications, we find that this is identical with the original expression,

$$\psi_1(1)\psi_2(2) - \psi_2(1)\psi_1(2)$$

A greater binding energy will be contributed by the sum, $\psi_1 + \psi_2$, which gives a proper function with a maximum along the double-bond direction; the difference, $\psi_1 - \psi_2$, on the other hand, will have a node perpendicular to the plane of the double bond and therefore passing through the other substituents that are bound to the carbon atom. This valence orbit will be the typical double-bond orbit with electrons above or below the node but never in plane with the other substituents. It is this orbit that can be made responsible for the rigidity of the double bond with regard to rotation. It also will contribute rather greatly to the polarizability of a molecule, since its electrons are spread out over great distances and are not bound very strongly.

We may expect to improve the valence orbits by making them more similar to those discussed for the CH_3 radical. In fact, both in the CH_3 radical and in a double-bond molecule an orbit has been considered which is antisymmetrical to the plane of the carbon and its substituents. The only difference is that for CH_3 only one electron is in that orbit, whereas in the double-bond there are two. Using the analogy of CH_3, we may expect that the single bonds and the double bond are arranged in a plane and that all valence angles have the value of 120°. The symmetry which caused the angles to be exactly equal to 120° is, of course, absent in ethylene. But it is plausible to assume angles greater than the tetrahedral angle, since this result follows both from the original chemical concept and also from a qualitative discussion of valence orbits

Spectroscopic evidence actually indicates that both the H–C–H and H–C≡C angles are equal to 120°. Electron diffraction experiments, on the other hand, lead to the result that if both H atoms in the CH_2 group are replaced by the methyl group, the CH_3–C–CH_3 angle is 111°. Although both of these facts are in agreement with the conclusions of the previous theoretical discussion, it is difficult to understand why a smaller valence angle is obtained in the case of the methyl substitution. Repulsion of the methyl groups would lead us to expect the opposite result.

Other double bonds such as carbon–nitrogen, carbon–oxygen, nitrogen–nitrogen, and nitrogen–oxygen (nitroso compounds) can be described similarly to the carbon–carbon double bond. Comparing, for instance, C=C with C=N, the only difference is this: On the nitrogen atom will be found (in addition to the electrons which participate in the double bond) a pair of unshared electrons and a pair of electrons belonging to a single bond; on the carbon will be found two pairs of electrons participating in single bonds.

When a bonding electron pair is thus replaced by an unshared electron pair, the orbit of the electron pair will be drawn closer into the atom. To compare, for instance, carbon and nitrogen, the bonding pair on carbon has been obtained by hybridization of s and p functions and combination with the wave function of the other partner in the bond. Not only will the unshared electron pair of the nitrogen atom occupy pure nitrogen functions but in addition it will be best to place the unshared pair into the $2s$ orbits which are closest to the nitrogen nucleus. This leaves, as we have seen, the $2p$ orbits available for the valences of the nitrogen. These orbits include right angles rather than tetrahedral angles with each other, and thus there will be less strain associated with a double bond if a nitrogen atom is at one end of it. Similar considerations apply to C=O and N=O double bonds where two unshared electron pairs are present on the oxygen atom. Lack of free rotation in a molecule containing a C=N or N=N double bond is, of course, to be expected.

The only double bond in this series that differs essentially from the rest is that in the O_2 molecule. Since on O_2 there are no further substituents, there is nothing in the molecule that would fix the plane in which the node of the double-bond function shall lie. Thus the possibility arises that the two double-bond electrons occupy double-bond orbits with different nodal planes. This actually is energetically favorable, because in this way the two double-bond electrons will have a greater average distance from each other, and a smaller coulomb repulsion will be obtained. The electrons being in different orbits may have parallel spins; in fact, the ground state of oxygen is a triplet, and oxygen is paramagnetic in contrast to all other double-bond substances.

In the classical stereochemical picture of the carbon–carbon triple bond, we obtain a binding energy much less than three times the single bond, since the natural direction of three valences cannot all simultaneously coincide with the line joining the carbon atoms. The smallest stress will be obtained if the remaining valence of the carbons lies on the continuation of the C–C line.

The same results are obtained in the valence-orbital method if we try to arrange a maximum overlapping of three pairs of orbits of the two carbon atoms. This will be attained by fitting together the bases of the two tetrahedra formed by the four valence orbits. The fourth valence orbit will then point in the correct direction. The energy will be less than that of three single bonds, because the overlapping of the orbits is less complete than in the case where the orbits point towards each other.

Instead of the three valence orbits including angles with the C–C axis, linear combinations may be used similar to those discussed for the double bond. One of these linear combinations has cylindrical symmetry around the C–C axis and corresponds to a full-strength single bond. The second linear combination has a node passing through the two carbon atoms; the two electrons in that orbit have similar properties to those of double-bond electrons; in particular, they are spread out more strongly, contribute less to the binding energy, and have a strong polarizability. The third orbit also has a node through the two carbons, and this node is perpendicular to the node of the second orbit. The electrons in this orbit again have double-bond properties. Since there are two perpendicular nodes, the triple bond does not define any particular plane as the double bond does. In fact, it can be shown that, apart from their being perpendicular to each other, the direction of the two nodes around the C–C axes can be chosen in an arbitrary way and that the resulting wave function of the triple bond has cylindrical symmetry. The situation is similar to that found for the neon atom; although neon contains p electrons with nodes through the nucleus, the composite wave function of the whole atom has nevertheless spherical symmetry.

The carbon–nitrogen triple bond and the nitrogen–nitrogen triple bond do not differ essentially in their electronic structure from the carbon–carbon triple bond. In replacing a carbon by a nitrogen, the main effect is that a bonding electron pair is converted into an unshared electron pair which will occupy the $2s$ orbit in the nitrogen atom. The nitrogen parts of the triple-bond orbits will then be supplied by the three $2p$ orbits. We shall expect that the strain on these perpendicular $2p$ orbits will be less than was the strain on the hybridized carbon orbits which included tetrahedral angles with each other. This helps to explain the great stability of N_2.

7.22 COMBINED VALENCE-ORBITAL AND MOLECULAR-ORBITAL METHOD In describing systems of conjugated double bonds it proves useful to apply the valence-orbital method to all elec-

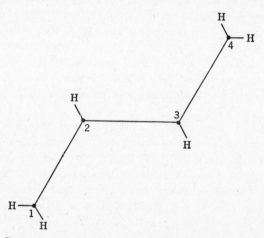

FIG. 7.22(1). System consisting of two conjugated double bonds, butadiene. Numerals 1, 2, 3, and 4 denote positions of carbon atoms.

trons with the exception of the double-bond electrons. The latter have even in the simplest double-bond compounds more extended orbits, and it seems reasonable therefore to use an approximation in which these electrons are allowed to move over a greater part of the molecule. Such an approximation is given by the molecular-orbital method.

We shall first consider two conjugated double bonds and assume that the four carbons, as well as all atoms attached to them, lie in a plane. In Figure 7.22(1) all substituents on the carbons designated as 1, 2, 3, and 4 have been chosen as hydrogens, and the lines joining the atoms indicate pairs of bonding electrons. All valence angles in the plane are 120° for the same reason that has been discussed in the example of ethylene. Only the single bonds are drawn in the figure. According to the valence-orbital method, two additional electron pairs should be present. The wave functions of these electrons should have a node in the plane of the molecule. According to the chemical formula one electron pair should be attached to the first and second carbon, and the other pair to the third and fourth carbon atoms.

We shall now try to distribute these last four electrons into orbits composed of the states on the four carbons still unfilled by the single-bond electrons. These vacant states are p states with their nodes in the plane of the molecule. One low state of this kind can be obtained by adding the four p states on the four carbon atoms; thus, a wave function is obtained which has no node except the one in the plane of the molecule. This molecular orbit can hold two electrons; for the two re-

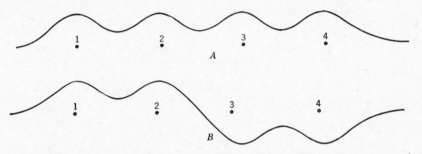

FIG. 7.22(2). Schematic representation of two lowest molecular orbitals composed of $2p$ states of four carbon atoms. The four carbon atoms are shown as lying on a straight line, and the nodes of the $2p$ electrons lie in a plane containing that line. The ordinate gives the amplitude of the ψ function along a line parallel to the axis passing through the carbon atoms.

maining electrons we have to construct an orbit which is orthogonal to the one just described and which contains as few nodes as possible. Such an orbit is obtained by superposing the wave functions on the carbons 1 and 2 with the same sign and subtracting from this the superposition of the wave functions on 3 and 4. The two lowest orbits which have now been constructed are schematically represented in Figure 7.22(2). In this figure, the fact that the four carbon atoms do not lie on a straight line * has been disregarded.

In the lowest orbit represented in Figure 7.22(2)A, the original wave functions have been superposed in such a way that the envelope of the resulting wave has no node within the molecule. The wave function of the next higher energy level shown in Figure 7.22(2)B corresponds to a superposition in which the envelope has one node between the atoms 2 and 3. Two orbits with still higher energies can be constructed from

* The arrangement of the carbon atoms on a straight line is, of course, not realistic. But the final result of the discussion is not influenced by this arrangement.

the p functions shown in Figure 7.22(3), in which the envelope has two nodes and three, respectively; these higher orbits remain empty.

It has been pointed out in the discussion of the molecular-orbital method that a molecular-orbital function without a node between two nuclei tends to draw the two nuclei together, whereas, if a node is found between two nuclei, they are pushed apart (bonding and antibonding properties). From Figure 7.22(2) it is clear that the atom pairs 1,2 and 3,4 are drawn together by the influence of both filled molecular orbits.

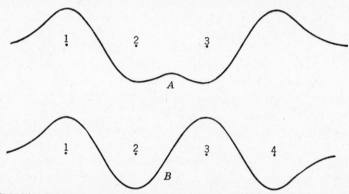

FIG. 7.22(3). Schematic representation of two highest molecular orbitals composed of $2p$ states of four carbon atoms. The four carbon atoms are shown as lying on a straight line, and the nodes of the $2p$ electrons lie in a plane containing that line. The ordinate gives the amplitude of the ψ function along a line parallel to the axis passing through the carbon atoms.

The distance between 2 and 3, on the other hand, would be diminished by the action of the functions shown in Figure 7.22(2)A but would be increased by the effect of the functions shown in Figure 7.22(2)B. Thus the distances 1,2 and 3,4 become shorter than the distance 2,3 in agreement with the simple double-bond picture which places the double bonds between the pairs 1,2 and 3,4.

Although the conclusions so far merely confirm expectations based on stereochemistry and on the valence-orbital method, the picture now being used suggests two more properties of a pair of conjugated double bonds. First it may be expected that the nodes of the four $2p$ orbits help to stabilize a common plane in which all four carbon atoms will lie. This statement is not contained in classical stereochemistry or in the valence-orbital picture, since in these presentations free rotation around the 2,3 link should be expected. The molecular-orbital method, however, merely suggests and does not prove the stability of such a plane. In fact, although the wave function shown in Figure 7.22(2)A helps to stabilize the plane, the wave function represented in Figure $7.22(2)B$ cancels at least part of this effect.

The second property of conjugated double bonds which is aptly described by molecular-orbital functions is the ease with which a pair of conjugated double bonds is converted into one double bond between the atoms 2 and 3. The wave function shown in Figure $7.22(2)A$ differs from a double-bond wave function between the atoms 2 and 3 only in that it extends further toward the ends of the molecule. If new substituents are linked to the carbons 1 and 4, room is created for two more electrons in the valence-orbital functions of the newly formed bonds. These electrons will be supplied from the wave function shown in Figure $7.22(2)B$. The orbits of low energy around the atoms 1 and 4 will then be filled by single-bond electrons, and the Pauli principle will exclude the electrons filling the states shown in Figure $7.22(2)A$ from the neighborhood of atoms 1 and 4. The orbit will shrink to an ordinary double-bond function around atoms 1 and 4.

The considerations just discussed can be easily generalized to cover the case of a chain of $2n$ carbon atoms linked alternately by double and single bonds. We shall assume again that all the carbon atoms and the atoms attached to them lie in a plane, and we shall construct molecular orbits from the carbon p wave functions with nodes in the molecular plane. $2n$ such wave functions can be constructed, the lowest having no node except the one in the molecular plane, and the next having one additional node in the middle of the chain. We can proceed in this manner, to the orbit of highest energy with $2n - 1$ additional nodes, that is, one node between every two neighboring carbon atoms. Of these $2n$ orbits, the n lowest will be filled by the $2n$ electrons which remain available if the single-bond valence orbits are filled with an electron pair each. The molecular wave function so obtained is analogous to the wave function for a pair of conjugated double bonds, and the essential conclusions which can be derived from the picture are also similar. It must be observed, however, that molecular orbitals of the kind here described will be interrupted whenever one carbon atom in the chain is linked to all its neighbors by single-bond electrons. After the energetically lower single-bond levels are filled, no additional free orbit is available on such a carbon atom, and this carbon atom will lie as a potential barrier across the path of the otherwise more freely moving double-bond electrons. Thus we see that conjugation will be interrupted as soon as two double bonds are separated by two (or more) single-bond links.

A particularly interesting example of conjugation is found in aromatic compounds. We shall discuss here only the simplest cases, namely, those of plane carbon rings with $2n$ members containing alternating single and double bonds between them. These ring systems have been discussed by Huckel and by Pauling from the point of view of wave mechanics.

The lowest wave function will be obtained from the "double-bond" p carbon electrons by adding the p functions of all carbon atoms. Higher orbits are constructed by multiplying the wave function of the lth carbon atom by sin $\pi kl/n$ and adding. (k is any integer which characterizes the orbit and which assumes values from 1 to n.) It may be noticed that, if we follow the chain around, the first carbon atom is identical with the $(2n + 1)$ carbon atom. Correspondingly, the multiplying factor for the first atom is sin $\pi k/n$; for the $2n + 1$ atom it is sin $[\pi k(2n + 1)/n]$ = sin $[2\pi k + (\pi k/n)]$; that is, the factors multiplying the wave functions of the first and $(n + 1)$ atoms are the same. More functions can be constructed by multiplying with cos $\pi kl/n$ and adding. Here k is an integer with the values from 0 to $n - 1$. If $k = 0$, the multiplying factor is one on every atom, and we obtain the simple sum which, as has been mentioned before, corresponds to the lowest energy. We now have n functions containing sine factors and n containing cosine factors. Altogether we have $2n$ functions, and it will be necessary to fill the n lowest of these with $2n$ available electrons.

Now we can show that a function containing sine factors corresponds to the same energy as a function containing cosine factors, if the k value appearing in the sine and cosine is the same. For instance the energy corresponding to the factors sin $\pi k/n$ and cos $\pi k/n$ is the same. This means that there exists a twofold degeneracy which actually is caused by the ring symmetry of our model. This twofold degeneracy is similar to that occurring for π electrons in diatomic molecules, in which case the degeneracy was caused by the cylindrical symmetry. We have described that degeneracy as due to the two possible rotational directions of the π electrons around the molecular axis. In an analogous manner the twofold degeneracy in our present ring model can be ascribed to the two possible directions in which the mobile p electrons can move around the ring. For the lowest state, $k = 0$, the motion can be said to have a zero velocity, and consequently no degeneracy is expected. Actually the $k = 0$ case does not occur among the sine functions but only among the cosine functions.

The lowest wave function can hold two electrons. The next energy is obtained for $k = 1$; here we have a twofold degeneracy, and four electrons can be placed. The same holds for higher functions. It may be seen that if the ring contains four members, and, if there are therefore four electrons available, these will fill the lowest level with $k = 0$ and also fill half of the available states for $k = 1$. Thus such a molecule is analogous to an atom in the middle of the periodic system, the outermost electronic shell being partially filled. If, on the other hand, we have a molecule with six carbon atoms, the available electrons will just suffice to fill the shells with $k = 0$ and $k = 1$. The molecule therefore will have a closed shell, and it will be analogous to a rare-gas atom. This closed shell may be used to account for the special stability of benzene. It must be borne in mind that, if a closed shell contains many electrons, then it is probable that the next excited energy level will be rather high above the closed shell, whereas, if shells contain only few electrons, such shells will have to follow closely on each other. For this reason we may expect that more energy will be needed to excite a benzene with its four electrons in the outermost closed shell than to excite a simple double bond or an open chain of conjugated double bonds with two electrons in the last orbit. Thus the electronic configuration of benzene is more difficult to change; that is, benzene is less reactive.

It may be easily seen that the statements about four and six carbon rings can be generalized to cover larger rings. In an eight-carbon ring, the $k = 0$ level would be filled with two electrons and the $k = 1$ level with four electrons, and there would remain only two electrons for the $k = 2$ level which would thus be only partly filled. We expect therefore that an eight-carbon ring with four conjugated double bonds would have a rather unsaturated character. On the other hand, in a ten-carbon ring the ten "double-bond electrons" just suffice to fill the $k = 0$, $k = 1$, and $k = 2$ levels, and a greater degree of saturation is therefore possible. In general 4, 8, 12, etc., carbon rings will be more unsaturated than 6, 10, 14, etc., carbon rings. We also would expect, on the basis of the molecular-orbital method, that rings with a lower number of members are more saturated because we find that, for instance, in benzene, the full $k = 1$ and empty $k = 2$ levels have a greater energy difference than the full $k = 2$ and empty $k = 3$ levels in a ten-membered ring.

Just as in the double-bond and the conjugated-double-bond systems, all valence angles in the plane of the molecule tend to have the value of 120°; therefore in a four-membered ring with two double bonds great strains are inevitable, and this will contribute to the instability of such a ring. In benzene no strains are present; an eight-carbon ring, on the other hand, cannot be set up in a plane without considerable strain. We can construct larger carbon rings without strain if some of the C–C–C angles are turned toward the inside and some toward the outside of the molecule. Two such rather simple molecules are shown in Figure 7.22(4). Each of the carbon atoms has a substituent attached. In the molecule shown in Figure 7.22(4)A the substituents on the carbons 1, 5, and 9 must be for steric reasons in the 1, 5, 9 triangle. If there is any possibility of realizing this, it will be by putting a trivalent sub-

stituent into the middle of this triangle. A ring such as shown in
Figure 7.22(4)*A* would be rather unsaturated on account of its 12 members. In a ring such as shown in Figure 7.22(4)*B* steric effects would
again limit the possibilities for substituents on the carbons 1, 4, 8, and
11. We would expect this 14-member ring to have greater stability,
and it is therefore perhaps more likely that it can be prepared chemically.

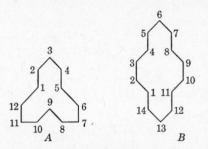

Fig. 7.22(4). Benzene-like rings without strain.

The electronic structure of the
familiar polycyclic compounds can
also be described by a molecular
skeleton consisting of single-bond
electrons and a number of double-
bond electrons roaming over the
whole molecule. In most of the
compounds not containing side
chains the number of the more
mobile electrons is equal to the
number of carbons. The mathematical description of their wave
functions is, however, more involved since the double-bond electrons
no longer follow simple cyclic paths. We may simplify the description
of these compounds by focusing attention on the longest cyclic path
that is possible in the molecule. Thus in naphthalene we may consider
all the double-bond electrons moving in an outer ten-membered ring
along the carbon atoms numbered 1, 2, 3, 4, 10, 5, 6, 7, 8, 9, and we

may disregard the possibility of the common single bond joining 9 and
10 becoming a double bond; or we may consider in pyrene the cycle 1,
2, 3, 12, 4, 5, 13, 6, 7, 8, 14, 9, 10, 11. The carbon atoms numbered

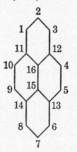

15 and 16 would then play the role of substituents, and they would

have to be joined by a double bond so that they would have just enough valences left to take care of the free valences on 11, 12, 13, and 14. Applying a similar procedure to the known polycyclic compounds, we find that the outermost cycle has $2 + 4n$ members; that is, the outermost cycle is always a ring of the kind that we have found to be particularly stable.

An interesting example of this rule is perylene in which we find an

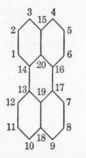

outer 18-membered ring 1, 2, 3, 15, 4, 5, 6, 16, 17, 7, 8, 9, 18, 10, 11, 12, 13, 14.   But by placing bonds into alternate links of this ring the valences of the carbons 20 and 19 cannot be satisfied.   The same difficulty is encountered if we assign to the outer ring 18 double-bond electrons. This perhaps accounts for the greater ease with which the electronic structure of perylene can be excited, giving rise to the yellow color of the compound.   Thus our explanation of the fact that rings with 8, 12, etc., members are not found is not fully satisfactory, since our procedure made it necessary to fix double-bond positions in an arbitrary way, and in the case of perylene it made a valence picture in the ordinary sense impossible.

7.23   ELECTRON MOBILITY IN CONJUGATED SYSTEMS   The great mobility of double-bond electrons in molecules containing conjugated double bonds gives rise to the great polarizability of such molecules.   As should be expected, the polarizability is particularly great if the electric field is applied along the molecular plane or in the case of an open zigzag chain along the chain direction.   For ring compounds such as benzene and naphthalene a peculiar magnetic effect is also to be expected.   It has been shown by London that the mobility of electrons around a ring gives rise to strong diamagnetism along an axis perpendicular to the ring plane.   Application of a magnetic field along the axis causes a change of the velocity of rotation of the electrons around the ring, accompanied by an increase of total energy.   Therefore, the plane of the ring tends to avoid being perpendicular to the magnetic field.   As an example we may quote naphthalene.   In this

molecule a magnetic field perpendicular to the plane will induce an approximately three times greater magnetic moment than a field which lies in the molecular plane. That is, the diamagnetic susceptibility is about three times smaller for a magnetic field in the molecular plane than for a field perpendicular to the molecular plane.

Further evidence for the mobility of the double-bond electrons is the change of reactivity on a rather distant carbon in benzene if appropriate substituents are introduced into the ring. Thus in aniline further substitution occurs preferably on the carbons in the ortho and para positions while nitrobenzene directs the next substituent into the meta position. This behavior contrasts with the more usual rule that ease of substitution on a group within a molecule depends primarily on the properties of that group and is modified mostly by immediately adjacent substituents.

7.24   RESONANCE   In discussing the ion OH_3^+ we mentioned that the positive charge is with equal probability on any one of the three hydrogens. This can be expressed by writing three structures for H_3O^+,

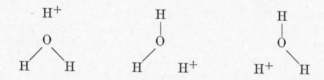

with one zero valent H^+ ion and one saturated H_2O molecule. We can represent each of these structures by a wave function and consider the real wave function of H_3O^+ as a sum of the three wave functions. Actually we have mentioned earlier that, if several wave functions have the same or similar energies, then by superposing these wave functions in an appropriate way we may succeed in lowering the energy. This is due to the fact that in the linear combination the wave function of the electron may possess a greater wavelength and thus a lower kinetic energy while at the same time the wave function attains higher amplitudes in regions of lower potential energy. In a crude general manner of speaking, the advantage of such linear combinations can be seen in the tendency of the electron to spread over as big a region as is consistent with a fairly low value of the potential energy. The procedure to approximate the correct wave function of a molecule by superimposing wave functions that represent familiar chemical structures has proved particularly useful since it permits the chemist to apply the symbolic language of quantum theory and still use his own customary expressions. Thus we use mutually exclusive chemical formulas and explain by the plurality of formulas an increased stability. This new procedure has been called resonance between chemical structures.

It would perhaps appear that the wave function of H_3O^+ as approximated by the resonance method is rather different from the wave function obtained from the valence-orbital method. Actually the difference is not so great. Comparing NH_3 and OH_3^+ in the valence-orbital method, we expect that the added charge on oxygen will draw the valence orbits so much closer to that atom that practically the whole free positive charge appears on the hydrogens, the charge of each of the protons being compensated to only a fraction of two thirds by the electrons in the valence orbits around them. In any one of the three structures that has been used, valence orbits reach out and practically neutralize two of the protons while the electron pair that ought to bind the third proton remains unshared on the oxygen atom. In superposing the wave functions which belong to the three structures we obtain a state where the orbit of each electron pair employed in the binding of a hydrogen consists two-thirds part of a valence orbit and one-third of an unshared orbit. This mixture resembles a valence orbit which has been drawn in somewhat toward the oxygen. Though a similarity between the two methods has been thus established, there is this difference between them. In the valence-orbital description of H_3O^+ each of the valence orbits is polarized independently of the others; that is, no phase relations between the electrons of different valence orbits are taken into account. In the resonance method, on the other hand, the valence electrons binding a proton are unpolarized as soon as any of the other two electron pairs is in the unshared state. It is not quite certain whether this sensitive interrelation between the electron pairs does not overemphasize the phase relations which actually have to exist.

The valence angles on OH_3^+ are obtained from the resonance method quite simply; stability will be expected if every H–O–H angle in the molecule is not very different from the H–O–H angle in H_2O; in this way all three resonating structures contain an H_2O with a but little distorted H–O–H valence angle. Assuming a value of about 105° for the H_2O angle, we obtain a pyramidal configuration for H_3O^+ giving a geometrical arrangement closely resembling that of NH_3.

The usefulness of the resonance method has been proved through many applications. We shall restrict ourselves here to a few examples.*
Resonance occurs in all the anions of all the symmetrical oxygen acids;

* For a more detailed discussion see L. Pauling, *Nature of the Chemical Bond*, Cornell University Press, 1940.

thus the CO_3^{--} ion can be written as a superposition of the formulae

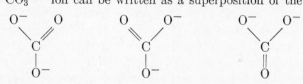

the O^- ion being univalent since it is isoelectronic with fluorine. The structure of the nitro group can be written with the help of a tetravalent N^+, (isoelectronic with carbon) and a monovalent O^-, as a superposition of

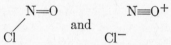

This presentation also accounts for the strong dipole moment of the group.

The ideas of resonance may be applied even if the resonating states do not have exactly equal energies. For instance, a resonance between the forms,

$$\underset{\text{Cl}}{\diagup}N{=}O \quad \text{and} \quad \underset{\text{Cl}^-}{N{\equiv}O^+}$$

has been proposed for the NOCl molecule. The second more unusual formula is justifiable on the basis of the electron affinity of Cl and on the basis of the increase of the NO binding when this molecule is ionized. Whereas in the symmetrical cases we must as a general rule superpose the wave functions with the same amplitudes, in the example given last, the coefficients in the superposition depend on detailed calculations which in practice cannot be carried out.

In the last example we have used wave functions in the superposition which themselves belong to slightly different energies. We may extend this procedure and use an increasing number of wave functions partly belonging to very high energy levels to obtain an approximation to the correct wave function of the lowest state. It can, of course, be shown quite generally that, even if the original wave functions have been very poor approximations, correct wave functions may be obtained by superposing a sufficient number of the original poor functions. However, it is technically hopeless to find even approximately correct coefficients in such a complicated case. The resonance method is useful only if the original wave functions have been good approximations, and in this case it suffices to superpose a few wave functions of equal or nearly equal energies.

The resonance method has been applied to describe the wave functions of diatomic molecules such as H_2. We can, for instance, describe the H_2 wave function by a superposition in which one electron is on each hydrogen atom and other functions where both electrons are near one nucleus while the other proton is bare, H^+, H^-. These approximations are poor when the two nuclei are as close together as they are known to be in the stable H_2 molecule. It seems therefore that for H_2 as for most of the other diatomic molecules the resonance method does not offer any great advantage in simplicity or accuracy, as compared with the molecular-orbital method. Although the resonance method seems perhaps more apt to utilize chemical intuition, the molecular-orbital method has proved a more flexible and accurate tool in correlating spectra of diatomic molecules with each other and with the properties of the molecules in their ground state. For the electronic states of complicated molecules, on the other hand, the resonance method often yields a very useful description.

One condition for resonance to be effective is that equilibrium configurations of the two resonating structures must not differ strongly. Resonance is possible practically only for two states with the same configuration of the atomic nuclei. Now, if the equilibrium configurations for the two resonating structures differ considerably, then the electronic energy of at least one of the two structures must be greatly raised by the distortion necessary to make the two nuclear configurations coincide. The energy thus lost will offset the gain in stability to which resonance can give rise; if, however, the two equilibrium configurations do not differ strongly, we can choose an intermediate configuration with no great loss of energy, and resonance will more than compensate that loss.

As an example for a small difference in equilibrium configuration we may consider the resonance in the carboxyl group where the two structures $\text{R}\!-\!\text{C}\!\underset{\text{O}^-}{\overset{\text{O}}{\Big<}}$ and $\text{R}\!-\!\text{C}\!\underset{\text{O}}{\overset{\text{O}^-}{\Big<}}$ resonate. The C—O and C=O equilibrium distances (1.4 Å. and 1.2 Å.) may be roughly estimated from the distances in alcohols and ketones, respectively; the difference is not very great.

Another class of examples in which resonance is probably prevented by too great a difference of the equilibrium configurations consists of compounds containing a hydrogen bridge. The two structures,

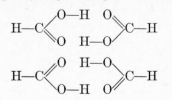

and

might be expected to resonate, but the distance in the O–H group is about 1.0 Å. while the distance between H and the oxygen atom to which it is not bound can be estimated from the structure of ice as about 1.8 Å.* The difference of the two distances is probably too great to permit resonance. The fact that bimolecular association with a binding energy of 14 kcal. is found must probably be interpreted as coulomb attraction and polarization effects acting between the hydrogen of one molecule and the oxygen of the other. The energy per hydrogen bridge, that is, half the association energy, actually does not differ much from the energy of the hydrogen bridge in water which we have explained in terms of van der Waals forces.

An example in which resonance is made definitely impossible by too great a change in configuration is the keto–enol isomerism. The hydrogen must move through a distance of more than 1 Å. if the transformation from the keto form to the enol form is to take place; consequently the keto and enol forms exist as separate chemical entities. This contrasts with the situation found in resonance where pure symbolic superposition of two structures is used to describe a single definite electronic configuration of a certain molecule.

As has been mentioned, we will expect in case of resonance an equilibrium configuration that is intermediate between the configurations of the two resonating structures. As an example confirming this rule, we may consider methyl nitrite in which the observed N–O distance lies between the distances expected for $N^+{=}O$ and $N^+{-}O^-$ bonds. (The ion N^+ is expected to behave in a way similar to the isoelectronic C atom; O^- will behave like an F atom.)

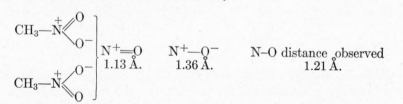

$$N^+{=}O \qquad N^+{-}O^-$$
$$1.13 \text{ Å.} \qquad 1.36 \text{ Å.}$$

N–O distance observed
1.21 Å.

7.25 RESONANCE DESCRIPTION OF CONJUGATED SYSTEMS For an open chain of conjugated double bonds, the chemical formula which belongs to the lowest energy is the usual one having alternate single and double bonds. Other forms of higher energy are obtained if charges on carbons or unshared single electrons on carbons

---

* In the case of dimerized formic acid, this distance seems to be actually smaller by about 0.1 Å.

are permitted. Thus for butadiene the following formulae may be considered:

(a) $CH_2{=}CH{-}CH{=}CH_2$

(b) $^-CH_2{-}CH{=}CH{-}CH_2{}^+$

(c) $^+CH_2{-}CH{=}CH{-}CH_2{}^-$

(d) $CH_2{-}CH{=}CH{-}CH_2$
                         | |

In the formulae (b) and (c) the C^- ion and the C^+ ion can be considered trivalent. They are actually isoelectronic with nitrogen and boron, respectively. In (d) there is a single unshared electron in each of the terminal carbon atoms. The resonance as shown by the formulae is effective only if the equilibrium configuration of butadiene approximates closely the equilibrium configuration of each of the four forms. This is possible only if all carbons lie in a plane; resonance seems therefore to favor a coplanar structure.

A much greater effect of resonance may be expected in benzene since at least two resonating structures, namely, the twin Kekulé formulae belong to the same energy. This accounts in the resonance description for the fact that benzene is much more stable than other unsaturated molecules or open conjugated systems. Actually the heat of combustion of benzene is 39 kcal. lower than the crude value which would follow from the additivity of bond energies. This discrepancy can be decreased by only 20 kcal. on account of the presence of three conjugated double bonds, and it has been proposed that the remaining difference is due to the peculiar and strong resonance in benzene. But the quantitative part of this argument suffers somewhat from the purely empirical nature and the crudeness of the bond additivity rule. On the qualitative side, it is highly satisfying that both Kekulé structures are needed to describe the electronic structure of benzene.

There is no immediate and simple reason why the resonance method should predict greater stability of 6, 10, 14, etc., membered rings than for 4, 8, 12, etc., membered rings (if necessary strains in some of these rings is disregarded). In this respect the results of the resonance method does not correspond exactly to the results of the method described in section 7.22.

Resonance between the two Kekulé structures does not suffice to explain the ortho–para-directing influence of some benzene substituents and the meta-directing influence of others. For this purpose further resonating structures must be introduced such as

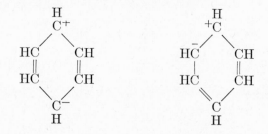

Although structures with ions in the ortho or para position are possible without deviating further from usual chemical rules, there is no simple structure with two ions, positive and negative, in the meta position. This correctly indicates a parallel behavior of the para and ortho positions.

Resonance with ionic contributions such as just mentioned has frequently been discussed in connection with more extended structures. The resonance in paranitrophenol is established by shifting simultaneously four double bonds.

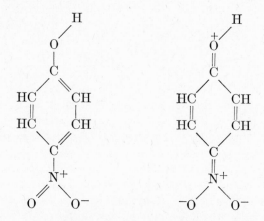

However, resonance is always weak if there are only very few electron configurations for which both resonating wave functions are appreciably different from zero. In fact, resonance is due to the overlapping of wave functions. Such overlapping is feeble if there is a great difference between the two resonating structures. Resonance in such cases will primarily proceed through intermediate ionic structures. We can always find such intermediate structures in which overlapping of the wave functions is considerable. In the preceding example the following series of structures can be used:

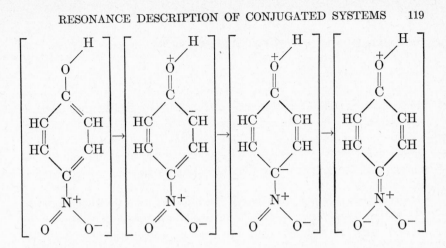

or another series:

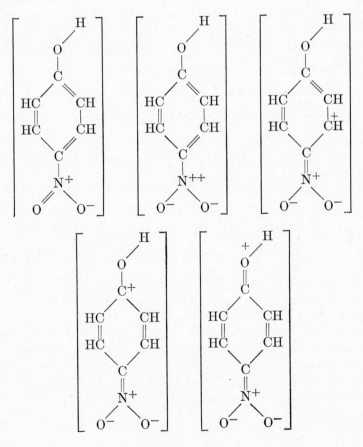

On the other hand, the intermediate ionic structures may have considerably higher energies and may, for that reason, be less available partners in the resonance.

Through the introduction of these ionic states, the electrons obtain greater mobility in the resonance picture. Accordingly, they behave more closely in the same way as was found in the modified molecular-orbital approximation (section 7.22). This may be considered as a special example of the general statement that the results obtained by different approximations converge when approximations are pushed far enough.

In the more complicated heterocyclic and carbocyclic rings, the number of resonating structures is considerable, even if we disregard ionic structures. For example, in anthracene we get contributions from the following structures:

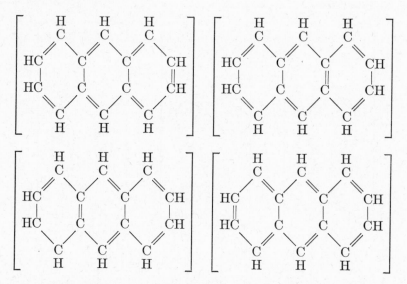

Perhaps one of the most complicated resonance situations is found in a carbon plane of graphite. Some of the structures for a limited part of the plane are shown in Figure 7.25(1).

Stability of some radicals may be explained by the great number of resonances which the removal of one atom makes possible. Thus if ionic structures are disregarded, the Kekulé resonances are the only ones possible in hexaphenylethane, whereas in triphenylmethyl the following structures are possible:

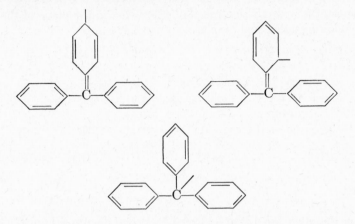

If we again disregard Kekulé resonances, the first of these structures will still stand for three different possibilities, and the second structure can be realized in six ways. A tendency for the ring and its substituents to

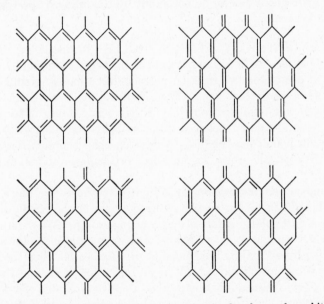

FIG. 7.25(1).   Resonating valence structures in the planes of graphite.

lie in a plane is a consequence of the resonance picture. In this respect there is a definite deviation from older stereochemical ideas. If, for instance, the hydroxyl hydrogen of phenol lies in the plane of the ring, the following additional resonating structures can be written:

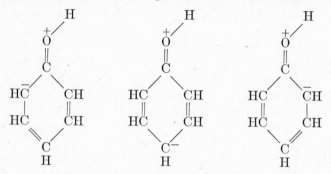

If, on the other hand, the hydroxyl hydrogen does not lie in the plane of the ring, these structures would become impossible, since they would violate the rule that if two atoms are joined by a double bond all their substituents must lie in one plane. The coplanar position of the hydroxyl hydrogen seems to be borne out by the infrared spectra of substituted benzenes.

7.26 BINDING BY ELECTRON HOLES In discussing the alkali halide molecules we found an example of one type of binding by electron holes. If one of the two reaction partners has a loosely bound electron while the other partner has a closed shell except for a vacant electron orbit, then the loose electron will fill the vacant orbit. The resulting electrostatic attraction between the ions holds the molecule together. A different, homopolar, binding by electron holes is obtained when two atoms with vacant orbits, for instance, two halogen atoms, react with each other.

To understand the homopolar action of the holes, we must bear in mind that filling of the vacant electron orbits of the reactants would lead to a particularly stable electron configuration. We shall use this closed-shell configuration as a standard of energy and judge the strength of binding by estimating how much energy is released when the missing electron orbits are filled. It will be an indication of chemical stability if the molecule releases less energy than the two separated atoms would. In other words, electron holes lead to a homopolar bond if the electron orbits of the holes have a higher energy in the molecule than in the separated atoms. The electron holes will thus have to "occupy" states which we have called antibonding, which of course means the same thing as saying that as many of the electrons present as possible have to be put into bonding states. For the particular case of F_2, the highest molecular-orbital function is an antibonding σ state obtained from p states of the separate atoms. The two holes in the F_2 molecule are both in this σ state. For an antibonding orbit the wave amplitude in the region between the two atoms is small, whereas the amplitude is large on the outside parts of the atoms. Thus the holes will be found with the smallest probability between the atoms, which again is merely a repetition of our earlier rule that in homopolar binding as many electrons as possible are located between the atoms. Similar statements hold for the other halogen molecules.

It may be noticed that holes behave, in general, in an opposite way to electrons, seeking to occupy the highest rather than the lowest orbits. An electric field draws them in the opposite direction to electrons, and in this way they behave as though they were carrying positive charges. In fact, if the closed shell is considered as a basic neutral structure, their presence does cause a positive charge. By using the simplified concept of positively charged holes, the behavior of halogen atoms may be discussed also in other than chemical respects. Thus in the theory of the halogen spectra it is permissible to a certain approximation to discuss the motion of one positively charged hole rather than the seven electrons in the outermost shell. The analogy with the positive charge is, however, not perfect because the hole tends to occupy the state with the highest kinetic energy which a positively charged electron would not do.

It is interesting to note in this connection that the application of the idea of holes in relativistic quantum mechanics has led to a theoretical prediction of the positron. In this curious application space is considered filled up with a continuous infinity of electrons in negative energy states. The existence of these states follows from relativistic theory, but they have never been observed. The state of space in which all the energy levels are filled up corresponds to a closed atomic shell. The electrons filling the negative states are assumed to be unobservable. If any of the electrons in these negative states is missing, this becomes noticeable as a positron. Owing to the peculiar properties of negative energy levels in relativistic theory, this positron behaves in every respect as a positively charged electron. In particular, it differs from our positive holes in that it tends to occupy low kinetic-energy states. But the positron retains the property of a hole in one respect. When it meets an electron, both the electron and positron may disappear, their energy being transformed into radiation. This process is a perfect analogue to an electron being captured by a rare-gas atom with a vacant orbit; the positron has played the role of the vacant orbit. This positron theory with its infinite number of unobservable electrons may seem unsatisfactory, and it may be actually replaced by a theory that places elec-

trons and positrons on an equal footing. But the "hole theory" shows
how close the similarity is between the positron and the vacant place of
an electron in an atom, and it is interesting to observe the influence
which our ideas of the known structure of matter had on the theory of
elementary particles.

8. FORCES IN THE SOLID STATE

8.1 INTRODUCTION In treating the solids we shall have to apply the concept of atomic forces to a great variety of structures. In many cases the forces are not very different from those encountered in molecules. We shall start by a rough classification of the forces acting within solids and then proceed by considering a few examples of the great variety of structures to which these forces can give rise. Following that, we shall treat the more common types of forces which have been described in previous chapters in connection with inner- and intermolecular forces acting within the solid. We shall emphasize, however, the problems which specifically arise in the discussion of the solid state. A more detailed discussion will have to be reserved for the metallic state which has no strict analogue in molecular structure. It will be shown that starting from the theory of the metallic state we may reinterpret all forces occurring in solids. As a final application we shall treat surface phenomena.

We shall not discuss the problem of liquids. The forces operating in liquids are to a great extent similar to the forces in solids. The essential difference is that the thermal agitation has destroyed the long-range order that may have existed in the solid and that it has greatly facilitated the exchange of molecules, thus decreasing the viscosity and producing a fluid. The questions connected with liquids thus concern statistical behavior rather than elementary forces or structures, and lie therefore outside the scope of this book.

The important question of the extent to which a solid is ordered will receive only occasional brief references. The degree of ordering distinguishes, in its extremes, crystals from amorphous substances, but there are many intermediate steps where the appearance is crystalline, and yet a certain element of disorder is present. This complex of questions too is essentially of a statistical nature, and we shall refer to it only where it has some bearing on the nature of forces governing the solid structure.

8.2 FORCES ACTING WITHIN SOLIDS Solids have often been called giant molecules. There are a few solids for which this description is entirely appropriate. Perhaps the best example is diamond in which each carbon atom is bound by four homopolar single bonds to four neighboring carbon atoms and where, proceeding along bonds, any carbon atom can be reached from any other carbon atom in the lattice. There are, however, many solids in which the nature of the forces differ considerably from those usually associated with the idea of a chemical bond. In heteropolar crystals such as the alkali halides, probably a greater contribution to the binding is made by simple coulomb potentials acting between the ions than in any molecules. In fact, polarizability of the ions within molecules tends to equalize charges and reduces polarity, whereas, in ionic crystals in which the ions are symmetrically surrounded by other ions, the resulting polarizing forces are much smaller.

A much greater qualitative difference exists between the weakly bound solids such as those obtained at low temperature by condensation of the rare gases and the ordinary chemical structures. In these weakly bound crystals, the attraction is due to van der Waals forces. The class of van der Waals solids is in fact quite comprehensive and includes the solids composed of molecules. For instance, solid nitrogen or solid iodine and also solid benzene and other hydrocarbons are representatives of this class. Their only analogue among proper molecules are weakly associated dimers or polymers in the gaseous phase which are usually not called molecules in the stricter sense of the word.

A further most important class of solids comprises the metals. We shall see that their properties differ very markedly from the properties of saturated molecules. Unsaturated molecules and radicals have some properties in common with metals, but the metals have so many unique characteristics that an analogy with any molecule is incomplete.

The discussion of solids is further complicated by the fact that the demarcation lines among the four kinds of solids just mentioned are none too sharp. Thus solids such as ice in which the main binding forces are dipoles constitute a smooth transition between the most weakly bound van der Waals solids and the ionic structures. Polarization in ionic solids gives rise to a transition of this crystal type into the homopolar structures. In fact, there is no quite clearly defined rule how many electrons shall be ascribed to one atom or ion and how many to another and we shall see later that the same crystal may be interpreted as homopolar or as heteropolar. Finally closely packed structures of any kind can go over almost imperceptibly into semiconductors and finally into metals.

In addition, it is possible that several types of binding are present in the same crystal. Threads or sheets of atoms may be held together by homopolar forces, whereas the interaction of these bigger units is of the van der Waals type. Polar structures may alternate with less polar bindings, and even the forces characteristic of metals may be most pronounced between some atoms, whereas in the cohesion of other atoms metallic properties play a lesser role.

In some respects, however, the study of solids is simpler than that of molecules. First, purely geometrical considerations of arrangements of atoms in space are more easily determined in solids and can indeed be obtained more readily by X rays and by electron diffraction. Second, metallic conductivity gives direct and important information about the behavior of electrons in metals. Finally, macroscopic properties, such as cleavage planes, hardness, or melting points, give direct hints as to the microscopic structures.

8.3   VAPOR PRESSURES AND MELTING POINTS OF SOLIDS

As has been mentioned, the physical properties of solids are very closely related to the type of forces operating in them. Two properties of these forces are important: (1) their strength and (2) their directed or undirected nature. Evidently, small forces are connected with a high vapor pressure as is the case in the van der Waals solids. In addition, we will expect that van der Waals forces are greater between heavier atoms and bigger molecules; this regularity has been known for a long time and can be illustrated by the vapor pressures in the solid state of the rare gases, halogens, or the series of hydrocarbons. The more tightly bound solids have a much lower vapor pressure. It is interesting to notice the lowering in vapor pressure which follows the polymerization of organic compounds and the formation of plastics.

The directed nature of forces influences the melting point more than the vapor pressure. The typically homopolar compounds like diamond have strictly directed valence angles, and correspondingly their melting points are sometimes so high that they are outside the range of convenient physical observation. In ionic lattices the forces merely require that there shall be a great number of oppositely charged ions close to each other while the similarly charged ions are kept as far apart as possible. Although these requirements are sufficient to stabilize crystal structures, they do not make the angular relations so rigid as to make melting practically impossible. In metals we find frequently a tendency for a great number of nearest neighbors, resulting in close-packed structures with not too rigidly fixed angles and comparatively low melting points.

8.4   SHEETLIKE STRUCTURES   As has been mentioned already, alternation of stronger and weaker forces within certain crystals can be inferred from macroscopic physical properties. Perhaps the best example is that of graphite where the atoms in plane sheets can be represented [Figure 7.25(1)] as one big unsaturated molecule. The different possible configurations of the conjugated double bonds give rise to the same kind of resonance phenomena as has been discussed in the examples of the closely analogous organic compounds. In these, the double-bond electrons could be represented as wandering all over the molecule, and this analogy suggests that the binding contributed by the double-bond electrons in the planes of graphite is essentially a binding by free electrons, that is, a metallic binding. This consideration is borne out by

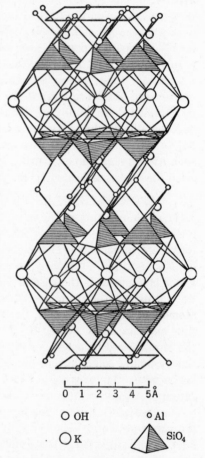

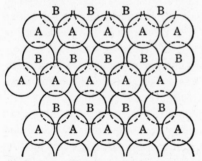

O OH   o Al

○ K   △ SiO₄

FIG. 8.4(1). Plan of a single sheet in the black phosphorus crystal. (See also *Structurbericht*, Vol. III, page 6, 1937.)

FIG. 8.4(2). Diagram showing the structure of muscovite mica, $(OH)_2KAl_2(Si_3Al)O_{10}$.

the metallic conductivity of graphite. The separate sheets in graphite are held together by much weaker forces, as shown by the exceedingly easy cleavage of the crystal. Actually the valence picture can be satisfied within one plane, and we will not be far off in saying that graphite consists of metallic and therefore exceedingly highly polarizable sheet molecules held together essentially by van der Waals forces which for big polarizable molecules are quite considerable but yet inferior to the strong forces operating within the sheets.

Another example of a sheetlike structure is found in black phosphorus in which the atoms are arranged in staggered sheets as shown in Figure 8.4(1). The circles marked A represent atoms slightly above, those marked B slightly below, the average plane of the sheet. Each atom has three neighbors satisfying the three valencies of phosphorus. The staggered nature of the sheets is due to the fact that in phosphorus, as in nitrogen, the valence angle is smaller than 120°. Separate sheets are held together by van der Waals forces. This simple picture is somewhat complicated by the fact that black phosphorus does possess an electric conductivity. Black phosphorus and graphite are examples of sheets within which homopolar bonds are the greatest stabilizing factors with various tendencies of the electrons toward free metallic motion.

A sheetlike structure is even more strikingly exhibited by the exterior behavior of the crystal in the case of the micas. But in the micas the structures become a little more complicated. One "simple" structure, that of muscovite is shown in Figure 8.4(2). In this case the sheets themselves have complex structures; the binding between the sheets as well as within them is of ionic character but the different ionic radii and charges insure an easier cleavage near the univalent alkali ions. In other micas the electrical neutralization within each layer is more perfect, and the interactions between layers are due only to multipole and polarization forces characteristic of van der Waals attractions.

8.5 THREADLIKE STRUCTURES We have just seen that some crystals far from constituting a homogeneous latticework can be naturally subdivided into sheets. In a few crystals, the natural subunits are one-dimensional structures or threads which in turn are held together by weaker forces. We may consider sulfur as one example.

In the ordinary rhombic sulfur one finds ringlike S_8 molecules in which each sulfur atom is linked to two neighbors; the valence angle of 105° causes the ring to be puckered. On being heated to about 200° C., sulfur becomes a very viscous liquid in which the rings have opened up, and the ends unite to form long chains. The long chains impeding each other's motion explain the high viscosity. If this liquid

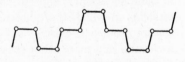

Fig. 8.5(1). Sulfur chains in stretched plastic sulfur.

is now cooled, amorphous sulfur is obtained which still consists of long chains in a disorderly arrangement. Amorphous sulfur has rubber-like qualities. On stretching, chains which originally were bending around in a random fashion assume the more orderly structure shown in Figure 8.5(1). The sulfur chains while retaining the valence angle follow in general straight lines. This more orderly arrangement causes sulfur to crystallize under high tension, a further peculiarity in which it resembles rubber. Somewhat similar crystalline structures are found for

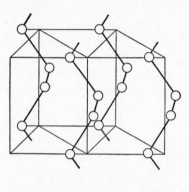

selenium and tellurium in which chains with each atom bound to two neighbors spiral round parallel axes, Figure 8.5(2).

Among the silicates there are also found threadlike arrangements of strongly bound groups. Thus in pyroxene minerals, for example, $CaMg(SiO_3)_2$, chains of SiO_4 tetra-

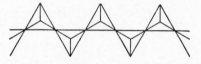

FIG. 8.5(2). Diagram showing the structure of selenium. The spiral chains extend indefinitely through the crystal in the vertical direction.

FIG. 8.5(3). Chain of tetrahedra in a pyroxene mineral.

hedra are found in which two neighboring tetrahedra always share one oxygen. One such chain is shown in Figure 8.5(3). The chains carry a total negative charge and are bound together by positive calcium and magnesium ions placed between them. Many of these silicate-containing chains show macroscopically a fibrous structure.

8.6 VAN DER WAALS SOLIDS In the last two sections we have seen how the difference in the nature of forces has brought about within the solids extensive substructures the presence of which manifests itself in the macroscopic properties of the body. There is a much larger class of solids in which the difference in strength of the forces causes finite spatial groups to exist as subunits. These groups can then be called molecules in a more strict sense.

The character of these solids is determined by the fact that with the use of relatively little energy they can be decomposed into smaller units. We shall treat in this section the case where this decomposition requires a minimum energy. This will be so if no dipoles are attached to the constituent molecules and the forces discussed in section 6.5 are responsible for holding the solid together.

Among the general properties of the van der Waals solids we have just mentioned is the small energy of sublimation. The fact that the van der Waals interaction between two nondipole molecules does not affect in first approximation their interaction with a third molecule means that there is no tendency towards the formation of bigger groups containing several molecules. Further, these van der Waals forces depend on direction only when the interacting molecules are not spherical and only insofar as these molecules tend to get into close contact and particularly tend to bring their polarizable parts as close together as possible. This will result in closely packed structures, and the absence of directional forces gives rise to easily deformable solids with low melting points.

The simplest crystals of this type are obtained by solidifying the rare gases. We shall leave out of consideration here helium, in which the very low van der Waals binding energy and the small mass of the helium atom make it necessary to take quantum effects into account when discussing the positions and motions of the helium nuclei. This makes helium a unique substance. The motion of all other nuclei in physico-chemical processes can always be described by classical theory in reasonable approximation and most often in excellent approximation.

In crystals of neon, argon, krypton, and xenon the atoms are arranged in the way in which spheres can be packed together most tightly. Each atom has 12 nearest neighbors. The melting points rise regularly with increasing atomic weight as would be expected from the greater polarizability in the heavier atoms.

But the agreement between expectation and experience does not extend to the finer details of the crystal structure. We shall give a detailed discussion of a structure in order to illustrate the difficulties which arise if one attempts to explain quantitatively even the simplest of the crystals.

The actual arrangement of atoms is that of cubic close packing. This structure can be described in terms of hexagonal sheets of atoms, one such sheet being shown in the Figure 8.6(1). The circles with the numeral 1 in their centers represent the atoms of a sheet. A second similar sheet is placed on top of the first, with the atomic centers situated above the points designated by the numerals 2. Thus each atom of the second sheet will touch three atoms of the first. The sheet lying above the second sheet will have its atoms vertically above the numbers 3 in the figure so that each atom of this sheet will again touch three atoms of the previous sheet. The atoms of the fourth sheet lie vertically above the atoms of the first and from there on the structure repeats itself. Thus each atom is surrounded by 12 other atoms, 6 from its own plane, 3 from the plane above, and 3 from the plane below.

A second close-packed structure of spheres is known which differs from the one observed in rare-gas crystals, namely, the hexagonal close-packed structure. This structure contains sheets similar to the cubic close-packed structure. The atoms in the first and second sheets have actually the same position as in the cubic close-packed arrangement. But the atoms of the third sheet do not lie perpendicularly above the

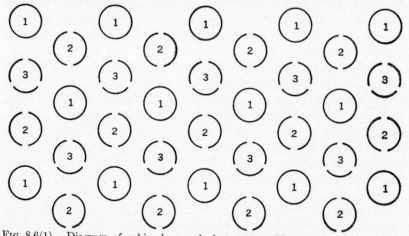

FIG. 8.6(1). Diagram of cubic close-packed structure. Numerals 1, 2, and 3 indicate atoms in successive crystalline planes. Starting from plane number 4, the structure repeats itself.

positions designated by the number 3 in Figure 8.6(1); they lie perpendicularly over the atoms of the first layer. Thus the layers alternate between the positions 1 and 2 rather than alternating cyclically among the positions 1, 2, and 3.

The number of nearest neighbors is the same in the hexagonal and cubic close-packed arrangements. If the lattice energy is considered as the sum of interactions between neighboring atoms, no difference is obtained for the energies of the two arrangements. It is then of interest to ask why the rare-gas crystals have cubic rather than hexagonal arrangements.

We might suspect that the cubic close-packed arrangement is stabilized by interaction between second and perhaps further neighbors. Though the van der Waals potential decreases with the sixth power of the distance, the great number of farther atoms could possibly make their influence significant. But if the sum of interaction potentials among all pairs of atoms is taken, it is found that the lattice energies for the hexagonal and cubic arrangements differ by less than one thousandth of their value, and whatever difference exists would tend to stabilize the hexagonal rather than the cubic lattice. The small value of the difference between the energies of the two arrangements would lead us to expect that a random mixture of the two lattice arrangements would result with a layer of type 2 or 3 following layer 1, a layer of type 3 or 1 following 2, and a layer of type 1 or 2 following 3, without any relation to the further removed layers.

It seems that in order to explain the stability of the cubic lattice it is necessary to assume that the forces within the crystal are not strictly additive; that is, the interaction between any two atoms is influenced to some extent by the configuration of other atoms. It is most likely that the bulk of the lattice energy is due to simple additive forces acting between pairs of atoms. In fact, the lattice energy can be estimated satisfactorily on this basis using the experimentally known constants for the rare-gas atoms and the formula for the van der Waals potential

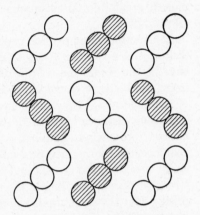

FIG. 8.6(2). The structure of benzene. The shaded molecules are displaced vertically relative to the others through one-half the height of the unit cell.

given in section 6.5. But the actual structure of the solid cannot be obtained without taking into account the presumably small nonadditive corrections which have to be applied to these potentials. That the actual structure of a solid depends on a delicate balance of energies is a rather common occurrence and explains the polymorphisms, that is, changes of structure at certain temperatures and pressures, that are so frequently observed.

Though the van der Waals forces are generally speaking nondirected, they nevertheless can produce somewhat complicated crystal arrangements if the molecules to be packed are nonspherical. The structure of benzene which may serve as an example is shown in Figure 8.6(2). The groups of three circles represent three C–H groups of a benzene ring whose plane is at right angles to the plane of the paper. The other three C–H groups are immediately underneath. The shaded molecules are displaced vertically with respect to the unshaded ones. Thus the crystal consists of alternating planes represented by the shaded and the nonshaded part of the figure.

The interatomic distances between atoms within a molecule are, as a general rule, somewhat greater in a van der Waals solid than in the corresponding gas. As an example we may mention iodine. The distance between two iodine atoms of the molecule is 2.65 Å. in the gas, whereas the distance in the solid is 2.70 Å. Great distortion of distances within molecules signifies, of course, a tendency to depart from the pure molecular lattice and an approach to a more uniform binding between all neighbors.

A somewhat more explicit explanation of the greater inner-molecular distances of a van der Waals solid can be given in terms of the dependence of the forces on polarizabilities. According to this theory, the interaction energy of molecules increases with increasing polarizability of the molecules. Now the polarizability usually becomes greater with increasing distance between the atoms within a molecule. The energy necessary to change slightly the inner-molecular distances is more than compensated by the increased interaction between the molecules. Generally speaking, the ground state of an isolated molecule represents the strongest possible binding of the constituent particles, and it is not surprising that the structure is somewhat loosened if the particles are subject to additional external forces.

8.7 DIPOLE STRUCTURES, THE HYDROXYL BOND AND THE HYDROGEN BOND Van der Waals forces holding crystals together are, of course, much stronger if they are produced not merely by the interaction of polarizabilities but by permanent dipoles. Attraction due to such dipoles will, of course, favor certain orientations, thus giving rise to quite complex structures.

If the dipole is due to a hydrogen-containing group such as OH or NH_2, the binding often shows a peculiar behavior which is not quite completely described by the simple picture of dipoles. We have already seen in discussing the interaction energy between water molecules that consideration of a detailed distribution of charges within the water molecule will have a decisive influence on the most stable configuration of these molecules with respect to each other. Thus the arrangement shown in Figure 8.7(1)A would be the most stable configuration of water molecules if we describe the electrical properties of the molecule by attaching to it one dipole moment bisecting the H–O–H angle. If, however, we take into consideration the existence of two distinct centers of positive charge in H_2O, we find that the configuration shown in Figure 8.7(1)B is probably the more stable one. The interaction energy for this configuration can be estimated, and we find that it is of the right order of magnitude to explain the binding energy of ice. In fact, the structure of ice can be described by placing four hydrogen atoms around each oxygen in a tetrahedral distribution. Two of these hydrogen atoms belong to the same molecule as the oxygen atom while two others belong to adjacent oxygen atoms and point toward the oxygen atom in question. The hydrogen atoms within the same molecule are rather closer to the oxygen atom than are the other two hydrogens; but beyond each of the four hydrogen atoms on four straight lines there are found four oxygens at equal distances from the original oxygen atom. Each O–O distance is a sum of two unequal distances 1.1 Å. found within a molecule and approximately 1.6 Å. found for the distance between the

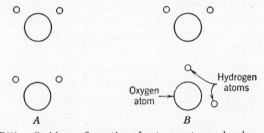

FIG. 8.7(1). Stable configurations for two water molecules assuming
A. Interaction of dipoles
B. Excess charges on individual atoms.

H atom of one molecule and the O atom of an immediate neighbor. Actually the X-ray investigation of ice fixes only the distance between O atoms, whereas the positions of the H atoms are inferred from spectroscopic data obtained in gaseous H_2O.

Because of the difficulty of packing tetrahedra closely, ice has a rather open structure and a low density. In this case the electrostatic forces trying to pull positive and negative charges as closely together as possible have produced the loose tetrahedral co-ordination. Any closer packing, though favored by the interaction of polarizabilities, would necessitate closer approach of charges of the same sign. We may consider this situation as the first though not the best example of an important principle in the building of ionic crystals which we shall call the principle of microscopic neutrality. In reality this principle, the name of which is self-explanatory, is merely a statement which helps in finding without a detailed calculation a configuration of charges with the lowest electrostatic energy.

Although the structure of ice can be explained by essentially electrostatic reasoning, there is some evidence that the hydroxyl groups both in OH_2 and in the ion OH^- tend to follow each other not in a straight line but rather in an angle not very different from the tetrahedral angle.

A relatively simple example of such a binding of OH groups is found in the structure of boric acid, B(OH)₃, which forms a layer crystal. Some layers are represented in Figure 8.7(2). The angular disposition of the OH groups is evident. We might again argue that the structure is mainly stabilized by electrostatic forces. Another possible explanation can be given in terms of directed valencies. If a positive charge approaches the OH⁻ ion, the most stable configuration will be found for that direction of approach in which a proton would be bound to OH⁻

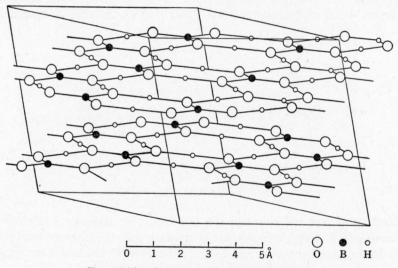

FIG. 8.7(2).   Structure of boric acid, B(OH)₃.

to form the H₂O molecule. In fact, an electron orbit can be constructed that protrudes relatively far in that direction and the electrons of which may meet relatively easily the approaching positive charge. From the pure electrostatic reasoning we might expect that the best possible line of approach of a positive ion A⁺ is along the O–H axis as shown:

$$A^+ \quad O\text{—}H$$

But the same detailed consideration of the electron orbits which explains why the H–O–H angle in water is not 180° may also cause the A⁺ ion to approach from another direction than along the axis.

The same kind of consideration can also be applied to H₂O when a positive ion approaches. Since the ion H₃O⁺ as well as the isoelectronic ammonia have a pyramidal structure, it is possible that the most favorable direction of approach for the A⁺ ion is in a direction outside the H₂O plane. Thus, not only is the A⁺ ion attracted to the negative re gion of the H_2O dipole, but also it is attracted in a directional way, the direction being determined by that of the bond which could be formed were the positive ion to approach closely enough to be incorporated in the molecule. The expression "residual valency" may be correctly applied to describe such a binding due to a preferential polarizability of the molecule that corresponds to a potential bond formation. The residual valence of the OH group which tends to attract positive ions roughly at a tetrahedral angle to the O–H axis, is sometimes called the hydroxyl bond.

A similar situation should occur with the NH_2^- ion where one would expect the A^+ ion to be attracted from a direction forming roughly tetrahedral angles with the N–H bonds. That NH_3 attracts a positive ion in such a way as to form a H_3N········A^+ tetrahedron is due both to the action of directed residual valences and to the simpler reason that the A^+ ion must approach the negative N from the direction which is not occupied by positive hydrogens.

The attraction of a hydrogen atom for a neighboring negative ion is so pronounced that a symmetrical structure has been suggested in which the hydrogen is equally strongly bound to the atom to which it was attached originally and to the other atom with which, according to the original picture, it should interact only with van der Waals forces.

As an example one may quote the dimerization of formic acid. If in this dimer the hydrogens of the two hydroxyl groups are placed symmetrically between two oxygens, two hydrogen bridges between the two formic acid molecules are formed. We have discussed this structure in section 7.24 and found that the energy of formation of the dimer may be explained without actual sharing of the hydrogens.

A direct decision could be obtained by determining the positions of the hydrogen atoms, but our diffraction methods are not capable of doing this. There is some indirect evidence in the formic acid dimer for the presence of resonance. All distances between neighboring C and O atoms have been found to be equal, whereas in the absence of resonance we would expect the $C\!\!=\!\!O$ distance to be smaller than the $C\!\!-\!\!O$ distance. It must be remembered that even the pure electrostatic van der Waals forces will stretch the original bond by which the hydrogen was held while causing an approach of the hydrogen to a neighboring negative ion. Thus a gradual transition is possible between the pure electrostatic binding and the resonance binding which occurs for symmetrically located hydrogens.

8.8   IONIC CRYSTALS   Simple examples of ionic crystals such as the alkali halides were among the first to be subjected to a theoretical discussion. The reason for this was that the main part of the binding energy is a simple electrostatic attraction, and thus the energy of formation of the crystal could be estimated from the ionic charges and the ionic distances. In order to obtain accurate results one must include, of course, other forces such as the interactions of the polarizabilities, the van der Waals repulsion forces, and also that part of the van der Waals forces which describes the polarization of one ion by the charge of the neighboring ions. The latter forces, though exceedingly important in a gaseous alkali halide molecule, are far less strong in an alkali halide crystal in which each ion is symmetrically surrounded by a relatively great number (six or eight) of oppositely charged ions, the fields of which cancel each other to a considerable extent. But just because the main effect cancels, the residual polarization is difficult to calculate and has not been taken into account. The effect of the other forces has been taken into account, and it has been proved possible to establish a relationship, with their help, between the energy of formation of the crystal and some other properties. Among the latter, the compressibility of the crystals is of particular importance since it gives a measure of the forces that are produced by changing the distance between the ions.

In Table 8.8(1) calculations on the energy of formation of the alkali halide crystals are summarized and compared with experimental data. (The fluorides have been omitted because for these substances experimental data are incomplete.) The first column contains the substances. The second column gives the electrostatic energies per molecule, that is, the work that has to be performed against electrostatic attractions and repulsions of point charges if the lattice is decomposed into isolated ions. This energy, as well as all the following energies, is measured in units of electron volts.

In the third column the energies are listed which are due to the interaction of polarizabilities. Only the forces between the highly polarizable negative ions are of importance. To calculate these, data on the spectra and refractive indices of the alkali halide crystals were used. It may be noticed that in this way not the properties of the free halogen ions were used as the basis of the calculation, but rather the properties of the halogen ions as modified by their surroundings in the crystal. The figures given in the third column are, therefore, semi-empirical, but their importance is comparatively small.

The potential energies due to the van der Waals repulsive forces are given in column four. In calculating this potential, it is assumed that the forces have the exponential form discussed in the previous chapter. But two constants (the factor in front of the exponential and the factor multiplying the interionic distance in the exponent) have been adjusted empirically. These constants have been chosen in such a way as to obtain the correct densities and compressibilities for the crystals. It is interesting to compare this empirical formula with the one given in section 7.3. There we have found that the exponent in the van der Waals repulsion force depends on the binding energy of the most loosely bound electron. In the present case this is the binding energy of the extra electron on the negative ion. (This binding energy is called the

TABLE 8.8(1)

LATTICE ENERGIES OF ALKALI HALIDES

Substance	Electrostatic Energy in e.v.	Interaction of Polarizabilities in e.v.	Van der Waals Repulsion in e.v.	Lattice Energy in e.v.	Experimental Lattice Energies by Mayer and Helmholtz	Experimental Lattice Energy by Saha–Tandon	Lattice Energies Obtained by the Born–Haber Cycle
LiCl	9.75	0.16	1.17	8.63	8.74		8.65
LiBr	9.07	0.14	0.98	8.16	8.23		8.19
LiI	8.23	0.16	0.79	7.56	7.60		7.65
NaCl	8.92	0.13	1.03	7.94	7.86		7.90
NaBr	8.41	0.12	0.90	7.58		7.65	7.60
NaI	7.77	0.14	0.74	7.10		7.23	7.17
KCl	7.99	0.17	0.94	7.17	7.22		7.12
KBr	7.62	0.16	0.82	6.71		6.90	6.74
KI	7.10	0.16	0.69	6.54	6.66	6.52	6.57
RbCl	7.68	0.20	0.87	6.95			6.98
RbBr	7.30	0.17	0.76	6.67	6.56		6.74
RbI	6.82	0.17	0.67	6.30			6.36
CsCl	7.08	0.33	0.77	6.51			6.58
CsBr	6.80	0.30	0.71	6.34			6.40
CsI	6.40	0.29	0.63	6.04	6.13		6.11

"electron affinity.") In the empirical van der Waals formula the exponential factor drops off somewhat more sharply than is predicted by our formula in the previous chapter, if the electron affinity of free negative ions is used in that formula. We may, indeed, expect that in the crystal the outermost electron of the negative ion may be a little more confined to the neighborhood of the ion than is the case for the free ion.

Column five gives the end result of the theoretical calculation, the "lattice energy." This energy is defined as the work needed to dissociate the lattice into pure positive and negative ions. Like all other energies in the table, the lattice energy is expressed in units of electron volts and is to be interpreted as the energy per alkali halide molecule. The lattice energy is calculated by adding the energies in columns two and three and then subtracting the repulsive energy in column four. Actually a further small correction was included in the figures of column five. Because of the uncertainty principle, atomic nuclei are not quite sharply localized even when they are in the lowest possible energy state. Thus the nuclei will not be found exactly in the equilibrium positions of the lattice to which the numbers of columns two, three, and four would apply. We can apply the needed correction by subtracting the "zero-point energy" of lattice vibrations from the value obtained from the previous columns. It should be emphasized that this correction is small and that it can be obtained with quite a high accuracy from the experimentally known lattice frequencies.

Column six gives the experimental values of lattice energies obtained by Mayer and Helmholtz. The procedure was to measure the concentration of alkali and halogen ions in the gas phase over a heated alkali halide crystal. The lattice energy can then be determined from simple thermodynamic relations. These measurements have been carried out for only a few kinds of crystals. In column seven are shown similar measurements by Saha and Tandon and by Tandon.

The last column gives the lattice energy obtained by a more circuitous procedure; the Born–Haber cycle. We consider the dissociation of the lattice into the ions in the following steps: (1) The lattice is decomposed into the solid alkali metal and the diatomic molecules of the halogen gas. (2) The alkali metal is evaporated, and the halogen molecules are dissociated. (3) The alkali atoms are ionized, and the electrons so obtained are attached to the halogen atoms so that we are left with positive alkali ions and negative halogen ions in the gas phase. The energy of each step mentioned has been measured. In this way we obtain an independent experimental value for the lattice energy. This value is shown in column eight.

It may be seen that the difference between theory and experiment is not greater than the difference between the various experimental figures. Of course, the theoretical derivation contained, in many instances, empirical constants; but these empirical constants were never adjusted to give the best fit for the lattice energies but rather to describe some other properties of the crystals such as density, compressibility, refractive index or the ultraviolet absorption. On the whole, it may be said that the agreement which has been obtained is a fine confirmation of the method used in calculating forces and energies within a polar solid.

Though the ions are fairly good subunits in these crystals and thus the crystals can be discussed in fairly good approximation by considering the interaction of these subunits, our discussion of the rare-gas crystals indicates that a detailed explanation of even the simplest lattice is very difficult. Thus the simple lattice theory applied to the alkali halides has failed to predict in a satisfactory way the frequency of those lattice vibrations in which all positive ions move in one direction and all negative ions move in the opposite direction. The indications are that in this kind of a displacement the restoring forces are of a somewhat different nature from those in the displacement which corresponds to a simple compression of the crystal. It will perhaps be necessary to introduce nonadditive forces, that is to assume that the interac-

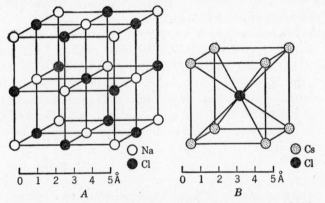

○ Na
● Cl

◉ Cs
● Cl

0 1 2 3 4 5Å   0 1 2 3 4 5Å

A   B

FIG. 8.8(1).   Structures of sodium chloride and caesium chloride.

tion between two ions is influenced by the presence and position of a third ion. Another problem, the complete clarification of which lies outside the scope of the simple lattice theory, is connected with the stability of the two crystal structures common among alkali halides, namely the sodium chloride and caesium chloride structures. The structures of these two salts are represented in Figure 8.8(1).

Qualitatively, it is easy enough to understand the factors which stabilize one or the other of these structures. If the two ions in the lattice are of very different sizes, that is, if the negative ion is very much larger than the positive ion, then the negative ions actually touch and form a cubic close-packed structure with the positive ions fitting into the interstices. In the sodium chloride structure, shown in Figure 8.8(1)A, each ion is surrounded by six ions of the opposite charge. But the second neighbors of each ion are 12 ions of a similar charge which have the same configuration as the 12 neighbors of a rare-gas atom in a rare-gas crystal.

Thus in sodium chloride structure the factor determining the configuration of the ions is the desire of the highly polarizable negative ions to be closely packed. In such a close packing the interaction of the polarizabilities of the negative ions are fully effective while the placing of the positive ions into the interstices more than compensates the repulsion of the negative ions.

The caesium chloride lattice is stable if the positive and negative ions are of comparable size. Then there is no room in the interstices of the closely packed negative ions for the positive ions, and that structure becomes more stable in which each ion is surrounded by as many oppositely charged ions as possible. This happens in the caesium chloride structure where the number of closest neighbors, which was six for sodium chloride, is increased to eight.

Quantitative calculations of lattice energies prove the stability of the sodium chloride type for very unequal ionic radii in agreement with experience, but, if the radii of the positive and negative ions are not very different, theory predicts a rather small energy difference between the two structures and is not quite sufficient to predict the structure of such alkali halides in every instance. Again, a more detailed description of the forces seems to be necessary before a complete explanation can be expected.

Although the number of ionic crystals is very great, the general principles governing their structure are the same as have been mentioned before. The structure is primarily determined by two factors: (1) the principle of microscopic neutrality which requires that ions of opposite charge should be as close as possible to every ion, thus giving effectively as uniformly neutral distribution of charge as possible; (2) the strong van der Waals repulsion which sets in rather abruptly when the ions approach to a distance where their electronic distributions begin to overlap. It is to be expected and is roughly verified that this distance can be written as the sum of two distances characteristic of the two neighboring ions called the atomic radii. We have already implicitly used these radii in discussing the alkali halides. The interplay of the coulomb forces and microscopic neutrality tending to draw opposite ions close together, with the influence of ion radii not allowing an approach of the ions beyond a certain limit, produces varied and sometimes quite complicated crystal structures.

8.9 IONIC COMPLEXES It often occurs in ionic crystals that a small group of ions is held together by particularly strong forces thus effectively forming a subunit in the ion structure. If these subunits are themselves neutral, we may expect them to be held together merely by van der Waals forces, and a van der Waals crystal is obtained. If on the other hand, the subunits happen to carry a net charge, we can consider them as great ions or more specifically as complex ions which themselves are building blocks of which the crystal is formed. Well-known examples of complex ions are CN^-, N_3^-, NO_2^-, CO_3^{--}, SO_4^{--}, NH_4^+, $[Fe(CN)_6]^{----}$, $CuCl_4^{--}$, and others. With the exception of the diatomic and triatomic ions, all examples are built around one central ion. The central ion is as a rule small and strongly charged and can hold neighboring ions by forces stronger than those by which the neighboring ions are held to further ions in the crystal. Since positive ions are usually smaller than negative ones, the central ion is as a rule positive, the only notable exceptions being NH_4^+, and H_3O^+ complexes in which the central atom has to be regarded as the negative constituent. Frequently the central ion has a positive charge so high that under normal circumstances we would expect it to attract electrons and at least partly neutralize its charge. Such are the C^{++++} in CO_3^{--}, the S^{++++++} in SO_4^{--}, and even the $Cl^{+++++++}$ ion in ClO_4^-. These ions achieve stability by attracting and polarizing negative ions so that the high ionization energy is compensated by the high electrostatic energy thus liberated. The net effect is that, for instance, in SO_4^{--} electrons of the S atom are shifted to the outside onto the O atoms, thus getting further apart while remaining in a region of moderately strong nuclear attraction. Of course, it is possible to represent ions like SO_4^{--} by starting with a more uniform distribution of charges and writing, for instance, the formula for SO_4^{--} as a resonance of structures of the type:

There are six such structures corresponding to six possible selections of two oxygens. Further structures can participate in the resonance; there is of course a continuous transition between the purely ionic structure and the one in which resonances between homopolar structures predominate.

The geometrical arrangement of the atoms or groups in the complex around the central atom can be considered from different angles. In the pure ionic description the electrostatic repulsion and the ionic radii will try to separate the outer ions or groups of the complex as far as possible from each other. This will very naturally give rise to a linear arrangement in a triatomic complex, to a symmetrical plane arrangement in a tetratomic ion like CO_3^{--}, to a symmetrical tetrahedron arrangement in an ion like SO_4^{--}, and to the arrangement on the six corners of a symmetrical octahedron in an ion like $CoCl_6^{---}$. It is significant that these geometrical configurations are always the stable ones if the total number of valence electrons in the complex is just sufficient to give rise to rare-gas shells around the outer ions while leaving the central ion bare. Other ions such as the bent NO_2^- and the low pyramidal SO_3^{--} do not satisfy the aforementioned condition and indicate that in such ions other forces than those due to electrostatics and van der Waals repulsion not only are present but also have an influence on the geometrical configuration. The previous statements about complex ions can be generalized to cover polyatomic molecules; thus CO_2 with 16 valence electrons is linear while $NOCl$ is bent. Of course, this does not prove that the former compounds are purely ionic but merely shows that, whenever a stable ionic structure can be written with all electrons accommodated on outer ions, the other important resonating structures will as a rule not give rise to directed valencies in directions that would prohibit the simple linear, planar, or tetrahedral structures.

The other way to determine the geometrical configuration of a complex ion is by considering the forces within the ion as directed valence forces. Thus the structure of NO_2^- can be written as a resonance of the two structures:

$$O=N-O^- \qquad\qquad {}^-O-N=O$$

Now we have seen earlier that the three valencies of nitrogen tend to include angles smaller than $120°$, and a bent structure of the NO_2^- becomes plausible. It is to be noted that such bent structures are never favored by the valence picture if the central ion does not carry some unshared electrons. Indeed, whenever all the orbits of a shell around the central atom are available for the construction of valence-orbital functions, we can always construct these functions in such a symmetrical way as to give rise to the same geometrical configuration as the one obtained from the pure ionic structure. We might imagine that the reason for the bent nature of NO_2^- is the presence of two unshared electrons on the nitrogen atom which occupy an orbit extending toward the third corner of a triangle, two corners of which are occupied by the O atoms.

A particularly interesting influence of directed valence orbits in complex ions is afforded by the $[Ni(CN)_4]^{--}$ complex. Surprisingly enough, the $(CN)^-$ groups occupy the corners of a square rather than the corners of a tetrahedron. To explain this we must use a description already implied in the previous discussion. We first take two electrons from the Ni atom so that we can form four $(CN)^-$ ions. Then we have to group these $(CN)^-$ ions around the Ni^{++} ion in such a way that the electrons of the $(CN)^-$ ions which are turned toward the Ni^{++} shall be able to penetrate as far toward the central ion as possible. One electron pair from each $(CN)^-$ ion will be used for that purpose, thus giving a partial single-bond character to the Ni–CN bonds. We have therefore to accommodate four electron pairs in four orbits around Ni^{++}; these orbits must be unoccupied in the original ion and indeed must be orthogonal in the wave-mechanical sense to those orbits already occupied. Now in Ni^{++} the $3s$ and $3p$ shells are filled, and eight more electrons are placed in $3d$ and $4s$ orbits. The angular dependence of a d orbit alone is a little difficult to write, but the hybridization of the s orbits and the five d orbits leads to the same angular dependence as that of the six functions x^2, y^2, z^2, xy, xz, yz. Of these six orbits, four are occupied by the eight $3d$ electrons, and two are available together with three somewhat higher $4p$ orbits. The latter have the same angular dependence as the functions x, y, and z. Using a linear combination of a p orbit with an unoccupied hybridized sd orbit, we may construct such an orbit which extends particularly strongly in one direction. The angular dependence of such an orbit can be written symbolically as $x^2 + x$, which function extends far in the positive x direction. If in addition to the p orbit of the type x which we have already employed we use just one more p orbit, for instance y, we may construct altogether four symmetrically situated valence orbits which can be written as $x^2 + x$, $x^2 - x$, $y^2 + y$, and $y^2 - y$, extending, respectively, in the positive x direction, in the negative x direction, in the positive y direction, and in the negative y direction. We actually obtain, therefore, four valence orbits pointing towards the four corners of a square by using two hybridized functions and combining them with two p functions.

If we had constructed the four valence orbits by using three rather than two p functions, it would have been possible to obtain a tetrahedral co-ordination for $[Ni(CN)_4]^{--}$, but $4p$ orbits lie higher than the $3d$ and $4s$ orbits so that it is reasonable to use as few of the p orbits as possible. By using other combinations of s, p, and d orbits we can obtain practically any co-ordination we choose. For instance, by using three hybridized sd orbits and three p orbits we may construct six orbits $x^2 + x$, $x^2 - x$, $y^2 + y$, $y^2 - y$, $z^2 + z$ and $z^2 - z$, pointing towards the six corners of an octahedron. This co-ordination is indeed quite common. But it should be noticed that a specific effect of directed valences in co-ordination complexes should be expected only if there are not too many orbits of the central ion available to be filled in by electron pairs drawn from the outer ions. If the number of the available orbits is too great, this will mean that the electron pairs can be accommodated in orbits of any geometrical configuration; that is, no pronounced directional effects exist. Thus it becomes clear why directed co-ordination bonds are found for those transition elements in which a

d shell is nearly filled and only few d orbits are free for occupancy by electron pairs participating in co-ordination bonds.

8.10 HOMOPOLAR CRYSTALS The best-known example of a crystal in which all atoms are linked together by strictly homopolar bonds is diamond, the structure of which is shown in Figure 8.10(1). Each carbon is surrounded by four other carbons situated on the cor-

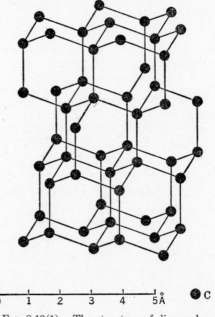

FIG. 8.10(1). The structure of diamond.

ners of a tetrahedron. The valence orbits can be considered the same as the C–C bond in a molecule.

Just as it is impossible to discriminate strictly in a general way between a homopolar and a heteropolar bond, so there exists a continuous transition between homopolar and ionic crystals. The diamond is, of course, strictly homopolar since there is no reason for the electron pair shared between two neighboring carbons to be attached more strongly to the one atom than to the other. A gradual transition from the homopolar to the ionic lattice takes place in the series of the crystals of diamond, aluminum phosphide, zinc sulfide, and silver iodide. The structure of ZnS is shown in Figure 8.10(2); AlP and AgI have similar lattices which differ from the diamond lattice in that each atom is now surrounded by four atoms of the opposite kind. A symmetrical surrounding of this kind may seem in the first moment rather strange for aluminum phosphide which consists of trivalent atoms. We may explain the structure chemically by assuming either that a crystal consists of univalent Al^- and univalent P^+ ions or that very small Al^{+++} ions occur in the interstices of the close-packed structure of very large P^{---} ions. The explanation involving univalent ions will probably be favored. But in reality it is largely a matter of definition which of the two ionic structures we adopt. The essential fact is that the sum of the valence electrons of aluminum and phosphorus is eight and therefore just sufficient to fill four valence orbits shared by the aluminum and phosphorus. We may arbitrarily associate all these eight electrons with the phosphorus giving none to the aluminum which would lead to P^{---} and Al^{+++} ions, or we might almost equally arbitrarily assume that one electron of each pair belongs to phosphorus and one to aluminum which will then lead to the Al^-, P^+ formula.

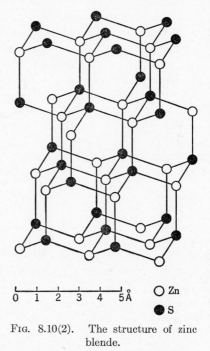

Similar statements may be made about zinc sulfide in which either the Zn^{++}, S^{--} or Zn^{--}, S^{++} formula can be postulated. The former electronic arrangement would indicate a pure ionic crystal, whereas in

○ Zn
● S

Fig. 8.10(2). The structure of zinc blende.

the latter formula homopolar binding is as important as the coulomb forces. In silver iodide the transition to an ionic crystal is practically completed since here the Ag^+, I^- formula will be definitely preferred to an assumption involving Ag^{---} and I^{+++}. Yet the electronic structure of the silver iodide crystal can be obtained by a gradual transition from the typically homopolar diamond crystal. This shows most clearly that the terms ionic crystal and homopolar crystal refer more to quantitative prevalence of certain forces than to a rigid classification.

8.11 THE METALS Metals are analogous to unsaturated molecules and to radicals. The binding of atoms in these compounds as well as in the metals is comparable in strength to the binding in saturated molecules. The unsaturated character is due to the fact that available electrons do not fill any closed shell. In the case of unsaturated molecules and radicals this leads to the striking property of high reactivity. In metals while such reactivity is present its effects manifest themselves only in surface properties. Thus we can explain why metal surfaces are, generally speaking, good catalysts, a fact which is discussed later in more detail.

But the unsaturated nature of the electron structure in metals has other important consequences. Lack of saturation means that not much energy is required to move an electron from an occupied into an unoccupied orbit. In fact, as we shall see later, the electronic-energy levels of a solid metal form a continuum, and an arbitrarily small amount of energy suffices to move an electron to a higher orbit. The electric conductivity of metals is a direct consequence of this fact since any small force suffices to move the electrons.

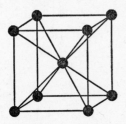

FIG. 8.11(1). Body-centered lattice.

The easy manner in which electron orbits in metals can be influenced also has an effect on the position of the atoms and on the restraining forces which tend to keep the atoms in their equilibrium positions. We have seen that directed-valence forces are due to a definite preference of electrons for certain orbits; such preference is to be expected to a lesser extent when a small amount of energy is sufficient to throw electrons into new orbits. Thus, in metals directed valences will not be expected. Actually, metals usually have close-packed structures in which atoms may be displaced with relative ease. The metals are therefore highly malleable and often have a low melting point (compared to the temperature at which they boil). All these facts show that the geometrical configuration of atoms is relatively unimportant as long as a sufficient number of atoms remain closely together. In fact it seems that metals are like van der Waals solids in this respect, their structure being stabilized by a general attraction and by a strong repulsion between atoms at small distances.

It is not surprising to find general attraction in an unsaturated compound where, if more atoms are close together, more electrons can be placed into low orbits. The short distance repulsion is due to the van der Waals repulsion between the closed inner shells of the atom.

The densest structures are based on the cubic and hexagonal close-packed arrangements. These are quite common among the metals. A further structure frequently encountered is the body-centered lattice shown in Figure 8.11(1), in which the atoms are packed only slightly less densely than in the close-packed structure. The formation of alloys is also a consequence of the unsaturated character of the metallic binding and of the resulting general attraction between metallic atoms of all kinds.

8.12 CONDUCTIVITY BY ELECTRONS, THE TOLMAN EFFECT It was indicated in the previous paragraph that metallic conductivity is due to the mobility of electrons. In fact it has been assumed for a long time that in metals the electric current is carried by electrons. The reason for this assumption was that the electric current in metals is not accompanied by transport of matter as it is in those cases where electricity is transported by ions. It is interesting that the idea of electronic conductivity can be demonstrated in a fairly direct manner by the Tolman effect which though experimentally rather delicate is conceptually very simple.

It follows from the idea of free electrons in a metal that, if a piece of metal is accelerated, the electrons, due to their inertia, lag behind. Hence the electrons will be crowded into the end of the metal which faces the direction opposed to the acceleration. This greater electron density causes electrostatic forces which prevent further electrons from flowing into the more densely populated region. A stationary equilibrium is reached when the electrostatic force, that is the field E, multiplied by the electronic charge e, is equal to the mass of the electron m times the acceleration with which the metal as a whole moves. It has been indeed found experimentally that, if a metal is accelerated, an electric field appears in the expected direction. According to the foregoing considerations $E \times e = m \times a$, and $E/a = m/e$. The quantities on the left-hand side can be measured, and their ratio actually agrees within the considerable experimental uncertainty with the m/e value of the electron.

Theoretically, the experiment is complicated by the fact that, when a metal is accelerated, mechanical stresses are set up within the metal, and these stresses may influence the electron density and produce effects comparable in magnitude with the Tolman effect.

8.13 FREE MOTION OF ELECTRONS It is convenient to describe the motion of electrons in metals in a way similar to the description of electrons in molecules by the molecular-orbital method. This method assumes that each electron can roam over the whole molecule or in our present case over the whole metal, and it is evidently adapted to describe electronic conductivity. However, electron orbits in a metal differ in several respects from molecular orbits. The most important difference is that the discrete set of orbital energies of a molecule is replaced by a continuous distribution of orbital energies in a metal. This makes it necessary to discuss electron orbits in a metal in some detail.

We shall first consider the limiting case of an electron which can move entirely freely within the metal. Than we shall introduce a weak periodic potential and investigate its effect on the motion of the electron. Finally we shall consider the opposite limiting case of a series of deep potential minima at considerable distances from each other, forming a lattice. For the sake of simplicity we shall restrict ourselves in most of these considerations to a one-dimensional model and to the motion of the electron in this one dimension.

The motion of electrons in the absence of an external field is, of course, easily visualized, and the description of this phenomenon by wave mechanics which will now be undertaken can be considered as a mere change in vocabulary and does not lead to new facts. Such new facts will emerge, however, from the wave treatment as soon as perturbing potentials are present. The following statements about free electrons furnish us with the proper vocabulary for the description of the motion of electrons in a potential field.

The free motion of an electron along a straight line is characterized by its velocity. More usually the momentum p is used which is related to the wavelength λ, connected with the motion of the electron, by the de Broglie relation, $p = h/\lambda$. The electron waves can be written

$$\psi = \sin \frac{2\pi x}{\lambda} = \sin \frac{2\pi p x}{h} = \sin kx$$

where x is the position at which the wave amplitude is taken and the abbreviation, $k = 2\pi p/h$ has been introduced. Thus the quantity k is a measure of p differing from the momentum only by the factor $2\pi/h$. We call k the wave number; it may be defined as the number of crests we meet if we proceed 2π cm. in the direction of the wave motion.

Instead of the sine wave we may with equal justification use the function, $\psi = \cos kx$. Neither the sine nor the cosine is used, however, for a description of an electron moving in a given direction. For the motions in the positive and negative x directions, the exponentials,

$$\psi = e^{ikx}$$

and

$$\psi = e^{-ikx}$$

are used, which functions are of course linear combinations of sines and cosines. Multiplication of the functions e^{ikx} and e^{-ikx} with the usual factor describing time dependence $e^{-i\omega t}$ gives

$$e^{i(kx-\omega t)}$$

and
$$e^{-i(kx+\omega t)}$$

In the first of these formulae the phase of the wave remains unchanged if both x and t increase in appropriate proportion, whereas in the second formula x must decrease with increasing t if the phase is to remain unaltered. This suggests that positive and negative k values correspond indeed to wave propagation in opposite directions and also to the motion of the electron in opposite directions.*

The original functions $\sin kx$ and $\cos kx$ are standing waves. They can be written as the sum and the difference of the progressing waves e^{ikx} and e^{-ikx}. If the wave function $\sin kx$ (or $\cos kx$) is given, we have certain knowledge of the absolute value of k and therefore of the absolute value of p the momentum. But this wave function also conveys the probability statement that the motion has equal chances to proceed in either direction.

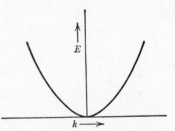

FIG. 8.13(1). Kinetic energy values E of an electron as a function of the wave number k.

To each value of k a certain kinetic energy belongs, according to the formula,

$$E_{\mathrm{kin}} = \frac{p^2}{2m} = \frac{h^2 k^2}{8\pi^2 m}$$

In Figure 8.13(1) we plot the energy values as a function of k which characterizes the different wave functions.

8.14 MOTION OF AN ELECTRON IN A WEAK PERIODIC FIELD Let the potential energy be a periodic function of the coordinate x. For the sake of definiteness we assume that shallow potential minima lie at the points $x = \cdots -3a, -2a, -a, 0, a, 2a, 3a, \cdots$ where the length a is the period of the potential. It will be simplest to assume that potential maxima lie in the middle between each pair of neighboring minima. We assume that the kinetic energy of the elec-

---

* It must be emphasized that the argument here presented is oversimplified. In particular it cannot be used directly for the derivation of the particle velocity from the wave theory. But the qualitative conclusion concerning the direction of propagation is correct.

trons is great compared with the fluctuation of the potential energy so that the momentum of the electrons will change but little during their motion.

For most momenta and correspondingly for most electronic-wavelengths, the electronic-wave functions do not differ much from the wave functions of free electrons, and the energy belonging to the function e^{ikx} continues to be in good approximation $k^2 \dfrac{h^2}{8\pi^2 m}$. But we shall show that for particular wavelengths of the electron a strong perturbation of the wave function and a corresponding change in the electronic energy results.

The original waves e^{ikx} describe an electron state in which the probability of finding the electron at any place is the same. If we return to the waves $\sin kx$ or $\cos kx$, the probability of finding the electrons in the minima or maxima of the waves will become great while the probability of finding the electrons at the nodes of the waves vanishes. In fact, it may be recalled that the probability of finding the electron in a region is proportional to the absolute value of the square of the wave function, and this expression is greatest on the wave crests and in the wave troughs. Now, if an electron wave fits into the periodic potential in such a way as to give rise to a great probability density of electrons in every potential minimum, a lowering of the energy is to be expected. If, conversely, the probability density is great on each potential maximum, the energy is appreciably raised.

If the wavelength is equal to twice the period of the potential $\lambda = 2a$ or $k = \pi/a$, then the function $\cos kx = \cos \pi x/a$, has alternately maxima and minima at $\cdots -2a, -a, 0, a, 2a, \cdots$ in the potential valleys. For this function therefore the energy is lower than for either of the two originally degenerate functions, e^{ikx} or e^{-ikx}. Conversely, $\sin kx = \sin \pi x/a$ has a node at the bottom of each potential minimum, so that for this function the electrons avoid potential minima, and a higher energy value results. It is easily seen that for an arbitrary value of k the energies will not be affected if the standing waves $\sin kx$ and $\cos kx$ are used instead of the progressing waves. This is so because the maxima in probability density for $\sin kx$ (or $\cos kx$) are for a general k distributed evenly between maxima and minima of the potential.

For $k = \pm \pi/a$, the standing waves $\sin kx$ and $\cos kx$ leading to strongly disturbed energy levels are actually the correct wave functions representing stationary states of the electrons. That progressing waves represent stationary states for general k values but not for $k = \pm \pi/a$ can be explained in another way. According to the interference condition, reflection of a wave by a periodic lattice is possible if the ratio of the wave functions of the incident and reflected waves is the same at analogous lattice points. Of course the incident and reflected waves must be progressive waves having the same kinetic energy and therefore having the same absolute value of k. For a general k, the ratio e^{ikx}/e^{-ikx} has different values at analogous lattice points. But for $k = \pi/a$, the ratio $e^{ikx}/e^{-ikx} = e^{2ikx} = e^{\frac{2\pi ix}{a}}$ changes by a factor $e^{2\pi i} = 1$ if x is increased by the amount a. Thus for $k = \pm\pi/a$ all lattice points scatter the wave in phase and re-enforce each other in converting the progressing wave e^{ikx} into the wave e^{-ikx} progressing in the opposite direction. Thus, even if one starts with a progressing wave $e^{\frac{i\pi x}{a}}$, reflections in the lattice will mix in the oppositely progressing wave and produce a standing wave.

The same situation which we met for $k = \pm\pi/a$ is generally true for $k = \pm n\pi/a$ where n is a positive integer. For all these values of k the interference condition is satisfied for the reflection of progressive waves.

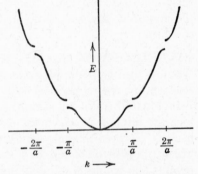

The energy of the electronic motion in a periodic field as a function of k is shown in Figure 8.14(1). If k is not close to a value $\pm n\pi/a$, the energy is the same as for a free electron. In the neighborhood of the

FIG. 8.14(1).   Energy of electronic motion in a weak periodic field of period a.

critical values, however, the energies are markedly disturbed, and at the critical value two different energies belong to the same value of k; the lower energy corresponds to a standing wave with its nodes at the maxima of the potential, the higher energy to a standing wave with its nodes in the potential minima. The strong perturbation of the energy near the critical values follows for reasons of continuity and can be calculated quantitatively with the help of perturbation theory.

It is interesting to notice that, if an electron moving in a weak periodic field is subjected to an external electric field, no electric current will result in first approximation. We may start with an electron at rest so that at the beginning $k = 0$. The action of an electric field will impart momentum to the electron, and the value of k becomes positive. But as soon as k reaches the value π/a, the electron is reflected by the lattice, k becomes $-\pi/a$, and the momentum is reversed. The electron now moves backward. The field causes an increase of k from $-\pi/a$ to zero. By the time the value $k = 0$ is reached and the reverse motion of the electron is stopped, the electron has returned to the place from which it started. The process then repeats itself. Thus a periodic motion is obtained, and the time average of the current is zero. Yet the motion of the electron in the periodic lattice can be used as a model for metallic conductivity. The potential minima represent atoms. They are not absolutely fixed but can vibrate, and collisions of the electrons with vibrating atoms gives rise to an effect resembling friction. The electron then may move in an external field at a constant velocity at which the friction is just sufficient to balance the action of the external force. In general, this constant velocity does not correspond to a value $k = \pm n\pi/a$, and a progressive motion of the electron will be produced by the presence of an electric field. It may be also noticed that, if no external field is present, the frictional terms will decelerate the motion of any electron so that we obtain no current in the absence of a field.

8.15 ELECTRON STATES IN STRONG PERIODIC FIELDS

We now turn to the opposite limiting case, namely, the behavior of an electron in a strong periodic field.

In Figure 8.15(1) we show the periodic potential consisting of deep separate minima in which the electron is to move. The levels drawn in each of these minima signify the energies of the stationary states which the electron would have if the potential had only a single minimum. The problem of finding the energy levels for this infinite series of

FIG. 8.15(1). Energy levels of an electron in a periodic potential. The tunnel effect is disregarded.

minima is somewhat analogous to the problem of finding the energy levels in a two-minimum problem. The latter question has been treated in sections 7.7, 7.8 and 7.9 and it was found that for every energy level of a single minimum two closely spaced levels appear in the two-minima problem. If the energy difference in any such pair is divided by h, we obtain the frequency with which the electron in the respective pair of levels can vibrate between the two minima.

For the lowest pair of levels where the electron has to cross a high potential barrier to get from one minimum to the other, the frequency of vibration and with it the separation of the two levels is very small. For high energies for which the barrier is smaller, the splitting becomes much greater, and near the top of the barrier it approaches in order of magnitude the energy difference between two neighboring levels of the one-minimum problem. The energy-level diagram for the two-minimum problem is shown in Figure 8.15(2). The full lines indicate energy levels in the one-minimum potential; the broken lines those in the two-mini-mum potentials. The two levels belonging to the lowest energy of the one-minimum potential have been drawn as a single broken line, since the difference of these two energies is too small to be made visible in the figure. To each pair of levels of the two-minimum problem there belong two wave functions obtainable in first approximation by the superposi-tion of the corresponding wave functions of the one-minimum problem

FIG. 8.15(2). Energy-level diagram for two minima. The solid lines show the en-ergies obtained when the tunnel effect is neglected. The dotted lines show the levels when the tunnel effect is taken into account.

in the two holes. One two-minimum wave function is obtained by adding the two one-minimum functions, the other by subtracting them.

In the periodic potential which has been shown in Figure 8.15(1), an infinity of energy levels belongs to each level. This is to be expected since infinitely many single-hole wave functions are available for each single-hole energy level, and from these wave functions one may form infinitely many linear combinations. The linear combinations to be used are similar to those which we have encountered when describing the mobile p electrons in benzene by the molecular orbital method. We shall number the holes from $-\infty$ to $+\infty$, and we denote the number of a hole by l. Let k' be a number greater than $-\pi$ but smaller than $+\pi$. Let also ψ_l be the wave function of an electron moving in the lth hole. It can be shown that wave functions $\Psi_{k'}$ for the electronic state in the periodic field can be obtained in good approximation by the expression,

$$\Psi_{k'} = \sum_{l=-\infty}^{l=+\infty} e^{ik'l}\psi_l \qquad\qquad 8.15(1)$$

The coefficients $e^{ik'l}$ are the phases with which the wave functions ψ_l are superposed, and the whole function $\Psi_{k'}$ can be considered as a wave of the states ψ_l passing through the periodic field. Different values of k' correspond to different wavelengths and to different energies. An exception has to be made for pairs of k' values which differ only in sign. These correspond to the same wavelength and to the same energy but to opposite directions of propagation. This can be seen from an analogy with the electron waves describing motions of electrons in an absence of a field (section 8.13). It may be noted that k' in equation 8.15(1) does not correspond directly to the k value of the free electrons. The latter quantity has the dimension of a reciprocal length while k' is a pure number. Actually k'/a (where a is the distance between minima) corresponds closely to k, since both can be considered as the factor with which the co-ordinate of the electron must be multiplied in order to get the phase of the wave. For the free electron this is evident since ikx appears in the exponent of the wave function. For an electron moving in a series of potential holes the co-ordinate x is equal to the number of the hole l times the distance between holes a so that $i\dfrac{k'}{a}x$ becomes equal to $ik'l$ which is the phase appearing in equation 8.15(1). Thus k'/a may be called the wave number for the case of strong periodic fields.

Because of the relation $e^{i\varphi} = e^{i(\varphi+2\pi)}$ two Ψ_k functions do not differ from each other if k' is changed by 2π. In fact all that counts is the ratio of factors on two consecutive lattice points l and $l + 1$, and this ratio,

$$\frac{e^{ik(l+1)}}{e^{ikl}} = e^{ik}$$

is not changed if we substitute $k' + 2\pi$ for k'. This justifies the restriction $-\pi \leq k' \leq +\pi$, since any k' outside this range describes exactly the same function as an appropriate k inside the range.

Two particular values of k' give rather similar results for the periodic potential as has been found for the two-minimum potential. For $k' = 0$ all phase factors in the sum 8.15(1) are unity; that is, the ψ_l functions are simply added. This recalls those wave functions in the two-minimum potential which have been obtained by adding the single-minimum wave functions. If on the other hand we set $k' = \pi$ (or in an equivalent way $k' = -\pi$), the factors in the sum 8.15(1) are alternately $+1$ and -1, corresponding to those wave functions of the two-minimum problem where the two single-minimum wave functions are subtracted. The energy difference of the levels belonging to $k = 0$ and $k = \pi$ is of the same order of magnitude as the energy difference between a corresponding pair of levels in the two-minimum potential. The values, $k = 0$ and $k = \pi$, correspond to no phase change and the largest possible phase change between neighboring single-hole wave functions. All intermediate k values corresponding to intermediate phase changes will give rise to intermediate energies and will fill with a continuous set of levels the range between the energy values belonging to $k = 0$ and $k = \pi$. We obtain thus the energy-level diagram shown in Figure 8.15(3) for the motion of an electron in the string of potential minima. The shaded energy regions in the figure are filled with a continuum of energy levels. Each of these strips corresponds to a level of the one-minimum problem, and each strip can be interpreted as the result of the splitting of a one-minimum level owing to the interaction of the infinitely many minima in the row. The lowest of these strips is so narrow that we prefer to represent it by a line. The higher strips increase rapidly in breadth just as the separation of the pairs of energy levels has

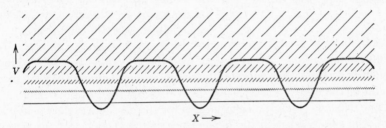

FIG. 8.15(3). Energy-level diagram for many minima. The shaded areas correspond to energy values that an electron in a stationary state may possess.

increased in the two-minimum problem. Above the top of the barriers, motion of the electron from hole to hole becomes possible without a tunnel effect, and in this energy region all energy levels are allowed, with the exception of narrow energy strips one of which is shown as an unshaded strip in the figure.

That an electron cannot possess all energies greater than the maxima of potential barriers separating the holes might seem at first surprising. But the effect becomes intelligible by comparison with the energy levels of an electron in a weak periodic field. Indeed for increasing kinetic energy of the electron the influence of potential minima diminishes, and we finally approach the case where the periodic field can be considered as weak. Now comparison with Figure 8.14(1) shows that in a weak periodic field not all electron energies are allowed. Narrow energy regions corresponding to k values in the neighborhood of $\pm n\pi/a$ are excluded.

Thus we see that for very strong binding of the electron its energy must lie in one of several narrow strips while the intervening broad strips of energy are forbidden in a like manner, as an electron in a hydrogen atom cannot have an energy intermediate between the stationary energy levels. For high-energy electrons the periodic field may be considered weak, and the permitted energy bands become broad while the forbidden strips are narrow. For intermediate electron energies the breadth of allowed and forbidden strips is of the same order of magnitude.

We now consider a narrow strip corresponding to a strongly bound electron. Within this strip a definite energy belongs to each value of

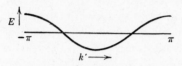

k' between $-\pi$ and $+\pi$. For sufficiently narrow strips it can be proved that this dependence is sinusoidal, as shown in Figure 8.15(4). The two ends of the curve at $k' = -\pi$ and $k' = \pi$ correspond to the same wave function. Actually the curve should be drawn on a cylinder and the two ends joined. In the figure the horizontal line for $E = 0$ corresponds to the value of the unperturbed one-minimum level. We see that half the k' values belong to lower and half to the higher energies, although it may happen that the maximum of the energy curve lies at $k' = 0$ rather than at $k' = \pm\pi$.

Fig. 8.15(4). Dependence of energy on k' (= wave number × lattice distance) in the case of a strongly bound electron.

The dependence of the energy on k' for the case of a strong field may again be compared with the dependence of the energy on k for a weak

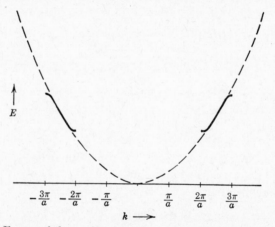

Fig. 8.15(5). Energy of electronic motion in a weak periodic field of period a. The full curve shows the energies in one Brillouin zone.

periodic field. For the latter case we may consider an energy band corresponding to k values between $n\pi/a$ and $(n + 1)\pi/a$. The same energy band appears also for k values between $-n\pi/a$ and $-(n + 1)\pi/a$. In Figure 8.15(5) we show that part of Figure 8.14(1) which corresponds to these k intervals. The full parts of the curve show the dependence of

E on k in the band corresponding to $\dfrac{-3\pi}{a} < k < \dfrac{-2\pi}{a}$ and $\dfrac{2\pi}{a} < k < \dfrac{3\pi}{a}$.

The dotted parabola corresponds to the relation between k and a for a free electron as shown in Figure 8.13(1). The actual E–k relation within the band considered is, save near the ends, practically undistinguishable from the dotted parabola.

The two points at $k = -2\pi/a$ and $k = 2\pi/a$ correspond to the same standing wave, namely, $\sin 2\pi x/a$. The other standing wave of the same wavelength, namely, $\cos 2\pi x/a$ belongs to the next lower energy band which is not shown in the figure. Thus it is permissible to join the two independent sections in Figure 8.15(5) giving the Figure 8.15(6). The two free ends of this curve again belong to the same wave function, namely, $\cos 3\pi/a$, the other standing wave $\sin 3\pi/a$ belonging to the next higher strip. The figure again should be drawn on a cylinder and joined at its ends.

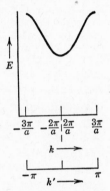

Figure 8.15(6) is thus quite analogous to Figure 8.15(4). The analogy can be brought out more clearly by comparing the abscissae. Since k'/a corresponds to k, the ranges $-3\pi < k' < -2\pi$ and $2\pi < k' < 3\pi$ correspond to the ranges $-\dfrac{3\pi}{a} < k <$

$-\dfrac{2\pi}{a}$ and $\dfrac{2\pi}{a} < k < \dfrac{3\pi}{a}$. As has been shown pre-

Fig. 8.15(6). Electronic energies in one Brillouin zone in a weak periodic field.

viously, a change of k' by 2π is merely a change in notation and leaves the wave functions unaltered. Thus the ranges for k' may be replaced by the ranges $-\pi < k' < 0$ and $0 < k' < \pi$ or by the single range $-\pi < k' < \pi$, as indicated in Figure 8.15(6). This is the same range which appears in Figure 8.15(4). The only difference between the two figures is that the curvature in the former is rather smooth, whereas in the latter sharp bends occur near $k' = 0$ and $k' = \pm\pi$.

8.16 MOTION OF AN ELECTRON IN A STRONG PERIODIC FIELD It may be assumed that the wave function at a certain time is confined to one minimum. According to the foregoing discussion, this function does not belong to a definite energy and does not describe a stationary state. In fact stationary solutions correspond to wavelike functions $\Psi_{k'}$ given in the formula 8.15(1). For a wave function localized in one minimum a time change of the probability distribution of the electron will ensue. In close analogy to the electron libration in the two-minimum problem, the reciprocal time required for the electron to spread from one minimum to the neighboring minimum can be estimated by dividing the breadth of the energy strip in question by Planck's constant. The higher the barriers between potential minima, the narrower are the energy strips, and the longer it takes for the electron to leave a certain minimum.

It might be expected that an electron after having penetrated a potential barrier and having arrived in a neighboring minimum may continue to proceed from minimum to minimum in a random way corresponding to diffusion. For the wave functions $\Psi_{k'}$ we obtain a more ordered motion. These functions correspond in their form to electron waves with a definite energy, a definite wavelength, and a definite momentum. Thus the waves represented by $\Psi_{k'}$ describe a definite motion of the electron in one direction just as plane waves having a definite k value do. The only difference is in the numerical relation between the electron wavelength and the electron velocity. The velocity, like all quantities involving time, is connected with the frequency ν of the electron wave, and this frequency is connected with the electron energy by Planck's relation, $E = h\nu$. Thus the narrower energy strips occurring for stronger binding give rise to slower processes, as has been already indicated by the slow spreading of a localized wave function from one potential minimum to the neighboring minimum.

If the foregoing arguments are carried through quantitatively, it is found that an electron with an energy near the minimum of one strip moves exactly like a free electron, except that it moves as though its mass were different from the electron mass. The narrower the strip is, the greater the effective mass will be. In fact, if we consider a certain wavelength, and (according to the de Broglie relation) a certain effective momentum, a greater effective mass must be assumed in order to explain the smaller velocities which occur when the energy strip is narrow.

The motion of the electrons in a strong periodic field can be described by the simple device of an effective electron mass only as long as $\mid k' \mid$ is small compared to π, that is, as long as the wavelength of $\Psi_{k'}$ is long compared to the lattice distance. In fact, such a description is good only as long as the energy curve of Figure 8.15(4) can be approximated by the lower part of an energy curve for a free electron such as shown in Figure 8.13(1).

In order to find the laws of the electronic motion for larger values of k, we have to discuss in some more detail how the electron velocity is obtained from the wave description of the electron. We will consider a wave packet, that is, a group of waves consisting of several crests.

According to the probability interpretation of the wave function, the electron must be found somewhere within the packet, since outside the packet the wave function vanishes. Therefore the velocity with which the electron moves in the lattice must be equal to the velocity with which the group of waves travels along. A group of waves can be obtained by a superposition of functions Ψ_{k}' with k' values corresponding to a certain not too extended range. The superposition must be arranged in such a manner that the waves shall cancel each other outside the group and re-enforce each other only within the limited extension of the group. In passing it may be remarked that such a wave group is the best illustration for the uncertainty principle. If we want to localize the electron with greater accuracy, we must construct a wave group of smaller extension, and for this purpose a greater range of k' values must be used, corresponding to a greater range of momenta.

It can be shown that for free electrons the group velocity and with it the particle velocity is equal to $\dfrac{1}{h}\dfrac{\partial E}{\partial k}$. For instance, considering Figure 8.13(1), we see that with increasing k and correspondingly increasing momentum values the slope of the energy curve $\partial E/\partial k$ also increases, and thus greater velocities will be found for greater momenta. The proportionality between momentum and velocity can be shown easily by taking into account that the curve in Figure 8.13(1) is a parabola. For electrons moving in a strong periodic field the velocity with which the electron is propagated in the lattice is given by $\dfrac{a}{h}\dfrac{\partial E}{\partial k'}$, where a again is the lattice distance. In this case Figure 8.15(4) shows that the slope of the energy curve does not continue to increase with increasing k' values. For k' greater than $\pi/2$ the slope and with it the velocity begins to decrease, and at $k' = \pi$ the slope and the velocity have become equal to zero. In this region the electron behaves in a remarkable way in that its velocity of propagation decreases while its energy continues to increase. Since $k' = \pi$ and $k' = -\pi$ are equivalent, a further increase of k' leads to negative k' values, and here we find that the energy begins to decrease while the slope assumes increasing negative values so that the electron moves faster and faster in a direction opposite that of the original motion. Finally, when k' passes the value $-\pi/2$, the negative slope assumes a maximum value, and a further decrease in energy is accompanied by a decrease of the absolute value of the velocity. This continues until at $k' = 0$ the velocity zero is reached again, and the cycle is completed. Thus, for $|k'|$ smaller than $\pi/2$, the behavior of the electron is normal since greater velocities correspond to greater energies. The behavior for $\pi/2 < |k'|$ is anomalous.

Comparing the present results with those obtained for electrons moving in a weak field, we find a marked analogy in spite of quantitative differences. In the weak field we found that, when k increased from zero towards π/a, the velocity increased in a normal manner. At π/a a reflection of the electron by the periodic field occurs, giving rise to a reversal of the direction of propagation. In the light of our statements about the connection between the electron velocity and $\partial E/\partial k$, we can now trace in greater detail how this change of velocity occurs. We see in Figure 8.14(1) that in the immediate neighborhood of $k = \pi/a$ the slope of the energy curve begins to decrease rapidly and reaches zero at π/a. The same slope is found for $k = -\pi/a$, but with increasing k values the slope assumes rapidly increasing negative values until within a short distance from $k = -\pi/a$ the value of the negative slopes correspond closely to an undisturbed parabola. In this range, where the slope varies rapidly, the electron is decelerated until its velocity is reversed. From there on the electron moves as a practically free particle.

The difference between the behaviors in the strong and weak fields is this: For strong fields the anomalous region extends from $k' = -\pi/2$ to $k' = \pi$ and from $k' = -\pi$ to $k' = -\pi/2$. In weak fields the anomalous behavior of the electron is confined to a narrow region close to $k = \pi/a$ and $k = -\pi/a$. Another important difference is the great effective mass in strong fields which, from our present point of view, can be explained by saying that in a narrow energy band the slope of the energy curve, and with it the velocity, will increase very slowly with increasing k'. It should be pointed out that under appropriate circumstances the effective mass may be smaller than the mass of a free electron. Thus we see from Figure 8.15(6) that near the minimum of the energy curve the slope increases rapidly with increasing k' values, a behavior opposite to the one with which we associated a high value of the electronic mass.

8.17 MOTION OF ELECTRONS IN A TWO- OR THREE-DIMENSIONAL LATTICE In a metal electrons move in the field of a three-dimensional array of ions. Their behavior will in many respects be rather similar to that of an electron in a linear lattice. The wave functions can be written in the form of plane waves. If the periodic field is weak, the waves are actually sine or cosine waves or simple exponentials. A stronger perturbation of these waves will arise only when certain interference conditions are fulfilled. If, for instance, we have a simple cubic lattice with a lattice distance a, strong perturbations will arise if the k value corresponding to the x component of the momentum is π/a or $-\pi/a$. The same holds if the k value corresponding to the y or z component of the momentum is π/a or $-\pi/a$. A graphic representation of these momentum values for which strong perturbations occur can be given for a two-dimensional lattice in the following way. In Figure 8.17(1) we plot in the horizontal and vertical directions ak_x and ak_y, respectively. Here a is the lattice distance of a simple square

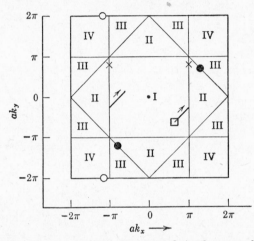

FIG. 8.17(1). Brillouin zones in a two-dimensional simple square lattice. Regions designated by the same Roman numeral form single zones.

lattice, k_x and k_y are $1/h$ times the x and y components of the momentum. Strong disturbances will arise in the neighborhood of the lines that separate the regions which in the figure are designated by Roman numerals. The figure has been restricted to the region where both $a \mid k_x \mid$ and $a \mid k_y \mid$ are smaller than 2π. Inclusion of further regions would increase the complexity without introducing new ideas. The lines of strong perturbation actually occur whenever a change of ak_x or ak_y or both of these quantities, by some multiple of 2π, leaves the kinetic energy unchanged. Thus the two x signs in the figure correspond to points for which ak_x has been changed by 2π. For the two white-circle points ak_y differs by 4π, whereas for the two black-circle points both k_x and k_y have been changed by 2π. For each of these pairs, the kinetic energy is the same because $\mid k_x \mid^2 + \mid k_y \mid^2$ and, therefore, the absolute value of the momentum has remained unchanged. It follows from the theory of diffraction in crystals that the lines of Figure 8.17(1) represent the wave numbers of those electrons for which interference conditions are satisfied and which therefore can be scattered elastically by the crystals.

In perfect analogy with the one-dimensional case the electrons will move along almost freely as long as they are far away from the lines shown in Figure 8.17(1). They will be strongly perturbed near the lines, and instead of crossing these lines they will be thrown across to another point of like energy changing their ak_x and ak_y values by multiples of 2π, according to the rules of crystal reflection. It may be noticed that, according to this rule, an electron which started in region I of Figure 8.17(1) cannot leave this region by any continuous motion owing to the action of external fields. Let us assume for instance that an electron has initially ak_x and ak_y values shown by the □ in Figure 8.17(1). In the absence of outside fields these values will be preserved, and the electron will continue to be represented by that point in the diagram. If an outside field acts, ak_x and ak_y change with time assuming new values, as shown by the line originating in Figure 8.17(1) in the open square. The direction in which the representative point moves is indicated by the arrow. When this line reaches the border of region I, it is reflected across to negative ak_x values. Since the same external field still acts and continues to cause momentum changes in the same direction as originally, the representative point continues to move along the direction parallel to its previous path, as indicated by the line and arrow on the left-hand side of Figure 8.17(1). Thus the point must remain in a region I. Similar arguments show that a point starting in one of the regions II will always continue to move in one of the regions II for which reason we may consider these four regions as being part of a single region. The same holds for the regions designated by III and IV in Figure 8.17(1).

The regions just described are called the Brillouin zones. They correspond in the one-dimensional case to the segments:

$$-\pi < ak < \pi$$

$$-2\pi < ak < -\pi \quad \text{and} \quad \pi < ak < 2\pi$$

$$-3\pi < ak < -2\pi \quad \text{and} \quad 2\pi < ak < 3\pi$$

In the absence of any perturbing field the kinetic energy is proportional to $k_x^2 + k_y^2$, and therefore we can picture an energy surface in the form of a paraboloid erected on Figure 8.17(1). In a weak periodic field this surface will be strongly perturbed near the boundaries of the Brillouin zones. Actually discontinuities will appear on the surface at the boundaries between the zones, so that it is impossible to get from one zone to another without an abrupt change in either k_x or k_y or the energy. This emphasizes again that we can get from one zone to another only by a process analogous to a quantum jump. It is important to notice that in crossing from region I to an adjacent point of region II the energy increases abruptly. In spite of this, all energies of region I are not necessarily lower than any energy of region II. Thus the corners of zone I in which $a \mid k_x \mid$ and $a \mid k_y \mid$ have values close to π correspond to higher momenta than the portions of zone II in which $a \mid k_x \mid$ is close to π and $a \mid k_y \mid$ is close to zero or in which $a \mid k_y \mid$ is close to π and $a \mid k_x \mid$ is close to zero. As long as the periodic field is weak, this portion of zone II has a lower energy than the portion of zone I described previously.

For strong periodic fields the simple sine, cosine, and exponential waves no longer describe the states of the electrons. We must use instead superpositions of wave functions describing the motions of electrons near separate minima, that is, near separate ions of the lattice. The coefficients appearing in the composite wave function are similar to those appearing in $\Psi_{k'}$ for the one-dimensional case with the exception that two constants k'_x and k'_y are needed to specify their state. These numbers correspond to ak_x and ak_y of the case of weakly bound electrons. The physical significance of k'_x and k'_y remains unchanged if a multiple of 2π is added to either of the two quantities. It can be shown that, if we retain the wave function in the single lattice cells but change k'_x and k'_y, wave functions are obtained which correspond to a single Brillouin zone. To obtain wave functions corresponding to a new Brillouin zone a new wave function must be used for the motion of an electron in the single minimum, and composite wave functions must be constructed by superposition. If we establish an appropriate correspondence between the wave functions near the single ions in a strong field and the Brillouin zones in a weak field, we can say that Figure 8.17(1) applies to strong periodic fields as well as to weak ones. At the same time we must replace ak_x and ak_y by k'_x and k'_y. All the qualitative statements about the Brillouin zones will then remain valid. For strong fields the energies within one Brillouin zone will differ but little, as is the case in the narrow energy strips in the one-dimensional lattice. In fact, the energy in each zone is nearly the same as the corresponding energy level in an isolated minimum. In the strong field we again find great effective electron masses. The reflections near the borders of the zones are replaced by an anomalous dependence of the velocity on the energy over a more extended region within the zone. In these respects the behavior of an electron in the two-dimensional case does not differ essentially from its motion in a linear string of potential minima.

The three-dimensional case does not differ from the two-dimensional one in any important respect. The Brillouin zones must be represented in three-dimensional space, and therefore their geometrical arrangement is somewhat more involved. This arrangement depends, of course, on the structure of the lattice. The simplest arrangement corresponding to a simple cubic lattice rarely finds actual application for a crystal. But the important conclusions about the separation of the energy into zones, the correspondence between crystal reflections and the boundaries of the zones, the confinement of a continuous electronic motion into a single zone, and the reflections and anomalous behavior of the electrons near the boundaries hold, however complicated the geometrical arrangements of the zones may be.

8.18 METALS AND INSULATORS There are few physical properties which resemble electric conductivity in changing so greatly for such apparently insignificant reasons. The slight change in lattice arrangement from diamond to graphite causes an increase in conductivity which is much greater than a factor 10^{10}. In fact, whatever conductivity exists in diamond is probably due to impurities or lattice imperfections, whereas graphite on the other hand is a good conductor.

The difference between conductors and insulators is due to the manner in which the Brillouin zones are filled up. For our present purpose we may represent the wave functions for both insulators and metals by electrons moving independently of each other in a self-consistent field. This means that each electron moves in the field of the nuclei and in the average field of the remaining electrons. Effects due to phase relations between electrons are neglected. This approximation is the same as that used in the molecular-orbital method, and it is one of the several methods which by making somewhat drastic approximations achieve rather far-reaching results.

The average field caused by the electrons has the same periodicity as the field of the nuclei. Since each electronic wave function is spread out over the whole crystal, a single missing electron causes an insensible change in the average field at any one point, and so each electron moves essentially in the same field, namely, in the periodic field of the lattice.

Having thus specified the nature of the orbits in which electrons move within a real crystal, we can now make the distinction between insulators and conductors. A crystal is an insulator if all electronic levels in a certain number of Brillouin zones are filled with pairs of electrons having opposite spins, so that according to the Pauli principle there is no room for further electrons in these zones; at the same time all other Brillouin zones are completely empty. A crystal is a conductor if one or more Brillouin zones are partly filled with electrons.

The distinction just described shows that insulators are analogous to rare-gas atoms and also to saturated molecules, whereas metals are similar to atoms with incomplete shells and also to unsaturated molecules. In this analogy the concept of closed shells corresponds to the concept of filled Brillouin zones, but, whereas the energy levels in an atomic or molecular shell are spaced at finite distances from each other, the energy levels within a Brillouin zone form a continuum. Thus in a metal the smallest forces suffice to transfer electrons into new orbits. This explains qualitatively not only the phenomenon of conductivity but also many other characteristic properties of metals. We have already mentioned that displacement of atoms within some metals is accomplished more easily than in insulators. In these metals the electrons can accommodate themselves to the new atomic position by changing their orbits in an appropriate manner. This is, in particular, to be expected when a Brillouin zone is about halfway filled so that there are many electrons which can easily change their orbits.

8.19 ELECTRON CONDUCTIVITY OF HEAT At the absolute zero, electrons of a metal, apart from filling some Brillouin zones completely, occupy the lower energy levels of one or more zones. All electron orbits up to a certain energy E_0 will be full; all levels higher than E_0 will be empty. The electrons occupying all states of a continuum up to a certain level are said to form a Fermi sea with the surface of the sea at E_0. If the temperature is raised, some electrons are lifted from levels below E_0 to levels above. But only the neighborhood of the surface of the sea is thus affected. The energy changes due to temperature excitation are small compared to the thickness of a relevant Brillouin zone of a metal. This thickness is usually of the order of an electron volt.

The excitation of electrons contributes to the specific heat but little since only the few electrons near the surface of the sea are affected. This contribution to the specific heat can be detected in some metals at very low temperatures where the specific heat due to vibrations is very small and at high temperatures where the vibrational specific heat is essentially constant.

The excited surface electrons contribute to a much greater extent to the thermal conductivity. In spite of their small number and the fact that they transport effectively only the relatively small additional energy imparted to them by temperature excitation, their effect is still important owing to the great velocity and to the long mean free path of the electrons. From a classical picture of the electronic motion we would expect the mean free path to be approximately equal to the lattice distance. But the discussion of electronic motion in a periodic field has shown that the propagation is essentially the same as for free electrons. This means explicitly that in a strictly periodic field electrons would have an infinite mean free path. The reason for the deflection of electrons in a crystal from a straight-line motion is the deviation of the field from complete periodicity caused by thermal motion of the atoms, by crystal imperfections or by collisions between electrons. At higher temperatures the thermal motion is of course most important, whereas below the Debye temperature the other two effects predominate. It should be noticed that collisions between electrons depend on phase relations of their motion which are not included in the original self-consistent field approximation.

Actually the relatively few electrons near the surface of the Fermi sea transport more heat in metals than the crystal vibrations which in insulators are alone responsible for thermal conductivity. Excitation of electrons by temperature is completely negligible in a good insulator, since in such substances the energy of the electron must be raised by several volts to lift it from the top of the highest full Brillouin zone to the bottom of the lowest empty one.

8.20   ELECTRIC CONDUCTIVITY IN METALS   Although from the foregoing it is clear why metals have a high electric conductivity, the details of this conductivity phenomenon are still to be explained. It is of interest to notice that the picture presented leads to an understanding of a number of finer effects, of which we shall discuss the decrease of electric conductivity in metals with increasing temperature and the Hall effect. For the purpose of this explanation we have to describe the mechanism of metallic conductivity.

We shall confine our attention to one incompletely filled Brillouin zone, since, as we have seen, such incompletely filled zones are characteristic for metals. The effect of the electric field is to increase the momentum of all electrons in the zone. In the interior of the Fermi sea this produces no change, since electrons move from one momentum state to another one which has been just vacated by an electron. Changes occur, however, at the surface of the sea where electrons accumulate in states with velocity components along the field, while they are depleted in the states with velocity components opposing the field. This new distribution possessing an excess of electrons with velocities along the field gives rise to an electric current in the direction of the field. This current would increase to extremely high values but for scattering of the electrons by crystal irregularities which tend to bring the electrons back into their original distribution. Above the Debye temperature the main reason for these irregularities is thermal vibrations, and we can show that the increase in the number of collisions is roughly proportional to the square of the vibrational amplitudes. This quantity in turn is directly proportional to the heat content of the lattice and increases linearly with temperature. Since the number of collisions which limit the size of the current is proportional to the temperature, it is to be expected that the conductivity varies as $1/T$, and this indeed is found to be true in rough approximation for most metals above the Debye temperature.

At lower temperatures the crystal vibrations die off rapidly, and in this region the conductivity increases with decreasing temperature more strongly than $1/T$. But the temperature variation in this region may be affected by crystal irregularities due to other causes than heat motion.

In some substances, many of which are not particularly good conductors, a sharp change occurs at a very low temperature of a few degrees above absolute zero. At this point the substances in question lose their electrical resistance completely, that is, become superconducting. No satisfactory explanation of this phenomenon exists at the present time. It may be due to a more involved interaction of the electrons with the lattice vibration.

A phenomenon which has contributed much to the understanding of electrical conductivity is the Hall effect. Let us apply a magnetic field to a metal through which an electric current is flowing. The magnetic field shall be perpendicular to the current. Then a gradient of electric potential arises in a direction perpendicular both to the electric current and to the applied magnetic field. The effect can be explained easily by the deflection of the moving electrons in the magnetic field. The sign of the gradient is determined by the sign of the electronic charge, and the correct sign is found in some substances which are said to show the normal Hall effect. But in many substances the Hall effect is anomalous; that is, it has a sign opposite to the expected one.

This anomalous effect may be explained by the presence of a Brillouin zone which is nearly completely filled up. It has been pointed out in previous sections that electrons near the border of the Brillouin zones move in a way opposite to the one expected. Actually electrons missing from the highest energy region in an otherwise full Brillouin zone behave in many ways like electrons of the opposite charge. The existence of positive electrons can indeed be formally explained by the absence of electrons in a Fermi sea of negative energies, not unlike an electron sea filling up a Brillouin zone. These negative energies must be introduced in a relativistic description of the electron motion. Dirac has assumed that the negative-energy states are usually filled up with electrons which, for an unexplained reason, we fail to observe. Only the holes in this distribution are observable. They are the positrons.

The absence of electric conductivity of insulators is not due, in the present picture, to the absence of "free electrons." On the contrary, the Brillouin zones of an insulator are completely filled with such free electrons. But the anomalous behavior of the electrons near the top of a Brillouin zone gives rise to currents which are just sufficient to cancel the currents due to electrons with a normal behavior. That the cancellation must be exact can be seen from the fact that a not too strong field can cause only continuous motion of electrons, that is, motions within the same Brillouin zone. Since the zone has been filled up completely to begin with, the field can produce no change. Any level vacated by an electron will be filled at the same time by another electron, and the net result is a mere redistribution of identical electrons among the available levels.

The Hall effect helps to establish the presence of electrons which behave in an anomalous manner. The existence of insulators may be said to depend on the presence of such anomalous electrons. Thus the Hall effect helps us to understand why insulators differ from metals.

We may use the Hall effect for another more practical purpose. A certain current in a conductor may be due to a few electrons moving at high speeds, or to many electrons moving with slow speeds. The deflecting magnetic force is proportional to the electron velocities. By observing the Hall effect we measure this deflecting force. Thus we obtain insight into the average velocity of the electrons, and we can also calculate how many electrons participate in carrying the current.

This number of "conduction electrons" is, in the alkali metals, approximately equal to the number of atoms in the lattice. In other metals we find that the number of conduction electrons per atom is not equal to one. In some very poor conductors, which are called semiconductors, the number of conduction electrons is quite small and strongly temperature-dependent. In semiconductors electric currents are carried by a few electrons which, for a given current, have a rather high drift velocity in the direction of the applied field. In such substances a magnetic field will strongly influence the motion of the electrons, and we obtain a strong Hall effect.

8.21 SEMICONDUCTORS, PHOTOELECTRIC CONDUCTIVITY, AND ELECTRIC BREAKDOWN For the poor conductors or semiconductors which we have just mentioned the rule that conductivity decreases with increasing temperature is not valid. A rapid increase of conductivity is observed instead, which can be described most easily by an exponential function of the form $e^{-\frac{C}{T}}$. We might be tempted to assume ionic conductivity for these substances and interpret the exponential temperature dependence by an activation energy which the ions in their motion must overcome. But no transport of matter has been observed for these substances. The definition of a true semiconductor is restricted to those examples for which the conductivity can be proved to be electronic.

The behavior of semiconductors can be explained by assuming that at absolute zero there are no partially filled Brillouin zones but that with a relatively small energy change we may lift an electron into an empty zone. It is not necessary that such an electron should originate from the top of a regular filled zone. Rather, it may be due to a more easily ionizable impurity in the crystal. With rising temperature an exponentially increasing number of electrons will appear at the bottom of the lowest empty zone, and these electrons give rise to the exponentially increasing conductivity. The temperature dependence is roughly proportional to $e^{-\frac{\Delta E}{kT}}$ where ΔE is the smallest energy which suffices to throw an electron into an empty zone.

The explanation of semiconductivity suggests that, if electrons could be placed in the free Brillouin zone of an insulator, conductivity would result. In a good insulator the quantity ΔE is too great to permit temperature excitation of electrons into an empty Brillouin zone, but absorption of light, mostly of ultraviolet light, causes a jump of electrons into such an empty zone. Indeed photoconductivity has been observed in many salts. The electrons liberated by light are usually trapped soon after their production. Impurities or crystal imperfections are quite effective in trapping such electrons; yet light of appropriate frequencies produces electrons in sufficient numbers to give rise to a conductivity which lasts as long as the crystal is illuminated and the transfer of electrons into the free zone is kept up. It is interesting to notice that heating or infrared illumination may cause conductivity if the crystal was previously illuminated by ultraviolet light of appropriate frequency. The smaller energies supplied by the temperature or by the infrared light, though not sufficient to lift a normal crystal electron into a free zone, may tear away an electron from the foreign atom that had captured it; thus the electron returns into the empty zone where it can move freely until it is recaptured.

The mobility of electrons in free zones may help to explain the rather complex phenomena encountered in the photographic process. Thus if an electron is thrown by light into a free zone, it will not fall back as a general rule into its original position but is trapped in some new position. Such trapped electrons may serve as nuclei around which reactions (for example, formation of metal crystallites) may start. This opens a possibility of understanding the nature of the latent photographic image.

The mobility of electrons in free zones also plays an important part in theories of electric breakdowns in insulators. The breakdown is thought to be due to the acceleration of an electron which happens to have gotten into the free zone. When this electron has gathered enough kinetic energy, it may collide with a second electron and lift it into the free zone. The same process is now repeated for the two electrons. Successive excitations give rise to an electron avalanche which finally turns enough electric energy into heat to cause local melting and to disrupt the crystal.

If a small electric field is present, electrons in the free zone will be prevented by collisions with lattice vibrations from accumulating enough energy, and no further electrons are lifted into the free zone. In fact, the electrons already present in this zone will soon be trapped and will lose their mobility. But, if the field applied to the crystal exceeds a certain value, free electrons can be accelerated until they have enough energy to excite further electrons so that an electron avalanche is produced. This explanation of the electric breakdown also shows why the field at which the breakdown occurs is so strongly dependent on impurities and crystal irregularities which contribute to loss of momentum and energy of the electron in the free zone.

8.22 CHEMICAL BINDING IN METALS AND INSULATORS

Metals occupy a definite region in the periodic system. The simplest representatives of metals are the alkalies which have in addition to closed shells just one loosely bound electron. In general, a relatively small ionization energy of the atoms seems to be favorable for metallic character of a solid. This explains why metals are grouped in the first columns of the periodic table in which the outermost electrons move under the influence of a comparatively low effective charge, while in the later columns of the periodic system there are a greater number of electrons in the outermost shell, and any one of these electrons moves in a more imperfectly shielded nuclear field and is therefore exposed to a higher effective charge. The requirement of low ionization energy can also be met by proceeding toward higher rows of the periodic table where the outermost electrons occupy orbits of higher quantum numbers and are farther removed from the nucleus. Indeed in the later columns of the system we find that the lighter elements are insulators while the heavier ones are metals.

In order to find the connection between the rules just stated and the requirement that imperfectly filled Brillouin zones should be present in metals, we shall investigate the electronic structure of solids of the simplest elements. We turn first to hydrogen. Ignoring the fact that hydrogen forms a molecular lattice, we shall place hydrogen nuclei in such a way as to form a simple lattice of the same kind as found for the alkali metals. This is a body-centered cubic lattice, that is, a simple cubic lattice with an additional atom at the center of every cube.

In order to investigate the motion of an electron in this lattice, we shall apply the rules derived for the motion in a strong periodic field. The electron-states must be obtained by linear superpositions of electronic motions around individual hydrogen atoms which are Bohr orbits perturbed to some extent by the influence of neighboring lattice points. If the number of atoms in the lattice is N, then there are N Bohr orbits available out of which we can form N independent linear combinations corresponding to waves propagated throughout the crystal. This is so because by forming linear combinations we cannot increase or diminish the number of states available. It was stated earlier (section 8.17) that one Brillouin zone corresponds to each electronic state of a cell. The Brillouin zone corresponding to the lowest hydrogen orbit consists therefore of N orbits and, according to the two possible values of the electron spin, requires $2N$ electrons to be filled up completely. But in a lattice of N hydrogen atoms only N electrons are available; this number is insufficient to fill the first zone, and a metal is obtained.

Let us now consider an arrangement of hydrogen nuclei in which pairs of nuclei are closer to each other than to any third nucleus. The elementary cells of the lattice now consist of two atoms, and, if N atoms are present, the number of cells is $N/2$. We consider again the lowest electronic orbit in a cell which in the present case is a bonding molecular orbit of H_2. The Brillouin zone corresponding to this state contains $N/2$ different orbits and can be filled up completely by the N available electrons. Therefore an insulator is obtained.

The state of the insulator just described does not differ from the state which we would obtain by filling each molecular orbit by the two hydrogen electrons. This as well as the formerly described procedure fills all the lowest bonding orbits, and it does not make any difference whether we first make up linear combinations of these orbits and fill all of them or whether we fill up all of the original orbits. It is significant to form linear combinations spread out over the crystal only as long as not all of the available orbits are occupied.

A similar situation was discussed in connection with the molecular-orbital method. There too it did not make any difference whether all molecular orbits, bonding and antibonding, obtained by linear combination of a state of one atom with a state of the other, are filled up by as many electrons as they can hold, or whether one filled up completely the atomic states from which the molecular orbits are constructed. In a Brillouin zone states of lower energy are analogous to bonding states, and states of high energy to antibonding states. The filling of the whole Brillouin zone gives rise to the cancellations of bonding and antibonding effects and to the distribution of electron pairs on the single cells. In the hydrogen lattice the result is that all forces between the molecules cancel out with the exception of van der Waals attraction and repulsion.

If the atoms are close together, the actual wavelength connected with a given k' value (sections 8.15, 8.17) is short. The electrons then have high momenta, high kinetic energies and also changes in electron states require high energy changes. Then it will be more difficult to effect displacements of atoms in the lattice since adjustment of the electronic orbits is impeded. In view of this, it will not be surprising to find that the displacements of the hydrogen atoms from the simple cubic lattice to a molecular lattice is not as easy at high hydrogen densities as it is at the ordinary low densities of hydrogen. Because of the great compressibility of hydrogen, high hydrogen densities can be produced relatively easily, and calculations actually show that at a pressure of a few hundred thousand atmospheres the hydrogen atoms should form a cubic close-packed lattice, and hydrogen should have metallic conductivity. It is not impossible that this metallic state of hydrogen exists at some distance below the surface of the great planets which are known to have a hydrogen envelope.

The structure of helium may be described from the point of view of the Brillouin zones in the same way as the structure of the molecular hydrogen crystal. If the crystal consists of N helium atoms, the Brillouin zone corresponding to the $1s$ state of helium contains N orbits which can be filled completely by the $2N$ available electrons. An insulator and more particularly a van der Waals crystal results.

In lithium the filling of the first Brillouin zone corresponds to the filling of the K shell. The valence electrons are sufficient to fill half the next Brillouin zone, and a metal is obtained. The same explanation of one valence electron per atom filling half a Brillouin zone certainly holds for the remaining alkali metals which have body-centered cubic structures.

From the arguments given so far, we would expect solid beryllium like solid helium to be an insulator. Actually the two beryllium electrons in the second shell are just sufficient to fill completely the second Brillouin zone. But we find here that a possibility mentioned in section 8.17

is realized; namely, there are some regions of a Brillouin zone which have a higher energy than certain regions of the next zone. A lower energy is obtained if one leaves a portion of the lower zone empty and moves some electrons into the lowest portions of the next zone. Thus we obtain two incomplete zones, and metallic conductivity results.

The example of beryllium shows that, even if the crystal structure is given and the number of electrons per cell is known, we may not be able to predict whether the substance is a conductor or an insulator. If the crystal field must be regarded as a strong periodic field, the Brillouin zones will form narrow nonoverlapping energy bands, and, if the right number of electrons are present, an insulator will be formed. If, on the other hand, the periodic field is weak, and the atoms are close enough together so that the kinetic energy associated with the spreading of electron waves through the crystal is more important than the binding to individual centers, then the Brillouin zones overlap, and metallic conductivity must be expected. In this, we see a confirmation of the rule that low ionization energies are favorable for metallic conductivity. Indeed, if the ionization energy is low, the electrons will be bound more weakly to the individual atoms, and a relatively weak periodic field may be expected.

If the number of electrons per cell is odd, the total number of electrons is an odd multiple of the total number of cells, while the total number of places available in a given set of Brillouin zones is an even multiple of the number of cells. Therefore atoms with an odd number of electrons may form insulators only when an even number of atoms (and therefore an even number of electrons) is placed in each cell of the crystal. One way of realizing this is to form the lattice from diatomic molecules. Thus, formation of homopolar bonds may lead to the electronic structure of an insulator where otherwise metallic conductivity would have to be expected. Such bond formation is favored if the outermost shell is incomplete, and if the ionization energy is great. The unoccupied places in the shell have energies similar to the occupied ones. This energy is low if the ionization energy is great, and thus much energy is to be gained by the sharing of electrons between neighboring atoms.

Generally speaking, if the ionization energy is great and the attraction centers are strong, it is favorable for the atoms to occupy positions for which localized electron orbits of low energy can be formed. These orbits may belong to diatomic molecules as in the halogens, to two neighboring members of a string of atoms as in sulfur, or to two neighbors in more complicated structures as in diamond. These orbits are then filled up with pairs of electrons, and an insulator is obtained whose structure can be represented by the molecular-orbital method and therefore by definite valence-bond pictures. If, however, the ionization energy is small, any molecular orbits that may be found will have a weak binding energy. In this case localization of electrons in molecular orbits does not lower the energy so greatly as does the spreading out of electron wave-functions over the crystal which latter wave functions give an uncertain position of the electron but at the same time lead to low momentum and low kinetic-energy values.

We have two simple methods of predicting metallic conductivity, a more empirical method connecting conductivity with low ionization energies and a theoretical rule requiring incomplete Brillouin zones for the presence of conductivity. But it is necessary to consider the possible electron orbits and with it the chemical properties of a substance in detail before we can say whether the actual crystal structures found will permit the filling of Brillouin zones. On the other hand, the criterion of low ionization energies is at best a qualitative guide and becomes less valuable when applied to crystals consisting of atoms with widely varying properties.

8.23 RESONANCE IN METALLIC CONDUCTORS

One way of representing chemical binding in a typical metal such as an alkali metal is to assume homopolar bonds between pairs of neighbors. The pairs may be arranged in an arbitrary manner except that all atoms must participate in one bond linking them to one of their immediate neighbors. Since in an alkali metal each atom has eight equivalent neighbors * there will be an indefinitely great number of possible arrangements of bonds. The actual state of the metal corresponds to a resonance among all these various valence pictures. Though for the formation of a homopolar bond between two metal atoms it would be more advantageous for two metal atoms to be closer to each other than to their other neighbors, an arrangement of a great number (8) of neighbors at equal distances is stabilized by the greater number of resonating states made possible by this configuration.

Although this picture of the metallic bond is helpful in correlating metals and unsaturated molecules having resonance structures, it does not yield a ready explanation of metallic conductivity. It is true that change from one resonating structure to another involves electronic motion. But any arrangement of a finite number of bonds gives rise

---

* It seems perhaps a little surprising that the alkalies, as the simplest metals, do not have a close-packed structure with 12 neighbors. In the actual body-centered structure there are in addition to the 8 nearest neighbors, 6 second nearest neighbors which are only $2/\sqrt{3}$ times farther than the nearest ones. Thus each alkali atom is surrounded by 14 fairly close atoms. In the resonance picture bonds with the second nearest neighbors must probably be taken into account.

to such electronic displacements the vector sum of which is zero, and such displacements cannot give rise to a net current. It would then become necessary to explain conductivity by the additional hypothesis that among the resonating states there are some with an electron pair on a single atom and some in which no valence electron or bond belongs to a given atom. This means an introduction of ionized states, a procedure which we also have to adopt when trying to describe the results of the molecular orbital method in terms of resonating atomic orbits and valence orbits.

As a second example for resonance in conductors we will consider the electronic structure of one layer in a graphite crystal. Figure 7.25(1) shows several resonating structures in a part of the crystal plane. As we shall see in the following paragraphs, the structure of the Brillouin zones does not require but also does not exclude the possibility of a partially filled zone. Actually the conductivity of graphite shows that a partially filled Brillouin zone is present. But the example also shows that resonance does not necessarily lead to incomplete Brillouin zones. Although the resonance is confined to a crystal plane, the motion of the conducting electrons need by no means be parallel to this plane. Thus conductivity is different from zero in a direction perpendicular to the plane, but the resistance may and does depend on the direction of the current.

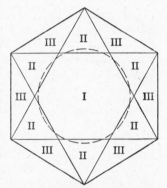

FIG. 8.23(1). Brillouin zones for a graphite plane.

We shall now investigate the conductivity of graphite from the point of view of the Brillouin zones. We shall consider here only the double-bond electrons, that is, those electrons, the wave functions of which possess a node in the graphite plane, and we shall restrict our discussion to the motion of the electrons in the plane. Then the Brillouin zones can be represented in a two-dimensional diagram. (Although such a two-dimensional picture gives qualitatively correct results, the third dimension must be included in any quantitative discussion.) Figure 8.23(1) shows the first three of these zones. The peculiar geometry of a graphite layer leads to the result that the available double-bond electrons can just fill the first Brillouin zone. If the motion of these electrons along the layer proceeds like the motion of free electrons insofar as their kinetic energy depends only on the square of their momentum, then the electrons of equal kinetic energy lie on concentric circles in the Brillouin picture. All states up to a certain circle will be filled; the dotted circle in 8.23(1) encloses the region occupied by the states of conducting electrons. The overlapping of the energy bands of two neighboring Brillouin zones causes the presence of unfilled zones and makes the substance a conductor.

There is no reason why other conjugated systems should not give metallic conductivity. Thus it should not be impossible to make plastics which would be good conductors.

8.24 ALLOYS When we describe the electron structure of metals by electronic states belonging to the periodic field as a whole and when we fill up these states successively with independently moving electrons, we

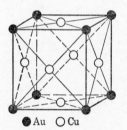

● Au ○ Cu

Fig. 8.24(1).   Ordered 1:3 gold–copper alloy.

relinquish the idea of ascribing definite chemical formulae or bond structures to the metals. Thus we deviate from the descriptions used in classical chemistry. That such a departure is necessary is shown by the behavior of alloys which elude a classification in the usual chemical categories.

The first remarkable fact about the alloys is the great readiness with which two or more different metals can form homogeneous structures. Among these structures regular arrangements or so-called superstructures are frequently found to be stable at low temperatures. The high-temperature arrangement is a more or less random distribution of atoms. Thus a 1:3 mixture of gold and copper gives at low temperatures after annealing the regular arrangement shown in Figure 8.24(1) where the gold atoms form a simple cubic structure with the copper atoms occupying the centers of the faces. At high temperatures the atoms occupy the lattice points of the close-packed cubic arrangement according to a random distribution.

On the one hand, the miscibility of metals would classify them with mixtures; on the other hand, the strong forces which hold together the atoms of different kinds seem to indicate chemical forces. Yet the rather indiscriminate nature of the forces acting almost equally between like and unlike atoms prevents the formation of very well-defined compounds. Metals have been described as electron compounds in which almost any kind of atom can be incorporated as long as one of its electrons can be lost with sufficient ease and pooled with the remainder of the metallic electrons. The only additional requirement is that the size of the remaining positive ion should not cause too great a distortion in the lattice. If the fit is poor, the miscibility is limited, and, after the ıraction of foreign atoms has exceeded a certain limit, a new geometrical arrangement of the atoms is formed.

The idea of an electron compound is supported by a most peculiar rule of Hume–Rothery. According to this rule certain crystal structures are favored if the ratio of lattice points to valency electrons in an alloy is close to certain numbers. Three such characteristic ratios are, $2:3, 13:21$, and $4:7$. According to a qualitative explanation of H. Jones, the crystal structures adopted for each of these ratios is such as to permit the surface of the Fermi sea to make contact with the surface of a Brillouin zone. We have seen that in weak periodic fields the only strongly perturbed electron motions are those represented by regions close to the boundaries of Brillouin zones. The perturbation is such as to lower the topmost energy region of a Brillouin zone and raise the lowest energy region of the following zone. [For the analogous behavior in the one-dimensional case see Figure 8.14(1).] The depression of the energy along the border where a Brillouin zone is in contact with a higher zone leads to the consequence that filling in of such border regions by electrons is energetically favorable, and this in turn explains why those crystal structures are stabilized which permit the Fermi sea to reach up in some places to the border of the Brillouin zone.

8.25 INTERSTITIAL STRUCTURES While in alloys atoms of different kinds replace each other, interstitial structures are formed when foreign ions which are small enough enter into the interstices of the normal lattice. In this way boron, carbon, or nitrogen may enter into various metals. In fact, the carbon in different forms of iron often is present in the interstices. The mechanical properties of a metal are influenced by the strain due to the atoms in the interstices.

The most interesting example of interstitial structures is the so-called solution of hydrogen in some metals, particularly in palladium. The pressure dependence of the solubility shows that hydrogen is dissolved in the atomic rather than in the molecular form. We shall describe the solution of a hydrogen atom as an independent addition of a proton and an electron to the metal. The hydrogen ion is a bare proton, the radius of which is negligible on an atomic scale. The reason why hydrogen is not soluble in many more substances is that the H_2 molecule is rather stable and that a great additional amount of energy is needed to ionize the hydrogen atom and to obtain the proton and electron. The latter particles are taken up eagerly by any metal, but in most instances the energy thus liberated is not great enough to compensate for the initial expenditures of dissociation and ionization.

In all metals a certain energy called the "work function" is needed to remove an electron from the metal. This energy ranges from about 1 volt for caesium to about 5 volts for heavy transition elements. The same amount of energy is gained if an outside electron is added to the metal. The addition of the proton to the metal also liberates some energy, since, as soon as the proton enters, the density of electrons around it increases, and the potential energy of the system is lowered.

It has been observed in palladium that hydrogen can diffuse freely through the metal and that under the action of an electric field the protons drift in the direction of the field. The latter experiment means that the charge of the proton is not completely neutralized by the charge of the electron cloud around it. Evaluating the results quantitatively, we find that the force on the proton is about 50 times smaller than would be the force on a free proton showing that the neutralization of the proton's charge is almost complete. In fact, if the proton were infinitely heavier than the electrons, a complete neutralization should always be expected in a conductor. Since the proton gathers the charge of one electron around itself within the lattice, we might think that it has returned to an atomic state not unlike the state of a gaseous atom. But in the gas the nearest orbit to the proton was filled with one electron. In the metal the proton is surrounded by electron pairs with opposite spins whose charge distribution differs radically from that found in the gaseous atom.

The fact that hydrogen atoms are held with sufficiently strong energy in palladium to balance the energy needed for dissociation and ionization and that at the same time the hydrogens can move practically freely within the palladium supports the idea of an electron compound. Formation of some definite palladium hydride, if it had enough energy to break the H–H bond, would probably hold the hydrogen in a fixed position and would not permit great mobility.

8.26 CHEMICAL PROCESSES ON SURFACES

The importance of surface effects in chemistry is primarily due to the catalytic action of surfaces. Although the details of this catalysis are greatly varied, complicated, and often obscure, the general reasons why surfaces speed up some reactions are not difficult to understand. The forces emanating from a surface are of different kinds. Van der Waals forces are always present, although on closer approach chemical forces may begin to act between the surface atoms and the adsorbed atoms. The chemical forces may be particularly pronounced at some active points. The indiscriminate attractive action of the van der Waals forces helps to create a greater concentration of reactants near the surface, whereas the chemical action of the surface may be useful in forming necessary intermediate compounds. The circumstance that different active places on the surface might have different kinds of chemical effects might help to account for the variety of catalytic effects observed for a single kind of surface.

All that has been said so far holds both for nonmetallic and for metallic catalysts. But metals can enter a chemical reaction in one more manner. They can accept an electron from a reactant, incorporating this electron into the Fermi sea, or they may give an electron to a reactant. The electron affinity of an insulator is usually quite small (a fraction of a volt), whereas the energy needed to pull out an electron from an insulator is often as high as 10 volts. In a metal the electron affinity is equal to the energy required for an electron to leave the metal, both of these quantities being called the work function. It is easy to see the reason for this difference between metals and insulators. In insulators the difference between "ionization energy" (that is, the energy required to draw an electron out of the insulator) and the electron affinity is equal to the energy gap between the top of the last full Brillouin zone and the bottom of the first empty zone. In metals both the "ionization energy" and the electron affinity are equal to the energy difference between the top of the Fermi sea and the energy of an electron outside the metal.

Thus metals are both good electron donors and good electron acceptors. Insulators in general are poor electron donors and also poor electron acceptors. The best electron donors among the metals are those with the lowest work functions, that is, the alkali metals. The best electron acceptors are the metals with the highest work functions which are to be found among the transition metals.

The ionization of reactants on metallic surfaces is facilitated by the fact that the ionic charge is partly neutralized by an appropriate increase or decrease of electron density in the adjacent metal surface. Since the reactant is in many cases in intimate contact with the metal surface, it might become ambiguous whether ionization has really taken place. The distinction between an ion and a neutral molecule is a sharp one only as long as there are no easily movable charges close to the ion.

The ease with which a metal can accept and give electrons, neutralize charges, and carry electrons to new places opens various possibilities to influence the electron structure of adsorbed molecules and thereby to facilitate chemical reactions.

9. MAGNETIC PROPERTIES OF MATTER

9.1 EFFECTS OF A MAGNETIC FIELD The motion of charged particles is affected by magnetic fields to a very much smaller extent than it is by electric fields. This is true as long as the motion of the particle is slow compared to light velocity, and it is in particular true for all valence electrons whose velocities are less than one hundredth of the velocity of light. Since practically all physical and chemical properties of matter in bulk depend on the behavior of the outer electrons, we must expect magnetism to play a much smaller role in the structure of matter than is played by electricity. This situation is not changed by the presence of the internal angular momentum or spin of the electrons. Though the spin is connected with a magnetic moment, this magnetic moment is of the same magnitude as the moment due to the orbital motion of electrons.

Though the interaction of atoms in molecules or in solids is not essentially influenced by magnetic effects, yet the spin plays an important part because opposite spin orientations for two electrons allow them to occupy the same orbit. Whenever such pairing of electrons occurs, the magnetic effects of their spins cancel. Conversely, whenever the influence of the magnetic moment of an electron is apparent in the magnetic properties of a substance, we can conclude that an unpaired electron is present, and this statement is of direct interest in connection with chemical structure. The magnetic effects of the orbital motion complicate this situation considerably; but the same effects may yield valuable information about the electronic orbits. For instance, in crystals containing rare-earth ions, magnetic measurements have helped to confirm the conclusion that the motion of the electrons in the internal incomplete shells is affected to a very small extent by the field of the neighboring ions.

A discussion of magnetism must of course also include the phenomenon of ferromagnetism, a phenomenon which does not affect very deeply the structure of the bodies involved and is not connected with particularly great energies but which is nevertheless striking and seems to require a peculiar compensation of forces occurring only in a small number of compounds.

9.2 THE MAGNETIC MOMENT   A magnetic moment is produced by a current enclosing a certain area. We shall consider only the simplest case in which the enclosed area is plane. Then the magnitude of the magnetic moment μ is

$$\mu = \frac{I\sigma}{c} \qquad\qquad 9.2(1)$$

where I is the intensity of the current, σ the enclosed area, and c the velocity of light. The magnetic moment like the electric moment is a vector. Its direction is perpendicular to the plane mentioned and is such that, if we look from the south to the north pole, the current appears to flow in a clockwise direction. The interaction of a magnetic dipole with a magnetic field is of the same kind as the interaction of an electric dipole with an electric field; namely, there is an orienting force on the dipole which tends to line up the dipole with the field. The energy of interaction with the field H is given by

$$-\mu H \cos \theta \qquad\qquad 9.2(2)$$

where θ is the angle included by the dipole and the field direction.

No atom has an electric dipole moment in its lowest state and as a rule not even in an excited state. On the other hand, magnetic moments are quite common in atoms. The reason which has ruled out electric dipole moments in atoms is that reflection in the center of the atom should invert the electric dipole, whereas in reality such an inversion leaves the charge distribution in an atom unchanged. If a circular current is considered, it may be seen immediately that inversion in the center of the circle merely interchanges diametrically opposite points of the circle but leaves the direction of the current unchanged. Actually, inversion leaves both the charge and current distribution in an atom unchanged, and, since the magnetic moment too remains the same under this operation, there is no general reason of symmetry which would cause the magnetic dipole to vanish.

The magnetic moment produced by the motion of the electrons in their orbits is connected in a simple manner with the angular momentum of the atom. If M is the angular momentum, one can show with the help of equation 9.2(1) that the magnetic moment is

$$\mu = \frac{eM}{2mc} \qquad\qquad 9.2(3)$$

where m and e are the mass and charge, respectively, of the electron.

Since the angular momentum of an atom is an integral multiple of $h/2\pi$, the magnetic moment of the atom must be an integral multiple * of

$$\mu_B = \frac{eh}{4\pi mc} \qquad\qquad 9.2(4)$$

This elementary magnetic moment, μ_B, is called the Bohr magneton. The simple relationship between the orbital magnetic moment and the Bohr magneton holds only as long as the electron moves in a spherically symmetrical field. In diatomic molecules and more generally in linear molecules, in which the field has cylindrical symmetry, the component of the magnetic moment along the axis of the molecule is still a multiple of the Bohr magneton. But, if the field is of a sufficiently low symmetry and is sufficiently strong, the orbital magnetic moment of the electrons turns out to be zero. This is in fact a very common occurrence in polyatomic molecules and crystals. Magnetic moments which differ from zero but are not multiples of a Bohr magneton occur in fields with a symmetry of three- or more-fold axes. If the symmetry is even lower but the microscopic field is extremely weak, the magnetic moment depends on the strength of the external field and vanishes when the external field goes to zero.

In addition to the orbital magnetic moment, electrons possess a magnetic moment connected with their spin. The magnitude of this moment is one Bohr magneton which may seem somewhat surprising in view of the fact that the spin angular momentum is only one half the unit $h/2\pi$. Thus relation 9.2(3) does not hold for the spin.† The resultant of spin and orbital magnetic moments can be obtained by adding the vectors which represent the two moments. The resultant will be, in general, no longer a multiple of the Bohr magneton, but it can be calculated in terms of Bohr magnetons by the quantum-mechanical vector-addition rule.

In contrast to the behavior of the orbital magnetic moment, the spin magnetic moment cannot be quenched by microscopic electric fields. The only coupling to which spin is subject in atoms, molecules, or crystals is coupling to magnetic fields, other magnetic moments, or other spins.

---

* Strictly speaking, this holds for the components of angular momentum and magnetic moment along a given direction. The actual length of the angular-momentum and magnetic-moment vectors is given according to quantum mechanics not by an integer l multiplied by an elementary angular momentum or magnetic moment, but rather by $\sqrt{l(l+1)}$ multiplied by the elementary quantity.

† This actually is a consequence of relativistic quantum mechanics.

9.3 TEMPERATURE-DEPENDENT PARAMAGNETISM A

paramagnetic substance is a magnetic analogue of a dielectric substance. In an isotropic paramagnetic substance, a magnetic field induces an average magnetic moment which is parallel to the magnetic field. The paramagnetism of many substances shows a temperature dependence of the same form as the temperature dependence of that part of the dielectric constant which is due to electric dipoles. In these substances the paramagnetism is actually produced by magnetic dipoles which can orient themselves freely in an outside magnetic field.

By an argument which is similar to that given in section 5.4 we find that the magnetization, that is, the magnetic dipole per unit volume induced by a magnetic field H, is

$$\frac{N\mu^2 H}{3kT} \qquad\qquad 9.3(1)$$

where N is the number of magnetic dipoles per unit volume. From this, we obtain for the magnetic permeability *

$$1 + \frac{4\pi N\mu^2}{3kT} \qquad\qquad 9.3(2)$$

The temperature-dependent paramagnetism previously described is of course found only for substances which do possess a magnetic moment. Such substances are relatively rare because in saturated compounds the spins are paired and their magnetic moments cancel while the orbits tend to form closed shells whose angular momentum and magnetic moment is zero. Notable examples for paramagnetic gases are oxygen and nitric oxide (NO). The former has no orbital angular momentum but two parallel uncompensated spins. The latter has one uncompensated spin and one unit of orbital angular momentum along the molecular axis. The temperature dependence of the paramagnetism of nitric oxide is complicated by the fact that the molecule has two low electronic levels. In the lowest level the spin and orbital magnetic moment cancel each other so that at low temperatures the paramagnetism disappears. But already at room temperature the next level in which the orbital and spin magnetic moments re-enforce each other is excited, and nitric oxide is paramagnetic. Owing to the weakness of magnetic

* In calculating this permeability we must not use integer multiples l of the Bohr magneton for μ. If μ is of orbital origin, then its value is $\mu_B\sqrt{l(l+1)}$, and, if it originates from spin alone, its value is $\mu_B\sqrt{l(l+2)}$. If both the orbit and the spin contribute or if the orbital magnetic moment is partly quenched, more complicated expressions are obtained.

coupling inside atoms, molecules, and crystals, it is not unusual to encounter a situation similar to that just mentioned. Levels which differ only on relative orientation of magnetic moments within an atom are apt to lie so close to each other that the temperature energy suffices to cause transitions between these levels.

An extensive class of paramagnetic substances is afforded by crystals containing rare-earth ions. The paramagnetism is due to the magnetic moments of the inner incomplete shell. This shell is sufficiently far inside the ion so that the microscopic fields of the crystal though having a noticeable effect do not complicate the calculation of the paramagnetic susceptibilities too greatly. Investigation of the magnetic properties of these ions has helped materially in clarifying the electronic structure of the incomplete inner shell.

Paramagnetism appears in other transition metal ions, but in these the incomplete shells are less completely shielded from the influence of the crystal field, and thus the theory of paramagnetism for these compounds is more involved. Paramagnetism of these ions may nevertheless serve as a guide in finding the electronic configuration in complex ions. According to the kind of co-ordination, the number of orbits on the central ion available for the electrons participating in the co-ordination bond may vary, and magnetic measurements can furnish information about the configuration of these electrons. This method has been used by Pauling to distinguish between the tetrahedrally co-ordinated doubly charged nickel ion in

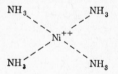

and the doubly charged nickel ion with plane co-ordination,

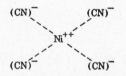

In the latter, eight electrons of the four co-ordination bonds (shown by dotted lines in the formula) must be distributed among four orbits (one $3d$ orbit, one $4s$ orbit, and two $4p$ orbits) which results in complete pairing of the electrons. Correspondingly no paramagnetism is observed. In the tetrahedral compound, five orbits (one $3d$ orbit, one $4s$ orbit, and three $4p$ orbits) are available for eight electrons of the co-ordination bonds. Two spins remain uncompensated, and the substance is, therefore, paramagnetic. (See section 8.9.)

9.4 MAGNETISM AND THE PRODUCTION OF LOW TEMPERATURES

The magnetic properties of rare-earth salts have been used to produce temperatures well below $1°$ K. We shall outline the principle on which this method is based.

Low temperatures are usually produced by transition of a system from a state of lower energy and small a priori probability to a state of higher energy and great a priori probability. The most common example of such a process is evaporation, in which process the molecules absorb energy in order to get into the vapor phase. The practical limitation of using such processes in the production of low temperatures is that after the temperature has been decreased to a certain extent almost all molecules will remain in the state of lowest energy. In order to reach low temperatures one must therefore utilize processes in which the change of energy is sufficiently small so that the process does not die off even at low temperatures. The fact that magnetic interactions are small, particularly if the magnets are not too close to each other, has the consequence that the orientations of magnetic moments retain their mobility even at very low temperatures.

The following procedure has been applied. A paramagnetic rare-earth salt is brought at liquid helium temperatures into a strong magnetic field. According to expression 9.3(2) the permeability at low temperatures is very high. By using sufficiently strong fields we can line up all atomic magnets with the external field.* In orienting the dipoles, the energy of the dipoles is lowered, and the heat thus released is carried away by the liquid helium. Then the system is as far as possible isolated against further heat exchange, and the magnetic field is slowly diminished until it reaches zero. During the process the magnets resume random orientation. This process is occurring while the magnetic field is still different from zero, so that the magnetic dipoles perform work against the magnetic field. The required energy is furnished from the store of heat energy of the substance so that the temperature is lowered. Factors limiting the temperatures which can be reached by this method are (1) interaction between the magnets which causes them to occupy fixed relative orientations if the temperature becomes too low, and (2) the slowness of exchange of energy between various degrees of freedom. We cannot completely escape both of these difficulties since

---

* In this case of saturation, the formulae 9.3(1) and 9.3(2) no longer apply. They were derived on the assumption that the orienting effect of the magnetic field introduces a small perturbation into the originally isotropic distribution of magnets.

high values of interaction prevent mobility, whereas too low interactions cause equilibrium to be established very slowly.

9.5 FERROMAGNETISM According to formula 9.3(2) paramagnetism can be enhanced by lining up a number of magnets parallel with each other. If for instance in an assembly of magnets, pairs of magnets were always forced to be parallel, we could replace N magnets of moment μ by $N/2$ magnets of moment 2μ. In the combination $N\mu^2$ which enters in equations 9.3(1) and 9.3(2), N is decreased by a factor $\frac{1}{2}$, but μ^2 is increased by a factor 4, and the paramagnetism is enhanced by a factor 2. In ferromagnetic substances very great numbers of elementary magnets are tied together into a so-called elementary domain. According to the state of the crystal, the large magnetic moment of an elementary domain may be tied rather tightly to certain directions in the crystal or else may be relatively free to change its orientation. The first is usually the case in a lattice full of irregularities such as hard iron. If such a substance is once magnetized, the elementary domains remain lined up, and we have a permanent magnet. In a more regular lattice, for instance soft iron, the elementary domains may return more easily to random orientations when the external field is removed.*

The main problem in explaining ferromagnetism is to understand the nature of the forces that cause the magnetic dipoles to remain lined up with each other. One can show that in iron and in similar substances, the orbital contribution to the magnetic moment is quenched by the field of the crystal, and we need consider only the electron spin. Free spins are indeed available in the incomplete d shell. In discussing the chemical bond, we have seen that forces causing relative orientation of spins may be due to the operation of electrostatic interaction between electrons and the Pauli principle. If in particular the symmetrical orbital wave function of two electrons has a lower energy than an antisymmetrical orbital wave function, then in the more stable wave function the spins will be opposed. This is the case in the lower state of the hydrogen molecule, for the electron pairs in the valence-orbit picture, and in general always when a maximum number of electrons are to be packed into a given number of states. But in the transition elements there is a surplus of free orbits, and under this condition there is no reason why the antisymmetrical state should not be the lowest. In this antisymmetrical state the spins must be parallel according to the requirements of the Pauli principle.

* Electric as well as magnetic dipoles have sometimes the tendency of parallel orientation within extended domains of some crystals. This occurs, for instance, in KH_2PO_4 and $BaTiO_3$. The resultant electric phenomenon is called ferroelectricity and is analogous to ferromagnetism.

At high temperatures ferromagnets become weaker, the magnetic moment of an elementary domain decreases, and at a certain temperature, the Curie point, ferromagnetism changes into temperature-dependent paramagnetism. If the Curie point is approached from the high-temperature side, the paramagnetism increases and becomes infinite at the Curie point. It is easy to understand qualitatively these effects. We shall start at low temperatures where the spins within an elementary domain are perfectly ordered. With rising temperature the distribution of spins becomes more random, and the moments of the domains decrease. The preferred orientation of each spin in the domain is determined by the action of the other spins in the domain so that, as disorder within the domain increases, the average orienting forces on each spin becomes smaller. Thus disorder will increase with rising temperature at an accelerated rate, and at the Curie temperature the magnetic moment of the domain has become equal to zero save for fluctuations. The fluctuations consist of correlations between neighboring magnetic dipoles; they cause the paramagnetism, immediately above the Curie point, to have exceptionally high values. The energy needed to introduce random orientation of the spins also causes a specific heat anomaly at the Curie point.

The value of kT at the Curie point gives the order of magnitude of the coupling between the spins. This energy turns out to be of the order of one tenth of an electron volt and is thus considerably smaller than energies of bond formation. The relatively small energy value may be explained by the fact that the interacting electrons are located at relatively great distances in the internal shells of different atoms and that the overlap of their wave functions which determines the relative spin orientation is small. We might perhaps expect that by bringing incomplete orbits closer together substances with higher Curie points might be produced. There are two reasons which make this expectation somewhat doubtful. First a variety of ferromagnetic substances is already known, and though some of them have quite low Curie points none has a Curie point higher than $2000°$ K. The second reason is that if the incomplete shells approach too closely to each other and if their functions begin to overlap considerably, we may expect that the interaction of the electrons in these shells becomes similar to the usual interaction of electrons in the outer shell, namely, that an attraction between electron pairs is associated with symmetrical orbital wave functions and opposed spins.

According to experimental evidence, conditions for the occurrence of ferromagnetism are satisfied if few electrons are missing from the $3d$ shell. Thus iron, cobalt, and nickel are ferromagnetic, but copper in which the $3d$ shell is filled is not ferromagnetic, and neither is manganese in which apparently too many electrons are missing from the $3d$ shell. In this connection it is interesting to note that ferromagnetism has been observed in copper–manganese alloys in which apparently some of the copper electrons are transferred to the manganese atoms.

9.6 TEMPERATURE-INDEPENDENT PARAMAGNETISM AND DIAMAGNETISM The effects discussed in the previous sections are exhibited only by a small fraction of substances. The magnetic effects in most substances are considerably weaker than those found for ferromagnetic substances and the typical temperature-dependent paramagnetic substances. In addition, the magnetic properties of most substances do not depend sensitively on the temperature.

One class of these more usual substances contains many of the metals and shows a weak temperature-independent paramagnetism. To explain this we must consider the distribution of electrons in the partially filled Brillouin zone of the metal. In the absence of a magnetic field, spins of both orientations occur equally frequently. But in the presence of a magnetic field the electrons will tend to have magnetic moments which are parallel to the magnetic field. This they can accomplish without violating the Pauli principle, if electrons with spins opposed to the field and having the highest kinetic energy are transferred to empty states in the same Brillouin zone in which the kinetic energy is somewhat higher and the spin is parallel to the field. The rise in the kinetic energy is at first overcompensated by a decrease in magnetic energy, but, after a number of electrons have made the transition just described, a too great change in kinetic energy will be necessary to transfer further electrons with spins opposed to the field into states with spins parallel to the field. It is seen that the circumstance limiting the number of electrons that can change their spins does not depend on temperature. It can be verified by simple calculations that the afore-mentioned ideas lead to a paramagnetic permeability of the magnitude observed in most metals.

A very great number of substances have a magnetic susceptibility which is smaller than 1. This means that a magnetic field induces in these substances magnetic dipoles which are opposed in direction to a magnetic field. These substances are said to be diamagnetic. Diamagnetism is as a rule a smaller effect than the temperature-dependent paramagnetism discussed in section 9.3.

Diamagnetism is in more than one way analogous to that part of the dielectric constant which is due to the polarizability of atoms or molecules. It is a small reaction to magnetic fields found in such systems which have no permanent magnetic moment. For saturated substances absence of a permanent magnetic moment is the rule, and this accounts for the great number of compounds belonging to this class. Diamagnetism is as a rule temperature-independent. The reasons for this are similar to the reasons for the temperature independence of the dielectric constant in nonpolar substances.

The explanation of diamagnetism is connected with the effects that a changing magnetic field has on charged bodies. Time-dependent macroscopic magnetic fields are known to induce currents in closed wires, and the resulting circular current has a magnetic moment. If initially no magnetic field is present and the field strength is then subsequently increased to a finite value, the induced magnetic moment is opposed in direction to the magnetic field. Under ordinary circumstances, the induced current is of course soon damped out by the resistance of the wire. The simplest way of explaining diamagnetism is to consider an atom as a microscopic conductor whose resistance is zero. Then it is clear that when a magnetic field is applied a current is induced which produces a magnetic moment opposed to the field. In the absence of resistance, this moment persists as long as the magnetic field remains unchanged. In view of the fact that electrons move in an unhindered way in the atom and that in stationary orbits they cannot lose energy by collisions, the picture proposed here is not unreasonable. Diamagnetic susceptibilities can be calculated by incorporating the magnetic and induction forces into the differential equation describing the atom. A really quantitative calculation can be performed, of course, only for those systems whose wave functions in the absence of a magnetic field are already known.

A few substances have large diamagnetic susceptibilities, and these susceptibilities often exhibit a rather complicated dependence on temperature and field strength. One striking example is metallic bismuth. The effect is due to the magnetic induction acting on the free electrons in the metal. In itself this should be a small effect, but if a Brillouin zone is very nearly full or if one has just been started, then the electrons may act as though they had a very small effective mass, and in this case the theory does predict strong diamagnetism. Another example of a substance with high permeability is graphite. It may be seen from Figure 8.23(1) that if graphite has incomplete Brillouin zones only few freely moving electrons and holes are to be expected, and all of these are close to boundaries of zones. It is also interesting to note that the diamagnetism of graphite has the anomalously great value only if the magnetic field is applied in a direction perpendicular to the strongly bound planes of graphite. Indeed electrons will be affected by the magnetic induction much more strongly if the induction forces lie in the graphite planes. This is the case if the magnetic field is perpendicular to these planes.

Superconductors act in some respects like infinitely diamagnetic substances. In fact, it is not quite clear whether, in describing this as yet unexplained phenomenon,* we should consider infinite conductivity or infinite diamagnetism as the main feature. If in the macroscopic model for diamagnetism which has been used previously the conducting closed wire were replaced by a superconductor, the magnetic moment induced by the field would persist indefinitely.

* By infinite diamagnetism we mean such diamagnetism which completely expels magnetic force lines from the substance in question.

10. MOLECULAR VIBRATIONS

10.1 INTRODUCTION In the development of quantum theory, the emphasis on spectroscopy was so great that sometimes it seemed as though quantum theory itself were merely a tool for finding spectroscopic rules. As quantum mechanics became a completed branch of physics, it was found to play the same rule for atomic and subatomic phenomena as is played by ordinary mechanics in the description of macrophysics. Spectroscopy retains, however, its importance as a direct method of finding atomic and molecular energy levels.

We shall be interested here in the method of getting such information from spectra and also in the general results to which these methods lead. Molecular spectroscopy will receive much more attention than atomic spectroscopy, some results of which have already been mentioned in connection with the theory of the hydrogen atom and the periodic table.

We shall consider in this chapter those spectra which are connected with molecular vibrations, that is the infrared and Raman spectra. In the following chapter the electronic spectra of atoms and molecules are considered.

10.2 MOLECULAR VIBRATIONS A diatomic molecule can vibrate in one definite manner. The vibration consists in the periodic change of the interatomic distance. If during the vibration the displacements from the equilibrium distance are small, then it is justifiable to assume that the restoring force varies proportionally to the displacement. Of course, in any actual molecule the dependence of the restoring force on the displacement contains quadratic and higher terms, but for small displacements these can be neglected. If we restrict the discussion to that of a linear dependence of the restoring force on the displacement, we obtain the model of a harmonic oscillator. The linear-force law is called the harmonic-force law, and the resulting sinusoidal variation of displacement with time is called harmonic oscillation. According to a simple classical treatment we obtain, for the displacement x,

$$x = a \sin 2\pi\nu t \quad \text{or} \quad x = a \cos 2\pi\nu t \qquad 10.2(1)$$

where a is the amplitude of the vibration and ν is the frequency. The two formulae differ only in the phase of the vibration. Linear combinations of the sine and cosine would give other possible phases. The frequency may be calculated from the proportionality constant k between restoring force F and displacement. ($F = -kx$, the minus sign indicating that the direction of the force is opposite that of the displacement.) The frequency is given by

$$\nu = \frac{1}{2\pi} \sqrt{\frac{k}{\mu}}$$ 10.2(2)

where μ is the reduced mass of the two atoms $\left(\dfrac{1}{\mu} = \dfrac{1}{m_1} + \dfrac{1}{m_2}\right.$, m_1 and m_2 being the masses of the atoms$\Big)$.

According to quantum mechanics, the possible energies of the harmonic oscillator are $(n + \frac{1}{2})h\nu$ where n can be zero or any integer. The lowest energy level $n = 0$ lies by the amount $\frac{1}{2}h\nu$ above the minimum of the potential energy corresponding to the equilibrium distance. This residual energy which the harmonic oscillator necessarily retains even at the absolute zero is called the zero-point energy. Its presence is due to the fact that according to the uncertainty relation one cannot localize the two atoms at exactly their equilibrium distance from each other and at the same time make the momentum and with it the kinetic energy exactly equal to zero. Thus the same reason which explains why the electron of the hydrogen atom does not fall into the proton also prohibits a harmonic oscillator from being absolutely at rest in its precise equilibrium position.

The vibrations of polyatomic molecules present a more complex picture. If by the displacement of atoms strains are produced in the molecule, an apparently disorderly motion results. There are, however, some vibrations, called normal vibrations, for which the motion is simpler. In a normal vibration, all atoms move in straight lines, and in addition all of them move in phase, their displacement changing with time in a sinusoidal manner. Thus each normal vibration has a certain characteristic frequency. On the other hand, the amplitude of the normal vibration can have any value. All this holds only if the forces are harmonic, that is, if they depend linearly on the atomic displacements from the equilibrium positions. For small displacements, the assumption of harmonicity is permissible. Even harmonic forces may be quite complicated since the components of the force acting on any atom may depend on the components of displacement of any other atom.

We can show that the number of different normal vibrations is equal to the number of vibrational degrees of freedom. This number is obtained by taking the total number of degrees of freedom of the molecule, that is, the number of independent ways in which atoms of the molecule can move, and subtracting the translational and rotational degrees of freedom. For an n-atomic molecule the total number of degrees of freedom is $3n$; there are always three translational degrees of freedom and mostly three rotational degrees corresponding to three independent rotations of the molecule about three perpendicular axes. But for linear molecules only two rotational degrees of freedom exist since the rotation around the molecule axis does not displace the atoms and must therefore not be counted as a degree of freedom. Altogether we find $3n - 6$ vibrational degrees of freedom and the same number of independent normal vibrations in a nonlinear molecule. The corresponding number for a linear molecule is $3n - 5$.

The knowledge of all normal vibrations of a molecule makes it possible to describe all the vibrational motions in a comparatively simple manner. This is possible because of two facts. The first is that normal vibrations may be simply superposed, by which we mean that from two or more normal vibrations we can construct an actual vibration of the molecule in which the displacement of each atom at each time is the sum of displacements which that atom would have according to the several normal vibrations. The second fact is that the normal vibrations form a complete system, by which we mean that any displacement in which no translation or rotation is involved can be obtained by superposing displacements characteristic of normal vibrations. A further very helpful fact is that, as a general rule, superposed normal vibrations not only proceed independently of each other but also give rise to independent effects in the various spectra. Therefore, apart from corrections and exceptions to be discussed later, the influence of each normal vibration on the spectrum can be considered by itself.

10.3 SYMMETRY OF NORMAL VIBRATIONS If in a molecule of known configuration the linear relation between restoring forces and displacements is given, it is possible to calculate the frequency and the form of the normal vibrations. However, the calculation is complicated for polyatomic molecules, involving as it does the solution of an equation of high order. In practice the opposite problem usually arises. The frequencies can be determined experimentally, and in addition some information may be obtained about the forms of the vibrations. From these data we wish to find what kind of forces arise when atoms are displaced. These forces are of direct interest in molecular structure and in chemistry since they insure the stability of the molecule and may enter in quantitative considerations of the mechanisms of chemical changes.

Unfortunately in most cases the experimental facts about the normal vibrations are too few to permit the calculation of all force constants. But the problem can be greatly simplified and sometimes completely solved by taking into account the molecular symmetry and the symmetry of the normal vibrations. In fact, considerations of symmetry often make it possible to find the form of normal vibrations without making lengthy calculations.

For the discussion of the vibrations of diatomic molecules, symmetry need not be considered, since for each molecule only one mode of vibration exists. One of the simplest examples among the polyatomic molecules is carbon dioxide. The three atoms of this molecule lie in a straight line, and the two oxygen atoms are at equal distances from the carbon atom. We can see easily that only one mode of vibration exists in the course of which the complete symmetry of the molecule is preserved.

FIG. 10.3(1). Totally symmetrical vibration of carbon dioxide.

In this vibration the carbon atom remains at rest while the two oxygen atoms move at the same rates in opposite directions. The displacements in this vibration are shown by arrows in Figure 10.3(1). It is evident that the vibration just described is a normal vibration. In fact, symmetry insures that the carbon atom will remain at rest while the equal displacements of the oxygen atoms produce equal forces so that the two oxygen atoms continue to move in phase. The reason why it is possible in this case to guess the form of a normal vibration without any calculations is that carbon dioxide possesses just one normal vibration of this symmetry type. Whenever we can construct more than one normal vibration of the same symmetry type, the form of the normal vibrations will depend on the force constants of the molecule, and more detailed calculations cannot be avoided. The carbon dioxide vibration mentioned is an example of a totally symmetrical vibration.

The remaining normal vibrations of carbon dioxide can also be obtained by using symmetry arguments alone. In these vibrations the two oxygen atoms move by equal amounts and strictly parallel to each other, while the carbon atom moves in the opposite direction, and its amplitude may be obtained from the rule that in a normal vibration the center of gravity of the molecule does not move. The vibrations which we are considering include two different types. In the one, all atoms move along the molecular axis. This vibration is shown in Figure 10.3(2). The symmetry properties of this vibration are described by the statements that the vibration is symmetrical to certain symmetry elements while it is antisymmetrical to others. We shall say that a normal vibration is symmetrical to a certain symmetry operation if the vibration remains unchanged when the symmetry operation in question is performed. For instance one operation belonging to a symmetry of carbon dioxide is reflection in any plane which contains the molecular axis. The vibration just described remains unchanged under the influence of this symmetry operation since the motion takes place along the axis. A vibration is called antisymmetrical to a symmetry element if the phase of the vibration is reversed by the reflection. For instance the vibration under discussion is antisymmetrical to the reflection in a plane which is perpendicular to the molecular axis and which passes through the equilibrium position of the carbon atom.

It is also possible that the parallel motion of the oxygen and the opposite motion of the carbon atom take place perpendicularly to the molecular axis. This gives the last normal vibration [shown in Figure 10.3(3)] of carbon dioxide.

FIG. 10.3(2). Normal vibration of carbon dioxide. This vibration is characterized by the statement that it is antisymmetrical to a plane passing through C and perpendicular to the molecular axis.

This vibration differs in one respect from those previously discussed, which were perfectly defined as soon as their amplitude was given. The vibration proceeding perpendicularly to the molecular axis may occur not only with an arbitrary amplitude but also in an arbitrary direction away from the axis. The vibrations in different directions have of course the same frequency since they can be transformed into each other by rotations around the molecular axis. If as in the present case vibrations differing in more than their amplitude belong to the same frequency, we speak about a degenerate vibration. If the reason for the degeneracy lies, as in the present case, in the symmetry of the molecule, we talk about a necessary degeneracy in contrast to the accidental degeneracies which may occur if the force constants of the molecule happen to satisfy certain relations.

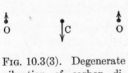

FIG. 10.3(3). Degenerate vibration of carbon dioxide.

There are infinitely many ways in which the carbon dioxide molecule can vibrate perpendicularly to the molecular axis. Yet we count this vibration as only two vibrations, or, in more technical terms, we speak about a twofold degenerate vibration. We do this because from two of these vibrations we can obtain by appropriate superposition any other vibration of the set. Thus the degenerate vibration corresponds to two degrees of freedom. This situation is similar to the well-known case of molecular translations. Although translations are possible in any direction in space, yet only three degrees of freedom correspond to translations since all translations can be obtained by appropriate superposition of translations in three perpendicular directions.

It is noteworthy that for degenerate normal vibrations we may and usually do apply a definition of normal vibrations which differs from the one given in section 10.2. Let us consider two vibrations which are perpendicular to the carbon dioxide axis and also to each other. If these vibrations are superposed with a phase shift, we find that all atoms move on ellipses rather than on straight lines. This motion in which all atoms still move with the same frequency is included in the usual definition of normal vibrations, and it is not required that all atoms move in phase and along straight lines.

We have now described all normal vibrations of carbon dioxide. This molecule has nine degrees of freedom, of which three belong to translations and two to rotations. From the four vibrational degrees of freedom, one is totally symmetrical, another is not totally symmetrical while also not degenerate, and the two remaining degrees of freedom are accounted for by a twofold degenerate vibration. All other motions of carbon dioxide can be obtained by superposing the simple motions just described. For instance, if the carbon atom is displaced at an angle different from 90° to the molecular axis, both the vibrations parallel and perpendicular to the axis will be excited. Since these vibrations have different frequencies a complicated motion results.

The types of normal vibrations found for carbon dioxide exhaust the possible kinds of normal vibrations for any molecule. If a vibration remains unchanged under all symmetry operations, then it is totally symmetrical. If the vibration does not remain unchanged under all symmetry operations but reverses its phase under the influence of some operations, then the vibration is nontotally symmetrical and nondegenerate (at least, as long as accidental degeneracy is disregarded). If, finally, some symmetry operations cause a more profound change in the vibration than mere reversal of sign, then we have a (necessarily) degenerate vibration. Most of the degenerate vibrations of molecules are twofold degenerate, but in molecules of cubic symmetry like CH_4 or SF_6, threefold degenerate vibrations occur (that is, vibrations where all the degenerate modes are obtained by the superposition of three independent vibrations). It may be observed that a degenerate vibration may be symmetrical or antisymmetrical to some symmetry elements. For instance the degenerate carbon dioxide vibration is symmetrical with regard to reflection in the plane which is perpendicular to the molecular axis and passes through the equilibrium position of the car-

bon atom; and the same normal vibration is antisymmetrical with
respect to reflection in the center of symmetry.

10.4 MOLECULAR ROTATION   According to classical theory, the
rotation of a diatomic or a linear polyatomic molecule is extremely
simple.   The rotation takes place around an axis which passes through
the center of gravity and is perpendicular to the molecular axis.   The
energy of rotation is given by the square of the angular momentum of
rotation divided by twice the moment of inertia.

In quantum theory, the foregoing statements still remain essentially
true, but one important addition must be made.   In classical theory
the angular momentum can assume any value, in quantum theory the
angular momentum must be zero or an integral multiple of Planck's
constant h, divided by 2π.   We may set the angular momentum M
$= jh/2\pi$.   The fact that M is an integral multiple of $h/2\pi$ is due to the
same reasons which in the hydrogen atom gave rise to the values 0,
$h/2\pi$, $2h/2\pi$, etc., for the angular momenta of the s, p, d, etc., electrons.
Substituting $jh/2\pi$ into the classical expression for rotational energy,
we obtain

$$E_{\mathrm{rot}} = \frac{h^2 j^2}{8\pi^2 I}$$ 10.4(1)

where I is the moment of inertia.   Quantum-mechanical calculations
show that the foregoing expression must be slightly modified and one
obtains, for the rotational energy in quantum theory,

$$E_{\mathrm{rot}} = \frac{h^2 j(j+1)}{8\pi^2 I}$$ 10.4(2)

The reason why the correct quantum expression 10.4(2) differs from the
equation 10.4(1) obtained by simple quantization of the angular momentum is connected with the uncertainty principle.   The angular momentum must be represented by a vector whose direction is parallel to the
axis of rotation.   It can be shown that the three components of the
angular-momentum vector cannot be known accurately at the same
time.   This causes an uncertainty in the direction of the rotational axis
which is the more important the lower the angular momentum.   Lack
of accurate knowledge of the components of M leads to the further consequence that j^2 in equation 10.4(1) must be replaced by $j(j+1)$.   It
may be seen that, though this effect increases with increasing j values, its
relative importance compared to the total rotational energy decreases.

The formula for the rotational energy levels of a linear molecule has
been discussed in some detail, because this formula enables us to calcu-

late the internuclear distance in a diatomic molecule from the rotational energy levels. By adjusting the formula 10.4(2) to empirical rotational levels we obtain the moment of inertia I, which is equal to the reduced mass of the two atoms times the square of their distance.

The theory of the rotation of a nonlinear polyatomic molecule is more involved according to both classical mechanics and quantum mechanics. The influence of rotation of nonlinear molecules has been analyzed in a few cases, and they have led to the determination of interatomic distances. As examples may be mentioned water and methane. The method is essentially the same as for linear molecules; quantization of the angular momentum leads to discrete rotational energy levels, the values of which depend on the moments of inertia. From these the internuclear distances may be determined for sufficiently simple molecules.

Further complications arise if the interaction of rotation and vibration is taken into account. In fact, rotations and vibrations can be discussed completely separately only as long as all vibrational amplitudes are small compared to interatomic distances. If atoms are held very loosely in their equilibrium positions, displacements become too large, and interaction of vibration and rotation becomes important.

10.5 THE INFRARED SPECTRUM The mechanism of emission of radiation is the production of electric and magnetic fields by oscillating electric charges. Molecular vibrations and rotations produce periodic oscillations of charges and give rise to emission (and absorption) of radiation. The frequency of this radiation is of course equal to the frequency of the molecular motion in question, and thus direct information about the latter frequency may be obtained. These frequencies lie in the infrared region. The well-known vibrational frequencies are mostly between 10^{13} and 10^{14} vibrations per second, while some vibrational frequencies and practically all rotational frequencies are still lower.

The study of frequencies lower than 10^{13} vibrations per second becomes increasingly more difficult so that most data refer to the higher-frequency region. The wavelength of the radiation in the important frequency region 10^{13} sec.$^{-1}$ to 10^{14} sec.$^{-1}$ varies * from 30×10^{-4} cm. to 3×10^{-4} cm. It is usual to give the reciprocal value of the wavelength which is called the wave number. The advantage of using wave numbers is that they are proportional to the frequencies of radiation and also to the energies of the light quanta. In the region mentioned, the wave number varies roughly between 300 and 3000 wavelengths per

* Vibrations in which lengths of bonds containing a hydrogen atom are strongly affected often have frequencies slightly above the upper limit of this range.

centimeter, or, if the customary notation is used, between 300 cm.$^{-1}$
and 3000 cm.$^{-1}$.

10.6 SELECTION RULES Though all vibrational and rotational
frequencies absorb radiation, the difference in absorption for different
kinds of motion is extremely great. Many vibrations or rotations absorb
radiation so weakly as to be practically unobservable in the spectrum.
The corresponding spectral lines are called forbidden lines. It is easy
to understand the difference between an allowed and a forbidden vibration by considering an example for each type.

During the vibration of the HCl molecule a net displacement of
charge accompanies the vibration, and so the molecule emits and absorbs radiation just as strongly as an isolated vibrating charge would.
This vibration is allowed and shows up in the infrared spectrum.

In the vibration of the N_2 molecule, a displacement of charges again
takes place, but no net displacement is produced by the vibration. In
fact, every displacement of a charge on one end of the molecule is balanced by an opposite displacement of a like charge on the other end.
These opposite displacements give rise to opposite values of radiated
electric and magnetic fields, and the sum total of the field intensity in
the radiation is zero. Thus no radiation is emitted, and it can also be
shown that none is absorbed. The N_2 vibration is therefore forbidden
in the infrared.

Though it would appear from the previous paragraph that the vibration of N_2 cannot give rise to any radiation, this statement is not absolutely correct. If it is taken into account that electric and magnetic
fields are not established instantaneously but spread with the finite
velocity of light, it is found that, by the time the electromagnetic effect
produced by one end of the molecule spreads to the other end, the displacement at the other end has undergone a slight change of phase.
Thus the cancellation of the effects of displacements at the opposite ends
of the molecule is not complete. But the fraction of the electromagnetic
field that is not canceled is very much smaller than the original field.
The ratio is obtained if the linear dimension of the molecule is divided
by the wavelength of the emitted radiation. This ratio is 10^{-4}, and,
since the intensity of emission and also the probability of absorption
depend on the square of the field, the forbidden frequency may be expected to appear with 10^8 times smaller intensity than an allowed frequency.

It is easy to find a criterion distinguishing allowed frequencies like
the vibration of HCl from forbidden frequencies like the vibration of
N_2. For our present purpose it is permissible to consider the molecule

as composed (1) of positive charges at the positions of the nuclei whose motion we shall think of as proceeding according to classical mechanics, and (2) of a negative-charge cloud corresponding to the probability distribution of the electrons which are described according to wave mechanics. When the configuration of the nuclei varies, the charge cloud of the electrons varies along with it. If in the course of a vibration or rotation the dipole moment of the whole system is changed, then the motion is accompanied by a net displacement of charge, and the corresponding frequency is allowed. If, on the other hand, the dipole moment remains unchanged during the vibration, the transition is forbidden. More specifically, the intensity with which the frequency of a molecular motion appears in the spectrum is proportional in very good approximation to the square of the change in dipole moment produced during the motion.

The rule which distinguishes between allowed and forbidden frequencies is called the selection rule. The appearance of a forbidden frequency in a spectrum is called a violation of the selection rule. One instance of such a violation has been described for the vibration of the N_2 molecule. Schematically, the effects of the N_2 vibration can be represented by the simultaneous vibration of two opposite dipoles. A charge distribution consisting of two opposite dipoles is called a quadrupole, and the resulting weak radiation is a quadrupole radiation, in contrast to the usual dipole radiation.

Selection rules may be violated for other reasons. For instance, while an N_2 molecule happens to be in a state of collision, its charge distribution may be sufficiently perturbed, so that complete cancellation of the dipoles produced by the vibration no longer occurs. It is clear that all selection rules which are based on the symmetry of molecules may be violated by collisions. But the resulting intensities remain small.

10.7 THE PURE ROTATIONAL SPECTRUM If a rotational frequency appears by itself in the infrared, we talk about a pure rotational spectrum. The name serves to distinguish the pure rotational spectrum from the rotational structure of vibrational or electronic bands in which the rotational frequency is superposed on a vibrational or electronic frequency. During a rotation the dipole moment of the system changes if the molecule possesses a permanent dipole moment. Change in direction of this dipole moment amounts to an oscillation of the charge, and the pure rotational frequency will be present in the spectrum. If the molecule has no permanent dipole, no change of dipole moment can occur during rotation, and the pure rotational spectrum is absent.

Appearance of the classical rotational frequencies in the spectrum corresponds in the quantum theory of a linear molecule to transitions between neighboring rotational levels. The pure rotational spectrum will have a different appearance according to classical theory and according to quantum theory. In classical theory the rotation can have any frequency, and an assembly of molecules will give rise to a continuous spectrum. In quantum-theory transitions between states $j = 0 \rightarrow 1$, $j = 1 \rightarrow 2$, $j = 2 \rightarrow 3$, etc., give rise to a discrete set of equidistant rotational lines. In fact, the formula for the rotational energy 10.4(2) gives for the energy difference of the jth and $(j + 1)$th levels $h^2(j + 1)/4\pi^2 I$, and this energy difference yields the frequency $h(j + 1)/4\pi^2 I$. From the frequencies, the moment of inertia I may be obtained which in turn determines the internuclear distance. It may be noticed that the quantized frequencies $h(j + 1)/4\pi^2 I$ correspond to the quantized angular momentum $h(j + 1)/2\pi$.

The intensities of the rotational lines are proportional to the square of the change in dipole moment occurring during a rotation. Since by rotation through 180° the permanent dipole moment is reversed, the total change amounts to twice the permanent dipole moment. Thus from intensity measurements in the pure rotational spectrum, the permanent dipole of a linear molecule may be obtained. But intensity measurements are difficult and usually not very accurate. Therefore this method of determining dipole moments is not a good one.

The question arises whether transitions may occur between rotational states of a diatomic molecule which are not immediate neighbors. Such transitions would correspond in classical mechanics to overtones of the rotation, that is, to integral multiples of the rotational frequency. Such overtones are to be expected according to classical radiation theory whenever a motion is not purely harmonic. But the rotation of a linear molecule can be considered as the superposition of two purely harmonic oscillations which are 90° out of phase. Therefore overtones of the rotational frequency will not occur, and correspondingly no other transitions than between neighboring rotational states must be expected for linear molecules. The more complete quantum theory of emission and absorption bears out this conclusion.

The selection rule that for linear molecules only neighboring rotational states combine can be violated by collisions. In fact, collisions produce a nonuniformity in the classical rotational motion, and thus the rotation can no longer be obtained from pure harmonic motions. Since the rotation of molecules may be easily influenced by collisions, this violation of the rotational selection rule may become important. It is interesting to note that in quantum theory the rotational selection rule is a consequence of the symmetry of space, according to which all orientations of a molecule in free space are equivalent. If the presence of a second molecule disturbs this symmetry, the selection rule ceases to operate.

We can formulate the rotational selection rule for a linear molecule in another manner which brings out the more essential aspects of this selection rule and which is capable of wide generalization. It has been noted that the angular momentum of the rotation can take on only integral multiples of $h/2\pi$. The rule that only neighboring rotational states may combine means, therefore, that a transition can occur only between states whose angular momenta differ by one of the quantum units $h/2\pi$. This latter formulation is the more general one since it brings out the connection between the selection rule and the angular momentum which is closely connected with the symmetry in regard to rotations. In fact, the angular momentum is a characteristic constant of the motion of a system as long as symmetry with respect to rotation prevails.

Quadrupole transitions give rise to transitions between rotational levels which are second neighbors. In such transitions the angular momentum may change by two units $h/2\pi$. Such transitions have a small intensity compared to dipole transitions. In nonlinear molecules a more complicated nature of the rotational spectra arises because the rotational axis may have any direction with respect to fixed axes in the molecule, and therefore the components of the angular momentum as well as its magnitude have a bearing on the rotational states and transitions. This results in a much greater number of states than were found for a linear molecule, and the resulting rotational spectra consist of many lines arranged in a complex manner. The selection rule governing this spectrum requires that the total angular momentum and also any component of the angular momentum which is a definite multiple of $h/2\pi$ must not change by more than one of the units, $h/2\pi$. It is, however, permitted that changes by $\pm h/2\pi$ takes place or that no change occur.

The complexity of the spectrum is particularly great for the asymmetric top molecules; as a rule all molecules fall into this class which possesses low rotational symmetry; in particular, no rotation smaller than 180° brings such a molecule back into a configuration similar to the original one. For instance, the water molecule which contains only a twofold axis (that is an axis about which rotation by $\dfrac{360°}{2}$ is required for performing a symmetry operation) passing through the oxygen atom and bisecting the H–O–H angle is an asymmetric top molecule. Its observed rotational lines are distributed all over the far infrared and are still observable for as short a wavelength as about 10^{-3} cm. These weak rotational lines are quite important in influencing the weather by absorbing the infrared radiation issuing from the heated surface of the earth. This blanketing effect is the main factor in limiting the drop of temperature at night.

The rotational spectrum of symmetrical top molecules is considerably simpler. These are molecules which have a higher axis of symmetry. An example is ammonia whose threefold axis reproduces the original atomic configuration by rotation through $\dfrac{360°}{3}$. The pure rotational spectrum of such molecules is at first sight as simple as that of a linear molecule. But, according to theory, to each line in the spectrum of the linear molecule there should correspond a great number of closely spaced lines in the symmetric top molecule.

10.8 VIBRATIONS IN THE INFRARED SPECTRUM As a general rule vibrations have from 10 to 100 times greater frequency than rotations. Their absorption lines lie in the more accessible part of the infrared, in the region between 300 and 3000 wave numbers, and the investigations of vibrations have been much more numerous than studies of pure rotational spectra. Owing to the considerably higher frequency of vibrations as compared to rotations, it is permissible in first approximation to think of the molecule as retaining a fixed direction in space during the period of one vibration. Thus vibrations may be discussed independently from rotations.

According to classical theory, harmonic vibrations may give rise to absorption and emission of radiation only if the frequencies of the radiation and of the mechanical motion are the same. In quantum theory the harmonic vibration has quantized energy levels of the magnitude (see section 10.2)

$$E = h\nu(n + \tfrac{1}{2}) \qquad\qquad 10.8(1)$$

where n is zero or a positive integer. We might expect perhaps that a transition may occur from any of these energy levels to any other energy level. But this would give rise to a multiplicity of energy changes and a corresponding multiplicity of possible emitted and absorbed frequencies, and thus quantum theory and classical theory would lead to essentially different results. The correspondence principle requires and the mathematical formalism of quantum mechanics confirms that in quantum theory as well as in classical theory the absorbed or emitted frequencies have the value ν. This means in terms of the energy levels that the vibrational quantum number n must change from n to $n + 1$ during an absorption process and from n to $n - 1$ during an emission. Then in each case the energy change is $h\nu$, according to formula 10.8(1), and the frequency of radiation is ν. Thus we have obtained the vibrational selection rule that n may change only by ± 1 in close analogy to the rotational selection rule mentioned in the previous section according to which a change in j must be ± 1 in the pure rotational spectrum of a diatomic molecule.

In a polyatomic molecule possessing several normal vibrations, only such a radiation frequency may be absorbed or emitted as agrees with the frequency of one normal vibration. This is due to the fact that normal vibrations proceed independently of one another. In quantum theory the energy levels can be written as a sum of expressions $h\nu_i(n_i + \frac{1}{2})$ where ν_i is a frequency of the ith normal vibration and n_i is the quantum number of the same vibration. In order that the frequency of the absorbed or emitted radiation shall agree with one of the frequencies ν_i, we must introduce the selection rule that in an infrared emission or absorption process only one of the quantum numbers n_i must change and that the change shall be either $+1$ or -1. The vibrational selection rules stated in the last two paragraphs retain their validity only as long as the vibrations are strictly harmonic. Exceptions from these rules are discussed in section 10.10.

As an example we shall consider again the vibrations of the CO_2 molecule. During the totally symmetrical vibration, Figure 10.3(1), the dipole moment does not change since in this vibration the molecular symmetry is preserved, and this symmetry is incompatible with a dipole moment. The nontotally symmetrical vibration which proceeds along the molecular axis, Figure 10.3(2), may produce a dipole moment. This can be seen most readily by attaching opposite charges to the carbon and oxygen atoms. Though such a model is certainly oversimplified, yet a vibration is not forbidden if any assumption consistent with the molecular symmetry leads to a finite change of the dipole moment during the vibration. By the same argument and the same model it can be shown that the degenerate CO_2 vibrations, Figure 10.3(3), may cause a change in dipole moment perpendicular to the molecular axis. Thus all nontotally symmetrical vibrations may appear in the infrared. Actually two strong bands have been observed in the infrared at 650 wave numbers and 2300 wave numbers. Subsequent considerations will show that the smaller frequency belongs to the degenerate vibrations.

10.9 THE VIBRATION–ROTATION SPECTRUM We shall consider a diatomic molecule vibrating and rotating at the same time. The vibration causes a change in dipole moment which may be represented at each instant by a vector of the magnitude $a \sin 2\pi \nu_v t$ lying in the direction of the molecular axis. Here a is the maximum change of the dipole moment, and ν_v is the vibrational frequency. We shall choose the plane in which the rotation proceeds as the xy plane of a co-ordinate system. Then the vibration may interact with radiation polarized in the x or y direction. We shall consider the first of these two directions; light polarized in the y direction will behave in the same way.

The emission and absorption of light polarized in the x direction is due to the x component of the vibrating dipole: $a \sin 2\pi \nu_v t \cos \varphi$ where φ is the angle included by the instantaneous direction of the molecule and the x axis. The dependence of φ on time is described by $\varphi = 2\pi \nu_r t$

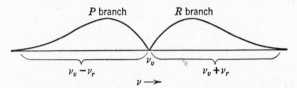

FIG. 10.9(1). Rotational structure of a vibrational line (Bjerrum double band). The structure shown is the one predicted by classical theory.

where ν_r is the rotational frequency. The complete expression for the x component of the vibrating electric moment can be written

$$a \sin (2\pi \nu_v t) \cos (2\pi \nu_r t) = \frac{a}{2} [\sin 2\pi (\nu_v + \nu_r)t + \sin 2\pi (\nu_v - \nu_r)t] \quad 10.9(1)$$

The last expression shows that the oscillating dipole moment can be considered as the sum of two terms, the first varying with the frequency $\nu_v + \nu_r$; the second with the frequency $\nu_v - \nu_r$. Accordingly, we see that the pure vibrational frequency ν_v cannot be absorbed or emitted. The two frequencies $\nu_v + \nu_r$ and $\nu_v - \nu_r$ appear in the spectrum instead. Since the rotational frequency ν_r is much smaller than the vibrational frequency ν_v, the two actual frequencies lie close to the pure vibrational frequency ν_v. It may also be observed that various molecules rotate with various frequencies ν_r. Since each molecule emits a pair of lines, a continuum of frequencies appears instead of the single vibrational frequency. The shape of the rotational structure is shown in Figure 10.9(1), in which the intensity is plotted as a function of the frequency. The center of the figure corresponds to the pure vibrational frequency ν_v. For this frequency the intensity vanishes. Toward shorter wavelength, one finds the continuum of frequencies $\nu_v + \nu_r$ constituting the so-called R branch, whereas toward longer wavelengths the frequencies $\nu_v - \nu_r$ form the P branch. The whole structure has the appearance of a double band in the spectrum which carries the name Bjerrum double band. The intensity distribution in both the P and R branches of the double band is due to the distribution of rotational velocities of the molecules. This distribution resembles to some extent the usual Maxwellian velocity distribution.* The separation of the two maxima depends on the average rotational frequency, and so with increasing temperature the maxima recede from each other. From this distance the moment of inertia of the molecule may be evaluated. But actually the breadth of the maximum makes this determination of the moment of inertia inaccurate.

If a Bjerrum double band is observed under higher dispersion, it is seen to break up into a series of rotational lines. This is due to the quantization of rotation. As has been stated in section 10.7, the rotational frequencies of a diatomic molecule can possess only the discrete set of values $\nu_r = h(j + 1)/4\pi^2 I$ where the integer j is the rotational quantum number, and I is the moment of inertia of the molecule. Thus the frequencies $\nu_v + \nu_r$ of the R branch and also the frequencies $\nu_v - \nu_r$ of the P branch form an equidistant set of lines. The lines of the R and P branches are produced when in addition to the change of vibrational quantum number, a change in rotational quantum number by ± 1 occurs. The absence of the pure vibrational frequency ν_v means that a change in vibrational quantum number never occurs without an accompanying change in the rotational quantum number. From the positions of the rotational lines, the moment of inertia I may be determined with considerable accuracy. It is experimentally much easier to study the vibration–rotation structure than to measure the pure rotation structure which lies in the far infrared.

If in a polyatomic molecule all atoms lie in a straight line and if in a normal vibration the dipole moment oscillates along the molecular axis, then the rotational structure will be the same as for a diatomic molecule. The conditions just mentioned are satisfied for the nonsymmetrical vibration of CO_2 shown in Figure 10.3(2). But linear molecules have other infrared-active vibrations in which the vibrating dipole is perpendicular to the molecular axis. An example is the degenerate CO_2 vibration shown in Figure 10.3(3). The rotational structure of this vibration differs from that of a diatomic molecule. For such

* It is actually a Maxwellian velocity distribution corresponding to the motion of a particle restrained to move in two rather than in three dimensions. The reason for this is that in enumerating all possible rotations of the molecule we must consider the possible motions of one of the nuclei in a plane perpendicular to the molecular axis.

a vibration the vibrating dipole may be parallel to the axis around which the molecule rotates, in which case the vibrating dipole moment is unaffected by the rotation so that the pure vibrational frequency ν_v appears in the spectrum. It may happen with equal probability that the vibrating dipole moment while still remaining perpendicular to the molecular axis is also perpendicular to the axis of rotation. In this case the rotation affects the vibrating dipole in the same way as has been described in connection with a diatomic molecule, and the frequencies $\nu_v + \nu_r$ and $\nu_v - \nu_r$ appear. If the oscillating dipole includes an arbitrary angle with the axis of rotation, the dipole still can be decomposed into a component parallel to the axis of rotation and into a component perpendicular to the axis of rotation. The former gives rise to the frequency ν_v; the latter to the pair of frequencies $\nu_v - \nu_r$ and $\nu_v + \nu_r$. The rotational structure of a vibration with the dipole moment oscillating at right angles to the molecular axis will consist of a line of frequency ν_v which contains half the intensity of the whole rotational structure and is called the Q branch, while the remaining intensity is distributed between P and R branches in a similar way as in a diatomic molecule. Thus there is a distinct difference between the rotational structure of a so-called parallel band in which the dipole moment vibrates along the molecular axis and a perpendicular band in which the change of dipole moment is perpendicular to the same axis.

In quantum theory the presence of a rotational structure with P, R, and Q branches means that a change of rotational quantum number by ± 1 and also by 0 may accompany the change in vibrational quantum number.

In CO_2 a typical Bjerrum double band appears with the center at 2300 wave numbers, showing that the corresponding vibration proceeds along the molecular axis whereas the band around 650 cm.$^{-1}$ possesses the additional sharp Q branch, indicating that this vibration is of the perpendicular type. We see that a study of the rotational structure serves not only to determine the moment of inertia but also to decide the correlation between observed frequencies and theoretical vibrational forms.

Only in a few polyatomic molecules is the rotational structure as simple as described in the preceding paragraphs. In most cases all nuclear equilibrium positions do not lie on a straight line, and then the rotational structure is much more involved. But it is nevertheless possible to obtain information about the moments of inertia and the vibrational forms by a more detailed analysis of the rotational structure.

10.10 VALENCE AND DEFORMATION VIBRATIONS Investigation of the vibrational frequencies by measurements in the infrared as well as by other methods has led to empirical relationships connecting the structure of a molecule, its vibrational frequencies, and the form of the corresponding vibrations. These rules are formulated in terms of the atoms participating in a vibration and in terms of the directions in which these atoms are displaced. It should be stressed in this connection that in general every atom participates in every normal vibration except when symmetry requires that the atom be at rest. However, in certain vibrations some atoms move much more strongly than other atoms, and moreover certain directions of motion may be strongly preferred.

It is an ill-defined but useful rule that in one normal vibration those displacements occur predominantly which, taken by themselves, that is, without other displacements being considered, would give rise to similar frequencies. There are two factors which cause a frequency to be high: the small mass of the atoms participating and the high value of the restoring force. Experience has shown that in accordance with chemical intuition restoring forces are great if the distance of atoms bound together by a chemical bond is altered; much smaller restoring forces arise if merely valence angles are changed. We may conclude that in high-frequency vibrations valence distances change. These are the valence vibrations. In low-frequency vibrations valence angles change; these are the deformation vibrations.

We can refine the previous statements, and we must also find the limitations of these qualitative rules. The valence forces are greater for double bonds and even greater for triple bonds. The influence of mass is still more important. Thus a hydrogen-valence vibration has so high a frequency as to be practically not coupled with any other motion within the molecule. Even the atom to which the hydrogen is directly linked participates but little in the vibration. Hydrogen has a valence frequency of 3000 cm.$^{-1}$ if linked to a carbon atom. In the N–H and O–H groups the hydrogen-valence frequency is 3300 cm.$^{-1}$ and 3600 cm.$^{-1}$, respectively. These values vary to some extent from molecule to molecule.

On the other hand, hydrogen-deformation vibrations have about the same frequencies as carbon-valence vibrations (about 1000 cm.$^{-1}$), and therefore in many hydrocarbons it is impossible to decide whether a vibration is due to change of valence angle of a C–H bond or to change of length of a C–C bond. The failure to classify such vibrations as belonging to one or the other type is due not merely to a scarcity of information but also to the fact that the two kinds of displacements strongly participate in the same normal vibration.

In CO_2 the two nondegenerate vibrations which proceed along the molecular axis are valence vibrations, whereas the degenerate vibration is a deformation vibration. In this case as in all linear molecules the distinction is sharp since it is based on symmetry arguments rather than on empirical rules. From the general statements just made, we may be led to suspect that from the two vibrations observed in the infrared the high one at 2300 wave numbers is the valence vibration, while the low one at 650 wave numbers is a deformation vibration. Study of the rotational structure has led to the same conclusion. The remaining valence vibration is the totally symmetrical vibration. Its frequency as will be seen later is 1300 wave numbers.

10.11 EFFECTS OF ANHARMONICITY By the statement that the oscillation of a molecule is purely harmonic we mean two things: (1) that the forces are proportional to the displacement of the nuclei, and (2) that all displacements of electric charges are proportional to the displacement of the nuclei. One consequence of the first statement is that no change of frequency occurs if the amplitude of the vibration changes. A further consequence of the same statement is that the displacements of the oscillating nuclei vary sinusoidally with time. However, a purely harmonic (that is sinusoidal) motion of the charge displacements follows from this only if the displacement of charges is proportional to the displacement of nuclei. In the present discussion we are interested only in changes of dipole moment during the vibration. Therefore we shall consider a vibration harmonic if proportionality exists between nuclear displacements and the resulting changes of dipole moments as well as between nuclear displacements and restoring forces.

Anharmonicity, that is lack of harmonicity, may accordingly be due to two things. First, the proportionality between nuclear displacements and restoring forces may not be satisfied. In this case we talk about mechanical anharmonicity. Or deviations may exist from the proportionality between nuclear displacements and the accompanying changes of the dipole moment. In this case there exists an electrical anharmonicity.

In practice, the concept of harmonicity is used only if the proportionalities mentioned are approximately satisfied and if the deviations from these proportionalities may be treated as small perturbations. In molecules of sufficiently rigid structure, displacements from the equilibrium positions are usually small compared to interatomic distances. For these relatively small amplitudes it is justifiable to assume in first approximation both the proportionalities mentioned. There will be, of course, quadratic and higher terms both in the dependence of the dipole moment on nuclear displacement and in the dependence of the restoring forces on nuclear displacement. But these "anharmonic" terms will as a general rule be smaller than the linear or harmonic terms, the ratio of the two being of the same order of magnitude as the ratio of nuclear displacements to internuclear distances. This consideration suggests that, in general, mechanical and electrical anharmonicities are about equally important, though in a special case one of the two may be considerably greater than the other.

The simplicity of a harmonic oscillation manifests itself in two ways: (1) The frequency is independent of the amplitude, and (2) the purely sinusoidal motion of the charges causes the appearance of fundamental tones only when overtones are absent. We shall first consider the theory of the overtones in classical physics.

If an oscillation is merely periodical without being sinusoidal in time, then the actual change of dipole moment can be represented as a sum of purely sinusoidal changes. There will be one term, the frequency of which is the same as the frequency of the oscillation. In another term the frequency is twice as great, in a third term three times as great, and so on. Of course, after the time $1/\nu$, each of the terms will have regained its original value since this time is equal to the period of the first term, twice the period of the second, and so on. Thus $1/\nu$ is the period of the composite motion. It can be shown that this decomposition of a periodic motion into a sum of sinusoidal motions is always possible. This decomposition is called Fourier analysis, and the resulting sum is the Fourier series.

In classical radiation theory, absorption and emission of radiation are closely connected with the Fourier series describing the dependence of the dipole moment on time. The lowest frequency absorbed or emitted is ν, and the intensity of the process is proportional to the square of the amplitude of the term in the Fourier series with the frequency ν (that is, the first term). This radiation is said to have the fundamental frequency of the motion and is called the fundamental tone or first harmonic. A frequency 2ν is likewise emitted or absorbed, and the intensity of this process is proportional to the square of the amplitude of the second term in the Fourier series. The corresponding radiation is often called the second harmonic or first overtone. Similarly the frequency 3ν is due to the third term in the Fourier series and is called the third harmonic or the second overtone.

Mechanical anharmonicity may manifest itself by a change of frequency with amplitude and also by the appearance of overtones. The latter effect may arise, since mechanical anharmonicity modifies the purely sinusoidal motion of the nuclei and may cause therefore a deviation from the sinusoidal variation of the dipole moment. But the connection between nuclear displacement and change of dipole moment is influenced by the electrical anharmonicity, and the appearance and intensity of overtones depend therefore both on the mechanical and electrical anharmonicity.

The frequency may either increase or decrease with increasing amplitude of the vibration. The latter behavior is to be expected if the potential energy plotted against the internuclear separation flattens out at great values of the nuclear displacement. In the flat parts of the curve the forces acting on the nuclei are small, and the time required for the motion through this part of the curve is longer than in case of a harmonic motion. Thus the vibration becomes increasingly slower as it extends into the region of greater nuclear amplitude. Since all diatomic molecules finally dissociate at great internuclear distances, the curve representing the potential energy must eventually become flat. It follows that in diatomic molecules the vibrational frequencies become very small for vibrations of high amplitudes. As a rule vibrations of moderate amplitudes already tend to have longer periods than the purely harmonic vibration that obtains for infinitesimal amplitudes. It occurs only as a rare exception that the frequency of a diatomic molecule increases with increasing amplitudes before the decrease at high amplitudes sets in.

We can obtain a rough estimate of the difference between the frequency of a finite amplitude vibration and that of the idealized infinitesimal vibration. This frequency difference is smaller than the vibrational frequency by approximately the square of the ratio between the nuclear displacement and the internuclear distance. The intensity of the first overtone or second harmonic is smaller than the intensity of the fundamental tone or first harmonic by approximately the square of the same ratio. In many practical cases the first overtone has 100 to 1000 times smaller intensity than the fundamental tone, and the frequency change between a one-quantum and two-quantum vibration is approximately 100 times smaller than the frequency of the harmonic motion.

In a polyatomic molecule anharmonicity produces, in addition to the effects mentioned, a coupling between the various normal vibrations. The frequency of a normal vibration will be affected not only by its own amplitude but also by the amplitudes of other normal vibrations as well. Also sums and differences of frequencies of two or more normal vibrations may appear. These are combination tones. Usually all these effects are as small as those discussed for a simple vibration. But, if the frequency of a normal vibration happens to be nearly equal to one-half the frequency of another normal vibration or if the sum of the frequencies of two normal vibrations is nearly equal to the frequency of a third normal vibration, resonance effects occur which may greatly enhance the importance of anharmonicity.

Anharmonicity manifests itself in quantum theory, just as in classical theory, in two ways. Corresponding to a change of frequency with amplitude, we find a change in the spacing of vibrational levels. Thus, an increase of vibrational energy and vibrational amplitude is accompanied by a change of the separation of neighboring levels and also by a change of the frequency associated with the vibration. If, as is usual, the frequency decreases with increasing amplitude, the spacing of vibrational levels decreases with increasing energy. If for high amplitudes the vibrational frequency tends towards zero, the spacing of levels also becomes vanishingly small. Such a convergence of vibrational levels occurs of course only for high-vibrational quanta which are practically never attained in the infrared spectrum. But the convergence has been observed often in connection with the electronic transitions in molecules and may be used to determine dissociation energies (see section 11.11).

The presence of overtones and combination tones is the second manifestation of anharmonicity in the classical theory. A corresponding phenomenon in the quantum theory is the appearance of transitions between vibrational levels that are not immediate neighbors. Transitions between second neighbors appear first while combinations between farther neighbors are increasingly less likely. If the vibrational levels were equidistant, the transitional frequency between second neighbors would be exactly twice the frequency of transition between first neighbors, so that a transition between second neighbors would have exactly the same frequency as the second harmonic has in classical theory. Actually the spacing of the levels is not quite uniform, and, though the transition between second neighbors is the equivalent of a second harmonic, it does not have exactly twice the frequency of the first harmonic.

In polyatomic molecules simultaneous changes of quantum numbers of more than one normal vibration may occur. This gives rise to the appearance of sums and differences of the frequencies of two and, with weaker intensity, of several normal vibrations. But in quantum theory as well as in classical theory, all these combination tones and the overtones mentioned in the previous paragraph have small intensities as compared to the intensities of the ground tones.

If the molecule possesses symmetries, then only some of the overtones and combination tones appear in the infrared spectrum. We may consider for example the antisymmetrical vibration of CO_2 in which all atoms move along the molecular axis [see Figure 10.3(2)]. It was stated that the frequency of this vibration (more specifically the fundamental tone of this vibration) appears in the infrared spectrum. We can show that, in addition, the third, fifth, and so on, harmonics appear while the second, fourth, and so on, harmonics are forbidden by the symmetry of the molecule.

It may happen that a fundamental tone and an overtone or combination tone have comparable intensities, either because the fundamental tone happens to be associated with an unusually small change of dipole moment and appears therefore with rather small intensity, or because the intensity of the overtone or combination tone is enhanced by resonance. The latter occurs if twice the frequency of one normal vibration is nearly equal to the frequency of another one. Then the two-quantum state of the first vibration ($n_1 = 2$, $n_2 = 0$) has nearly the same energy as the one-quantum state of the second vibration ($n_1 = 0$, $n_2 = 1$).

For actual occurrence of resonance it is further necessary that the anharmonic terms in the potential energy (that is, the terms increasing more than quadratically with the nuclear displacements) should not be small compared to the energy difference of the two close lying levels. In fact, it is required that anharmonic terms of a certain kind shall be present which couple the two normal vibrations with each other. If such coupling terms are permitted by symmetry and if they do not happen to be too small, two new mixed states will appear instead of the simple states, $n_1 = 2$, $n_2 = 0$, and $n_1 = 0$, $n_2 = 1$. These mixed states are then displaced toward high and low energies from the common position of the two original levels. The displacement divided by the original frequency is roughly proportional to the *first* power of the ratio between vibrational amplitude and interatomic distance so that the effect is considerably greater than the usual change produced by the anharmonicity (which is proportional to the square of the same ratio). Both mixed levels partake of the properties of both of the original quantum states; if a strong transition to one of the original states is possible, then strong transitions to both mixed states will occur. For instance, the transition from the ground state $n_1 = 0$, $n_2 = 0$ to the state $n_1 = 0$, $n_2 = 1$ might be permitted as a ground tone, whereas the transition from the ground state to $n_1 = 2$, $n_2 = 0$ may have at best the intensity of an overtone. Then transitions from the ground state to the two mixed states will both appear with strong intensities.

The same kind of resonance may occur if the sum of two frequencies are nearly equal to a third frequency. In this case the levels ($n_1 = 1$, $n_2 = 1$, $n_3 = 0$) and ($n_1 = 0$, $n_2 = 0$, $n_3 = 1$) may interact. Such interaction apparently occurs in CCl_4. The vibration of the carbon atom against the chlorine tetrahedron has a frequency of 750 cm.$^{-1}$ Instead of this single frequency, a doublet is observed. This is due to the fact that the 750 cm.$^{-1}$ vibration resonates with the sum of two other frequencies which have the values 450 cm.$^{-1}$ and 300 cm.$^{-1}$ It should be added that this quantum effect is simpler than the corresponding classical effect. The quantum treatment becomes involved only if resonances between higher quantum states are taken into account.

The resonances mentioned are sometimes called accidental degeneracies. Their presence may complicate infrared spectra and may lead to false conclusions by giving to overtones the appearance of ground tones. A reliable analysis of infrared spectrum requires consideration of all the available frequencies, of the symmetry properties, and, if possible, of the specific heats and the Raman spectrum.

10.12 INFRARED SPECTRA IN SOLIDS, LIQUIDS, AND SOLUTIONS

When a molecule is closely surrounded by others as is the case in solutions, liquids, or solids, its vibrations as well as its electrical dipole are changed so that its infrared spectrum is modified. If the intermolecular forces are small as compared to the forces holding the molecule together, the vibrations depending primarily on the latter forces remain essentially unchanged. The molecular rotation, however, will be almost always strongly influenced. With the exception of cases of so-called free rotation (which in reality is never quite free in the condensed phase) the rotational motion is actually transformed into a vibration about an equilibrium orientation. In solids this orientation is fixed in space, whereas in liquids the vibration is aperiodic, and the orientation executes a "Brownian" motion. The translation of the molecules is likewise transformed into a vibration or Brownian motion. In solids and in many liquids all degrees of freedom of a molecule may be considered as vibrational. For instance, in water and in ice rotation and translation are replaced by vibrations having roughly the frequencies of 500 and 160 cm.$^{-1}$

The change of rotation into vibration replaces the pure rotational spectrum by frequencies corresponding to a faster oscillatory motion. At the same time the rotational structure of the internal molecular vibrations is effectively eliminated. This structure contained sums and differences of vibrational and rotational frequencies. Instead of this structure we now have combination tones between internal vibrations and the orientational vibrations which have replaced rotation in the liquid, solid, or solution. But these combination tones have as usual a small intensity compared to the fundamental tones, so that the strongest absorptions in the spectra correspond to simple vibrations. The disappearance of rotational structure gives rise to a narrowing down of the absorption region which belongs to vibration. This effect is, however, often overcompensated by the one mentioned in the next paragraph.

The internal vibrations are never completely uninfluenced by the neighboring molecules. If a molecule is in a disordered surrounding (liquid or solution), the internal frequencies will be affected differently according to the changing surroundings. For this reason the frequencies are broadened as well as shifted. Strong broadening effect is to be expected if the interaction between molecules is great, as is the case in strongly polar liquids. The various vibrations will of course be broadened to different extents. The greatest broadening would be expected for translational or rotational vibrations, whereas the proper internal vibrations are usually less affected.

The over-all displacement of a vibrational frequency may be in either direction, but a lowering of the frequency is the rule. This may be made plausible in the following way. Electronic states in molecules adjust themselves to give the lowest energy and therefore the strongest possible binding. If molecules in the condensed phase attract each other, the total energy of the system is lowered, but at the same time the electronic configuration of the molecule is so modified as to give no longer so great a bond strength within the individual molecule. Concurrently, a lowering of the frequency may be expected.

The influence of neighboring molecules also affects the intensities of infrared transitions. If a symmetrical molecule is placed in unsymmetrical surroundings, the symmetry reasons for the absence of a frequency from the infrared spectrum are no longer strictly valid. Thus vibrations appear which are forbidden in the gaseous state. At the same time the magnitude of the dipole-moment change in an allowed vibration may be different in the condensed phase from what it is for the isolated molecule. It is of interest to consider a hypothetical example. Let the contribution of the intermolecular forces to the vibrating dipole be approximately one tenth of what we choose to call a normal dipole-moment change for an allowed vibration. Then the amplitude of a vibrating dipole is changed from 1.0 to 1.1 and the intensity from 1.0 to 1.21, that is, by 21 per cent. If, on the other hand, the vibrating dipole of 0.1 strength is induced in a forbidden transition whose original vibrating dipole is zero, the resulting intensity is 0.01, that is, 1 per cent of the intensity in an allowed transition. Thus it is seen that comparatively great changes of intensity in allowed transitions are compatible with relatively faint appearance of forbidden vibrations. Frequently the arrangement of the surrounding molecules will accommodate itself to a lesser or greater extent to the symmetry of the molecule under consideration, and then the intensity with which a forbidden transition appears in the condensed phase may be very small or even zero.

Although in liquids and solutions it has not been possible to take into account the effect of neighboring molecules on the spectrum in other than a qualitative way, a quantitative treatment of these effects is possible in crystals. In fact, crystals can be considered as giant molecules, and we may discuss mathematically the normal vibrations of the crystal as a whole. If a crystal consists of N atoms there will be $3N$ degrees of freedom, and, as N goes to infinity, the normal vibrations of the crystal will cover a continuum and often several continua. The quantitative treatment of these vibrations is made possible by the crystal symmetry. This allows the simplifying assumption that, for each normal vibration of the crystal, the vibrations in different cells differ from each other only in phase. Furthermore, if the cells are numbered systematically by three indices corresponding to their three-dimensional arrangement, then the vibrational phases in different cells can be represented by a linear function of the indices characterizing the cell.* A normal vibration of a crystal is then characterized by the form of vibration within one cell and by the linear function determining the phase relation between the cells.

For every crystal there exist vibrations where the motion mainly consists in the displacement of cells with respect to each other. These are essentially elastic vibrations and are known as the acoustical branch, because the vibrations produced by sound in the solid belong to this continuum of frequencies.

If each cell consists of one atom only, then the acoustical branch comprises all the vibrations of the crystals. If, however, there is more than one atom in a cell, there will be further branches in which the main vibrations consist of the relative motion of atoms within one cell. Since some of the vibrations of these further branches appear in the infrared spectrum, they are often referred to as optical branches. In molecular crystals such vibrations may closely resemble vibrations of isolated molecules; however, all molecules in the crystal will participate with the same amplitude and with regular phase shifts. The frequency too will not differ greatly from the frequency of an isolated molecule and will not be strongly affected by the phase shifts between neighboring molecules. Thus all frequencies within the branch lie in a narrow region.

The frequencies within a branch are more strongly influenced by the phase relation between cells whenever the main vibration does not take

---

* This is in close mathematical analogy to the properties of the wave function of an electron moving in a periodic field. The vibrational phase corresponds to the exponent in the complex factor appearing in the electronic wave function.

place within isolated atom groups or molecules. As an example we may consider the sodium chloride crystal whose elementary cell consists of a sodium and a chlorine atom. A vibration of these two against each other involves equally important displacements of each of the atoms against atoms in neighboring cells, and the frequency will greatly depend on the phase relations. In this case the optical branch covers a greater spectral region.

From the whole continuum of crystal vibrations only a very few may appear in the infrared spectrum as strong fundamental tones. The translational symmetry of the crystal requires that in an infrared-active vibration all crystal cells shall vibrate in the same phase;* otherwise the effects of the various vibrating cells would destroy each other by interference. Thus, at the most, one vibration of each branch may appear in the infrared. The acoustical branch never contributes to the fundamental tones appearing in the infrared. In this case equal phase in all cells means a simple translation of the whole crystal. Thus, if each cell contains only one atom, no fundamental tone is to be expected at all in the infrared spectrum. In more complicated crystals fundamental tones do appear and should, according to the simplified theory given here, be sharp lines. Their sharpness is due not to lack of interaction between the constituents of the crystal but to their perfectly ordered positions and regular vibrational motions.

A study of the infrared spectra of solids yields direct information about the direction in which a change of dipole moment occurs during a vibration. In the gas an analysis of the rotational structure is necessary to obtain this information. In crystals it is merely necessary to observe the dependence of the absorption strength on the relative orientation of the crystal and the direction in which the incident beam is polarized.

Although among the fundamental tones only a discrete set can appear in the infrared spectrum, there is to be expected a continuum of the weaker overtones and combination tones. This is due to the fact that for the appearance of overtones and combination tones it is only required that the phase differences in the combining vibrations be related to each other in a certain manner, and it is not necessary that, in the individual normal vibrations, the vibrations of all cells shall proceed in the same phase. The importance of overtones and combination tones is enhanced by the fact that under the usual experimental conditions there is more absorbing material in a crystal specimen than in the chamber

* In a strict sense this statement would be true only if the infrared radiation had an infinite wavelength. The fact that the wavelength though long compared to the lattice distance is nevertheless finite necessitates an insignificant modification.

containing an absorbing gas so that weak absorption is more easily observed.

10.13 SCATTERING OF LIGHT The scattering of light by atoms and molecules is due almost exclusively to the electronic displacements under the influence of the incident electrical vector. This displacement is governed by the polarizability which is essentially a property of the ground state of atoms and molecules. Furthermore one specific kind of scattering, the Raman effect, affords a method which is fully as important as the analysis of infrared spectra for studying molecular vibrations. Experimentally the investigation of light scattering is simpler than work in the infrared, and thus the Raman effect has yielded more material about molecular vibrations than any other method.

The process of light scattering is the following. The incident electric vibration induces a dipole in the atom or molecule. This dipole vibrates with the same frequency as the incident radiation. The vibrating dipole emits in turn electromagnetic waves, and these are the scattered radiation. It may be seen that this mechanism of scattering changes only the direction of propagation of the light and not its frequency.

The intensity of the scattered light depends on the polarizability of the scattering particles, and it is possible to measure the magnitude of the polarizability by determining the scattered intensity. We have seen, however, in section 5.11 that the polarizability is not characterized by a simple number but rather by a tensor. This tensor may be represented by an ellipsoid whose longest axis coincides with the direction of greatest polarizability and the shortest axis with the direction of least polarizability. The total intensity of scattering depends on the mean value of the polarizability which is the same quantity that appears in the formula for the dielectric constant.

Additional information may be derived from the scattering of light by a more detailed investigation of the orientation of the electrical vector in the scattered radiation. We shall assume first that the polarizability of the scattering particle is spherical. This means according to our previous discussion, section 5.11, that the inducing electric force and the induced dipole moment are always parallel to each other and that the proportionality constant between these two vectors does not depend on the orientation of the electric force with respect to the scattering particle. These assumptions are fulfilled for a rare-gas atom or for a molecule of cubic symmetry such as CH_4, CCl_4, or SF_6. We assume that the incident radiation is linearly polarized. This means that the electrical vector has a fixed orientation. We shall choose its direction as the x axis. Since we assumed that the polarizability of the scattering particle is spherical, the induced dipole moment also vibrates in the x direction. If the scattered radiation is observed, its electrical vector still will point in the x direction; that is, it will still be completely polarized.

Let us assume on the other hand that the polarizability of the scattering particle is anisotropic. Then the induced dipole moment is not parallel to the incident electrical vector but deviates from it by tending to be oriented in a direction of greater polarizability. Thus, if the incident electrical vector is again parallel to the x direction, the induced dipole moment points in general in a different direction. If light scattered in the z direction is observed, then the scattered radiation will have x and y components. The magnitude and even the sign of the y component depend on the orientation of the scattering particle. If light is scattered by an assembly of randomly oriented molecules with anisotropic polarizability, the scattered radiation is not completely polarized. In this way it can be decided whether or not the polarizability of the scattering particles is spherical or whether it has a certain anisotropy.

A quantitative measure of the anisotropy may be obtained by measuring separately the intensity of the radiation scattered in the z direction having an electrical vector parallel to the y direction and the radiation scattered in the same direction but with an electrical vector parallel to the x direction (that is, the direction of the electrical vector in the incident radiation). The ratio of these two intensities is known as the depolarization factor. If no anisotropy is present, the scattered electrical vector has no y component, and the depolarization factor is zero. The most anisotropic polarizability a molecule can possess is one where along one axis the polarizability is very great compared to the polarizabilities in any direction perpendicular to that axis. In this limiting case, the depolarization factor approaches the value $\frac{1}{3}$.

Though a measurement of the depolarization factor does not suffice to determine all components of the polarizability ellipsoid, it gives nevertheless a good idea of the deviation of the polarizability ellipsoid from a sphere. Conversely, we can give a quantitative expression for the depolarization factor in terms of the components of the polarizability tensor. In practice, depolarization factors lie usually rather closer to their lower-limit zero than to their upper-limit $\frac{1}{3}$. A large depolarization factor indicates a markedly elongated or else a very flat molecule. Double bonds and particularly a system of conjugated double bonds lying in the direction or directions of greatest length within the molecule contribute to a large depolarization factor.

10.14 THE RAMAN EFFECT If light is scattered by a vibrating molecule, not all of the scattered radiation has the same frequency as the incident light. There appear in the scattering additional frequencies which contain the frequency of the vibration. This effect was predicted theoretically; it is named after Raman who first succeeded in finding it. Its great importance lies in the fact that, by measurements in the readily accessible spectral regions of the visible and near ultraviolet, values of molecular frequencies may be obtained.

A superposition of the vibrational frequencies on the frequency of the incident light can be explained with the help of a simple classical model. We write for the incident electrical vector

$$E = E_a \sin 2\pi\nu_l t \qquad 10.14(1)$$

Here E_a is the amplitude of the vibrating electrical vector, and ν_l is the frequency of the incident light. The induced dipole moment is then given by the expression,

$$D = \alpha E_a \sin 2\pi\nu_l t \qquad 10.14(2)$$

We now assume that during the molecular vibration which proceeds with the frequency ν_m the polarizability α suffers a small change having the same frequency,

$$\alpha = \alpha_0 + \alpha_1 \sin 2\pi\nu_m t \qquad 10.14(3)$$

Substituting equations 10.14(3) into 10.14(2), we obtain

$$D = [\alpha_0 + \alpha_1 \sin 2\pi\nu_m t]E_a \sin 2\pi\nu_l \qquad 10.14(4)$$

$$= \alpha_0 E_a \sin 2\pi\nu_l t + \tfrac{1}{2}\alpha_1 E_a[\cos 2\pi(\nu_l - \nu_m)t - \cos 2\pi(\nu_l + \nu_m)t]$$

The first term on the right-hand side gives rise to scattered radiation of the unchanged frequency ν_l. This constitutes the main part of the scattering and is called the Rayleigh scattering. The second term is much smaller because the polarizability varies only by a small fraction during the vibration. This term gives rise to the sum and difference tones of the light frequency ν_l and the molecular frequency ν_m.

The intensity ratio of the Raman scattering and the Rayleigh scattering may be roughly estimated as follows. A usual small-amplitude vibration may be assumed to produce a fractional change in the polarizability which is of the same order of magnitude as the ratio between vibrational amplitude and the distance of the atoms in the molecule. This ratio α_1/α_0 is also the same as the ratio of the amplitudes of the electrical vectors in the Raman and Rayleigh radiation. The ratio of the intensity of these two scattered radiations is then approximately given by the square of the ratio of the vibrational amplitude and the interatomic distance. As a rule, the Raman scattering in a gas is from 100 to 10,000 times weaker than the Rayleigh scattering.

According to formula 10.14(4) the two frequencies, $\nu_l - \nu_m$ and $\nu_l + \nu_m$, should appear with equal intensity. This prediction is not verified by experiment. The frequency, $\nu_l - \nu_m$, appears almost always with greater intensity, often with considerably greater intensity. This line conforms to Stokes' rule for fluorescent radiation, according to which the fluorescent light has a lower frequency than the original radiation. Accordingly, the line $\nu_l - \nu_m$ is called the Stokes line while the line $\nu_l + \nu_m$ is the anti-Stokes line.

The quantum explanation of the Raman effect makes it clear why these two lines differ in intensity. According to the original rough formulation of this argument, the light quantum $h\nu_l$ may be absorbed by the molecule even if the frequency ν_l is not in resonance with any electronic frequency and if accordingly there exists no excited state with any energy $h\nu_l$ above the ground state. The absorbed light quantum may be retained, however, by the molecule only for the very short period which would be necessary for an absorbing molecule to establish the fact of lacking resonance. After that period the quantum is reradiated, but it may happen that part of the original energy $h\nu_l$ is retained by the molecule in the form of a vibrational quantum $h\nu_m$. Then the reradiated or scattered quantum carries the diminished energy, $h(\nu_l - \nu_m)$, and the scattered frequency is therefore $\nu_l - \nu_m$. Conversely, if the molecule was originally in a higher vibrational state, it may give up to the outgoing light quantum the energy of a vibrational quantum $h\nu_m$, so that the outgoing energy is $h(\nu_l + \nu_m)$, and the outgoing frequency is $\nu_l + \nu_m$. Since, according to the Boltzman distribution, the number of molecules in higher vibrational states is smaller, there is a greater chance for the emission of the Stokes line.* It can be shown that in the limiting case of high temperatures $(kT >> h\nu_m)$ the intensities of Stokes and anti-Stokes lines become equal in agreement with the classical argument.

The previous simple quantum argument not only is successful in explaining the greater intensity of the Stokes line but also helps to elucidate the relationship between the Raman effect and fluorescence. The latter phenomenon is usually described as the actual absorption of one light quantum followed by an emission from the upper quantum state into which the absorption has thrown the atom or molecule. The re-emitted light may have the same frequency as the absorbed radiation, or it may have a different frequency, according to whether the system returns into its original state or into a different state. The Rayleigh scattering and Raman effect go over continuously into fluorescence when the incident radiation approaches resonance. While this happens,

* This statement is true only if the usually insignificant dependence of scattered intensity on frequency is neglected.

the polarizability and with it the scattering increases rapidly. There is also an increase of the time during which the quantum may be considered as absorbed by the molecules, owing to the fact that more and more time is required to distinguish between the frequency of the incident radiation and the proper frequency of the electrons within the molecule. If finally the frequency difference becomes smaller than the breadth of an absorption line, the usual description of fluorescence becomes fully justified.

A more elaborate quantum argument is needed to prove that in the proper Raman effect, that is, in the case of complete lack of resonance, there is very little likelihood of the molecule acquiring or losing more than one quantum of one normal vibration. Likewise it is possible but difficult to derive the selection rules operating in the Raman effect and the depolarization factor in the Raman effect if the quantum theory is used as the starting point of the investigation. It is much easier to approach these problems from the standpoint of classical theory. An extension of the derivation in the beginning of the section gives the required answers, and it can be shown that the results are in need only of two major corrections: (1) The Stokes and anti-Stokes lines are of unequal intensity, and (2) the classical treatment is valid only in the absence of resonance, that is, if the difference of the incident frequency and any molecular-absorption frequency is great compared to the frequency of molecular vibrations.

10.15   THE VIBRATIONAL RAMAN SPECTRUM   The discussion in the previous section involved the assumption [see equation 10.14(3)] that a normal vibration of frequency ν_m causes a variation of the same frequency in the polarizability. This assumption is justified in first approximation as long as the polarizability changes linearly with the displacement of the vibration. For diatomic molecules this is generally the case. But in polyatomic molecules symmetry frequently prevents such a linear variation.

Consider for instance the nonsymmetrical nondegenerate vibration of CO_2, Figure 10.3(3). Since all atoms remain lined up along the molecular axis during the vibration, the polarizability remains an ellipsoid of revolution. The only change that can occur during the vibration is a change in the length of the axes of this ellipsoid. If the variation of polarizability with the displacement were a linear one, opposite displacements in the vibration would correspond to opposite changes in the length of the axes. But opposite displacements are obtained by reflection in the center of symmetry of the molecule, and such a reflection, while changing the sign of the displacement, leaves the polarizability ellipsoid unchanged. Since the change in the polarizability cannot both alter its sign and remain the same, our assumption that the polarizability varies linearly with the displacement must have been erroneous.

It is of course to be expected that the vibration just considered does cause a change in polarizability. But such a change must be at least quadratical in the displacement, and, if the displacement is small, quadratical effects are much less important. Therefore the vibration may appear only very weakly in the Raman effect. Furthermore we have seen that opposite displacements of the vibration give rise to the same change of the polarizability. But it takes only half a vibrational period for the displacement to change over into the opposite displacement. Thus the polarizability resumes its original value after half a vibrational period so that the polarizability changes with twice the frequency of the vibration. Therefore the vibration itself will not appear at all in the Raman effect. Its weak manifestation in the Raman spectrum will be limited to the second (and possibly higher) harmonics.

From the preceding example we see that the ground tone of a vibration may be forbidden in the Raman effect for reasons of symmetry. The details of the argument given in the foregoing can be actually generalized into the statement that in a molecule possessing a center of symmetry all vibrations are forbidden in the Raman effect which are antisymmetrical to the center of symmetry, that is, which change their sign if a reflection in the center of symmetry is performed. For instance, in CO_2 all nontotally symmetrical vibrations are antisymmetrical to the center and consequently forbidden. The totally symmetrical vibration, on the other hand, is allowed in the Raman spectrum. It is useful to notice that the corresponding selection rule in the infrared spectrum is just the opposite. If a vibration is symmetrical to the center, then no change of dipole moment can occur during the vibration, and the vibration is forbidden in the infrared. If, on the other hand, the vibration is antisymmetrical to the center, the vibration may occur in the infrared unless it is forbidden by other symmetry considerations. Investigation of both infrared and Raman spectra is useful not only because the results complement each other, but also because they help to determine the symmetry of the molecule. Appearance of the same frequency in both spectra (if the frequency really corresponds to the same vibration and is not due to chance coincidence) proves that the molecule has no center of symmetry. For instance, in CO_2 two of the three frequencies of normal vibrations may appear in the infrared spectrum only, while the third is allowed only in the Raman effect.

Antisymmetry to a center is by no means the only reason why a vibration may be forbidden in the Raman effect. In order to decide whether the ground tone of a vibration may appear in the Raman effect, it is necessary to investigate for each vibrational type whether a linear variation of the polarizability is consistent with the symmetry. For instance, in ethylene the vibration which consists of a twisting of the two CH_2 groups around the axis of the double bond is symmetrical to the center of symmetry and is nevertheless forbidden in the Raman effect. This vibration is also forbidden in the infrared, so that, while in ethylene no vibration can appear in both the infrared and the Raman spectra, we have an example of a vibration which is forbidden in both spectra.

A few statements about Raman selection rules are valid for all molecular symmetries. For instance a totally symmetrically vibration is never forbidden in the Raman effect.

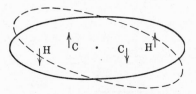

Fig. 10.15(1). Normal vibration of acetylene and corresponding change of polarizability.

Nontotally symmetrical vibrations may appear in the Raman spectrum. As an example we may consider the normal vibration of acetylene shown in Figure 10.15(1). This figure shows in addition to the displacements a tracing of the original polarizability (full line) and the polarizability changed as a consequence of the displacement (broken line). The lengths of the axes of the polarizability ellipsoid remain in first approximation unchanged but not the orientation of the axes. A change in the orientation influences the induced dipole moment and creates a component of this vibrating moment that contains the vibrational frequency and gives rise to the appearance of the fundamental tone in the Raman spectrum. The vibration used here as an example is one of the simplest illustrations that could have been used, but the vibration is apparently so faint in the Raman effect that until now it has not been identified with complete certainty. It is an empirical fact that nontotally symmetrical vibrations involving primarily the motion of hydrogen atoms are often very weak in the Raman effect.

Investigation of the polarization in the Raman scattering provides a useful way to recognize nontotally symmetrical vibrations. It can be shown that in such vibrations the sum of the lengths of the axes of the polarizability ellipsoid remains unchanged in first approximation. This type of polarizability change makes it possible to calculate the depolarization factor, and the value $\frac{3}{4}$ is obtained. This value is greater than $\frac{1}{3}$ which was the maximum obtainable for the Rayleigh scattering. But the Rayleigh scattering is due to the polarizability which as a rule does not assume negative values; that is, no component of the electric field produces a component of the dipole moment in the opposite direction. The

Raman effect, on the other hand, is due to a change of the polarizability, and for a degenerate vibration this change is actually positive in some directions and negative in others. The anisotropy resulting from the positive and negative changes arising during such vibrations is of course greater than the anisotropy in the molecular polarizability which is due to differences between positive polarizabilities. Actually the anisotropy and depolarization factor obtained in nontotally symmetrical vibrations are the greatest possible, according to the simple polarizability theory of scattering.

Multiples, sums, and differences of the normal frequencies are sometimes observed superimposed on the frequency of the incident light. This appearance of overtones and combination tones in the Raman effect is due to effects similar to those causing the appearance of these frequencies in the infrared spectrum, that is, to mechanical and electrical anharmonicities. Electrical anharmonicity means in this case a nonlinear dependence of the polarizability on the displacements. Overtones and combination tones are less frequently observed in the Raman effect than in the infrared spectrum. This is due to the fact that the Raman effect gives small intensities even for the ground tones. The intensity ratio of ground tones to overtones and combination tones is not expected to differ in the Raman and infrared spectrum.

In symmetrical molecules, selection rules operate for the overtones and combination tones as well as for the fundamental tones in the Raman spectrum. However, even harmonics are never forbidden.

In addition to the vibrational Raman lines, there exist in gases a pure rotational Raman effect, and the vibrational lines have a rotational structure. However, many Raman observations are made in the liquid state. One reason for this is the weakness of the Raman effect. The liquid state is of course not appropriate for studying the rotational structure.

The rotational Raman effect is due to the change in orientation of the polarizability ellipsoid during rotation. For diatomic and linear molecules, the twofold rotational frequency appears rather than the rotational frequency itself, since rotation by 180° brings the polarizability ellipsoid back into a position equivalent to the original one. Thus the frequency of polarizability change caused by the rotation is equal to twice the rotational frequency. In nonlinear molecules the simple rotational frequencies appear in addition to the double rotational frequencies. The vibration–rotation spectrum is due to the rotation of the polarizability change caused by the vibration. The structure arising in this way has been studied only in a few examples.

10.16   THE ISOTOPE EFFECT   Even if both the infrared spectrum and the Raman spectrum of a molecule are investigated, a number of molecular frequencies may not be found. For instance benzene has 20 normal vibrations. Of these, all but four are forbidden in the infrared spectrum, and only seven may appear in the Raman effect. All the predicted frequencies have been observed and identified and are in agreement with the presence of a center of symmetry. The Raman frequencies are never duplicated in the infrared spectrum. But even so only 11 of the 20 frequencies are found. The remaining nine vibrations are forbidden in both infrared and Raman spectra. Though in other molecules all normal frequencies may be obtained from the spectra, this is as a rule not sufficient to obtain all the elastic constants of a molecule. In order to find out the restoring forces arising from all the possible distortions of the molecule, it is necessary to know, in addition to all frequency values, the specific forms of the vibrations associated with each frequency. Information about the elastic constants of a molecule, though perhaps not so fundamental as the knowledge of the equilibrium positions, will probably prove increasingly helpful in the discussion of reaction mechanisms.

Measurement of molecular spectra in which certain atoms have been replaced by isotopes not only makes it possible to test the validity of an interpretation of Raman and infrared spectra but also offers the additional data needed for finding the form of molecular vibrations and elastic constants of the molecule. It has been mentioned in section 4.4 that substitution of isotopes does not affect the interaction of atoms and therefore does not change the force constants. But by altering the masses participating in the vibrations, we produce a change in frequency. It is easily seen how such frequency-changes can be used to obtain information about the form of a vibration. If for instance an atom remains at rest during a normal vibration, substitution of this atom by an isotope does not change the frequency. The more strongly the substituted atom participates in a vibration, the greater will be the resulting frequency change.

Isotopic substitution may effectively destroy molecular symmetry, and it may thus cause the appearance of previously forbidden frequencies. Lastly, simple rules exist concerning the ratio of products of frequencies before and after substitution. The exact form of these rules depends on molecular symmetry, and thus the rules can be used to verify assumed symmetries.

10.17   THE VIBRATIONAL SPECIFIC HEAT   One of the most striking proofs that classical mechanics cannot be applied to inner-molecular processes without some modification is obtained from the fact that at low temperatures vibrations do not contribute to the specific heat. According to quantum theory, this is to be expected since, as long as kT is small compared to the quantum $h\nu$ of the vibration, the excitation of a vibrational quantum is very improbable. If, on the other hand, the temperature is sufficiently high so that kT is great compared to $h\nu$, many vibrational quanta are, as a rule, excited. Then the correspondence principle is applicable, and the classical value of k per vibrational degree of freedom (or R per vibrational degree of freedom in a mole of the substance) is obtained for the specific heat. For intermediate temperatures quantum statistical calculations give, for the contribution to the specific heat by a harmonic oscillator c_ν,

$$c_\nu = k \left(\frac{x}{\sinh x} \right)^2 \qquad 10.17(1)$$

Here, x stands for $h\nu/2kT$, ν is the frequency of the harmonic oscillator, and the hyperbolic sine (sinh) is the function $\frac{1}{2}(e^x - e^{-x})$.

In a polyatomic molecule each normal vibration contributes a term c_ν, according to formula 10.17(1), to the specific heat. In each case one has to substitute for ν the frequency of the normal vibration in question. Two- or threefold-degenerate normal vibrations must be counted as two or three normal vibrations of the same frequency. In a solid it is necessary to sum over the very great number of different vibrations.

At low temperatures, x in equation 10.17(1) becomes great, sinh x increases exponentially, and the vibrational contribution to the specific heat approaches zero as an exponential function. This exponential behavior is characteristic of the vibrational specific heat of molecules. In solids the acoustical branch contains some vibrations of arbitrarily small frequencies. Thus for any given low temperature there exist a number of vibrations for which the ratio x is unity or smaller. These vibrations contribute to the specific heat amounts roughly equal to k, whereas vibrations of higher frequencies give diminishing contributions, which, as the frequency increases, can soon be neglected. In solids we find therefore that at low temperatures the specific heat is proportional to the number of vibrations whose quanta are comparable to kT or are smaller. This number, and with it the specific heat, varies at low temperatures as T^3.

The measurement of specific heats is useful in giving additional information about vibrational frequencies. In many solids specific heat furnishes until now the only available information about vibrations. But, owing to the rather gradual variation of equation 10.17(1), specific-heat measurements are not apt to yield very accurate values of the frequencies, and it is necessary to know the specific heat over a considerable temperature range to obtain useful information.

Specific heats of gases may help to establish molecular frequencies. The vibrations of ethylene may be quoted as an example. This molecule has 12 normal vibrations of which six are permitted in the Raman effect while five are infrared-active. The 12th vibration consisting of a torsion of the two CH_2 groups about the double-bond axis is forbidden in both spectra. The specific heat has been used to estimate the frequency of this vibration. A value of 750 or 800 wave numbers was obtained for the frequency on this basis. It was verified later by interpreting weak lines in the infrared and Raman spectra * that the value 800 cm.$^{-1}$ is approximately correct.

Data about specific heats of a very great number of gases have been obtained from the measurement of sound velocities. These data are unreliable unless cognizance is taken of the fact that often the period of the sound is too short for the vibrational energy to get into equilibrium with the translational and rotational energies.

As soon as the vibrational frequencies of a molecule are known, the vibrational specific heat can be accurately calculated. For highest accuracy one must take into account the effects of anharmonicity and of the interaction between vibration and rotation. Knowledge of the accurate specific heats is needed in calculations of thermodynamical properties and of chemical equilibria. Comparison with the experiments makes it then possible to check any assumptions which may have entered in the calculations. For instance, the question of free rotation in ethane has been elucidated by using data on specific heats and also by considering the $C_2H_4 + H_2 \rightleftarrows C_2H_6$ equilibrium. It was found that the forces opposing torsion of the CH_3 groups are considerable, so that barriers of about 3 Kcal. ($\frac{1}{8}$ electron volt) restrict internal rotation. Of course these barriers are still sufficiently low to permit fast interconversion of any isomers which may be constructed from appropriately deuterized ethane. So in the sense of structural chemistry, though by no means in the sense of physics, the rotation may be considered free.

* Although the torsion vibration cannot occur as a permitted fundamental frequency, its first overtone may occur in the Raman spectrum, and the fundamental frequency shows up as a weak forbidden band in the infrared. The presence of this weak band is probably due to interaction of the vibration with the rotation of the molecules.

11. ELECTRONIC SPECTRA

11.1 ATOMIC SPECTRA Although the electronic motion in atoms is in principle capable of exact treatment, the problem is in practice hopelessly complicated. The relative simplicity of the spectra involving nuclear vibrations is due to the small amplitudes of these motions. On the other hand, the motion of the electrons extends over the whole atom. Only in one particular case, namely, that of the hydrogen atom, has a complete solution been obtained in a simple way. But for other atoms, where the number of interacting particles exceeds two, mathematical experience has shown that no simple solutions are to be expected.

The interpretation of atomic spectra nevertheless has been possible by using a semiempirical procedure. Three circumstances facilitate such an analysis: (1) The high symmetry of the atoms makes it possible to give a rigorous classification of atomic states and to establish selection rules for the transitions between these states. (2) By making simplifying assumptions some of which are rather drastic, a complete system of atomic levels can be obtained which though admittedly crude, has proved useful. (3) By varying external conditions, for instance, by applying a magnetic field, experimental information can be obtained about the nature of an atomic line so that in the analysis of the spectrum one has a more reliable guidance than quantitative comparisons with crude calculations.

11.2 SYMMETRY PROPERTIES OF ATOMIC STATES The potential acting within an atom depends only on the relative positions of the constituent particles. The problem of finding the inner-atomic motions is therefore the same whatever the orientation of the co-ordinate system in which the atomic motion is described. In this sense the problem of inner-atomic motion is spherically symmetrical. Of course, it does not follow that each solution of the problem, that is, each atomic state, is spherically symmetrical.

The co-ordinate system in which the motion of electrons within the atom is to be described can be changed not merely by a rotation but also by reflection; such reflection will not change the form of the problem any more than a rotation. Actually it is unnecessary to consider all possible reflections. It is sufficient to take into account reflection in the center of symmetry which involves replacement of the x, y, and z co-ordinates by $-x$, $-y$, and $-z$. This inversion together with all rotations permits the construction of every symmetry operation which leaves the problem of inner-atomic motion invariant.

The systematization of all symmetry operations, the classification of atomic states made possible by the symmetry, and finally the common properties of atomic states belonging to one symmetry class are treated in group theory. We have discussed simple applications of group theory in connection with the simple vibrations of polyatomic molecules. In that case, normal vibrations rather than quantum states were classified according to symmetry. The selection rules which we have obtained from the molecular symmetry are among the properties investigated usually by group-theoretical methods. We shall not give here the mathematical details of group theory nor its application to atomic spectra, but shall restrict ourselves to the presentation of simple results and their connection with other facts of atomic physics.

The classification of atomic states according to symmetry is twofold. First, with respect to inversion (reflection in the center of mass) the wave function describing the state may be either symmetrical or anti-symmetrical. In the first case the wave function remains unchanged if the signs of all co-ordinates are reversed. In the second case the wave function changes its sign when the same operation is carried out. States whose wave functions are symmetrical or antisymmetrical with regard to the center are called, respectively, even and odd states. The property of a state of being even or odd is called the parity of the state. The difference between even and odd states cannot be interpreted in an immediate intuitive manner in classical theory. But the distinction between these states is of great importance in selection rules.

Second, we must consider the classification of the atomic states with respect to rotations. This classification is closely connected with a classical property: each atomic state is characterized by its angular momentum. In fact, angular momentum of a system is conserved as long as there are no external fields which disturb the spherical symmetry, and classification with respect to rotational symmetry is rigorously valid under the same conditions.

If at first the spin of the electrons is disregarded, the angular momentum may have only the values zero or an integer multiple of $h/2\pi$. In this respect atomic proper functions behave in the same way as the simple proper functions describing the electronic motion in the hydrogen atom. There we have seen that the angular momentum may have the values zero (s states), $h/2\pi$ (p states), $2h/2\pi$ (d states), $3h/2\pi$ (f states), and so on. States relating to a whole atom rather than to a single electron are called S, P, D, F states if the corresponding angular momenta are 0, 1, 2, 3 times the "quantum" of angular momentum $h/2\pi$. In close analogy to the spherically symmetrical s states of hydrogen, the S states of an atom remain unchanged under any rotation. The ground states of all rare-gas alkali and alkaline-earth atoms are S states. The P states are threefold degenerate just as the p states in hydrogen. Under the influence of rotation these degenerate states transform among each other in the same way as the three degenerate p states of hydrogen. In fact, the transformation properties of the P states are due to the spherical symmetry rather than to any special property of the hydrogen problem. Thus these transformation properties persist as long as there is spherical symmetry. In a like manner D, F, etc., states behave like d, f, etc., states of hydrogen. The degree of degeneracy is 5, 7, etc., for these states, respectively, and the degenerate states transform as in the case of hydrogen. There is just one difference between the symmetry of the hydrogen states and that of the states of higher atoms. In hydrogen all states with an even angular momentum (s, d, $\cdots$) are even with respect to inversion, and all states with odd angular momenta (p, f, $\cdots$) are odd.* In higher atoms there exist both even and odd S states, even and odd P states, and so on.

If the spin of the electrons is taken into account, we find that the total angular momentum (including the spin angular momentum) can have the values $\frac{1}{2}$, $\frac{3}{2}$, $\frac{5}{2}$, etc., in units of $h/2\pi$ whenever the number of electrons is odd.† The half-integer values of the angular momentum are due to the fact that the spin of the electron itself is $\frac{1}{2}h/2\pi$. The states with angular momenta $\frac{1}{2}$, $\frac{3}{2}$, etc., are 2-fold, 4-fold, etc., degenerate. The transformation properties of these degenerate states under the influence of rotations are somewhat more complicated than those of the states with integer values of angular momentum. If the atom contains an even number of electrons, the angular momentum can be shown to be an integral multiple of $h/2\pi$. In that case the degree of degeneracy and the transformation properties are the same as for S, P, D, etc., states.

The selection rules regulating transitions between these states are analogous to certain selection rules discussed in the previous chapter. We have seen that in molecules possessing a center of symmetry only such vibrations could appear in the infrared spectrum as are antisymmetrical to the center. The corresponding selection rule in terms of

---

* A similar statement is true for rotational states of simple diatomic molecules. This will be of importance in the theory of ortho and para hydrogen.

† The possible presence of a nuclear spin is left out of account here. If present it manifests itself only in the appropriately named hyperfine structure.

atomic states is that only transitions between even and odd states are permitted, but all transitions between even and even or odd and odd states are forbidden.

In the infrared-rotational and vibrational–rotational spectra of diatomic molecules we have seen that the angular momentum can change only by 1 or -1. In the vibrational–rotational spectrum of polyatomic linear molecules, transitions accompanied by no change of angular momentum were also permitted. It can be shown that general symmetry arguments exclude all other changes of angular momenta in absorption or emission spectra for atoms or molecules. Thus transitions between states with the angular momenta 0 and 1, 1 and 2, 2 and 3, 1 and 1, 2 and 2, etc. (all angular momenta measured in units $h/2\pi$) are allowed, whereas for instance a transition between states with angular momenta 0 and 2 is forbidden. There is only one additional selection rule; a transition cannot occur between two states with zero angular momenta. The reason for this rule is that, if the angular momentum is zero, the state is spherically symmetrical. The transition between two spherically symmetrical states may be considered as a pulsation of a spherically symmetrical charge distribution, and, according to classical electrodynamics, such a pulsation does not emit any radiation.

The selection rules concerning parity and angular momentum are due to symmetry with regard to reflections and rotations. Therefore these selection rules may be violated if the symmetry is temporarily impaired by collisions. The fact that the analogous selection rules in vibrational spectra concern infrared transitions which are due to dipole radiations indicates that the atomic transitions previously discussed are due to an effect similar to the absorption and emission of radiation by a vibrating dipole. The usual theory of optical transition probabilities is based on a generalization of this dipole radiation. But in connection with the extremely weak infrared spectrum of N_2, section 10.6, we have pointed out that radiation may be emitted or absorbed by a vibrating quadrupole. Weak transitions in atomic spectra are produced by quadrupole radiation and further types of radiation. For such kinds of radiation different selection rules operate.

The interpretation of observed atomic frequencies in terms of differences between energy levels leads to a knowledge of the energy states of the atom. The application of selection rules makes it possible to find out the symmetry properties of the energy levels. The goal of the analysis is the knowledge of the energy values and symmetry properties, but the analysis would be very hard to carry out without the use of supplementary theoretical considerations and experimental devices.

11.3 ATOMIC MODELS The same crude description of atomic proper functions which we have used in connection with the periodic system is also the one employed in the classification of atomic states. In this simplified atomic model we shall at first disregard the spins of the electrons. As a further simplification we assume that there are no phase relations between the motions of the electrons and that each of them moves in the field produced by the charge of the nucleus and the average field of the other electrons. This simplification is equivalent in quantum theory to the assumption that the wave function can be written as a product of wave functions of the separate electrons. We finally introduce the simplification that the field in which each separate electron moves is spherically symmetrical; if the actual average field of the remaining electrons does not fulfill this requirement, we take the average of that field over all orientations before employing it in further calculations. The model just described is called the Hartree model.

Since in this model each electron moves in a spherically symmetrical field, each has a definite orbital angular momentum and is accordingly described as an s, p, d, etc., electron, the small letters emphasizing that the notation is used for single electrons. The s states of which an electron is capable are numbered with increasing energy giving $1s$, $2s$, $3s$, etc., states. These symbols have been used for the hydrogen orbits and also for the hydrogen-like orbits in higher atoms. The present definition remains valid even if the orbits are very unlike the hydrogen orbits, but it coincides with the previous definition whenever the orbits resemble those in the hydrogen atom. A similar notation is introduced for the p orbits, but to preserve the correspondence with the hydrogen notation we start with $2p$, $3p$, etc. For the same reason the lowest d state is called $3d$.

From the angular momenta of the separate electrons, the total angular momentum of the atom can be composed. The rules of this procedure may be described in terms of classical mechanics: one replaces each angular momentum with a vector of a length proportional to the absolute value of the angular momentum. The total angular momentum is obtained by arranging the angular-momentum vectors of the electrons in arbitrary directions and then adding these vectors. But the restriction is imposed that the resultant vector must be again an integral multiple of $h/2\pi$ or else zero. If, for instance, we have a d and a p electron with angular momenta $2\dfrac{h}{2\pi}$ and $\dfrac{h}{2\pi}$, we obtain for the vector sum the values $3\dfrac{h}{2\pi}$, $2\dfrac{h}{2\pi}$, and $\dfrac{h}{2\pi}$. These correspond to an F, a D, and a P state

This vector-addition rule may be derived rigorously by group-theoretical methods. As long as the Pauli exclusion principle need not be considered, the results are the same as those obtained from the simple vector picture.

We use as the symbol of an atomic state the product of the symbols for the single electronic states composing it and add the symmetry symbol of the atomic state as a whole. Thus the lowest state of the carbon atom is written $(1s)^2(2s)^2(2p)^2P_g$. Here $(1s)^2$ stands for the product of two $1s$ functions and indicates the presence of two electrons in the K shell. Similar statements hold for $(2s)^2$ and $(2p)^2$. The symbol P shows that the total angular momentum is one (in units of $h/2\pi$) which is one of the possible results if the angular-momentum vectors of four s electrons and two p electrons are added. The subscript g indicates that the atomic state is even. (An odd atomic state would be indicated by the subscript u.) That the state in question is even is due to the fact that, apart from the s electrons each of which has an even wave function, the atom contains two p electrons which according to previous statements are odd. But the product of two antisymmetrical functions is symmetrical, and so the product of two odd functions gives an even state.

The symbols $(1s)^2$ and $(2s)^2$ prescribe in an unambiguous way the product of the indicated electronic wave-functions. On the other hand, the expression $(2p)^2$ leaves the question open which of the three degenerate p states or which linear combination of such states each electron occupies. Actually the symbol $(2p)^2$ is somewhat misleading, because according to the somewhat involved quantum theory of the vector-addition rule we cannot construct a state of definite angular momentum (for instance a P state) by ascribing to each p electron a definite wave function and taking the product. It is necessary to construct a sum of products; for instance to obtain a P state, we may place the first electron in a p_x state and multiply it by the p_y * wave function of the second electron, then take the p_y state of the first electron and multiply it by the p_x function of the second electron, and take the difference of these products. In this way we obtain one of the degenerate P states and more particularly a state which in analogy to the notation just used we should call P_z. Linear combinations of products such as have just been described amount no longer to independent motions of the electrons but rather to motions with some definite phase relation. This is so because the square of the total wave function giving the probability of the different electron configurations is no longer the product of the squares of single electron-

---

* The p_x and p_y states are similar to the states which have been designated in section 2.2 by $(2x)$ and $(2y)$.

wave functions and therefore can no longer be written as the product of independent probabilities. The three atomic states,

$$(1s)^2(2s)^2(2p)^2S$$

$$(1s)^2(2s)^2(2p)^2P$$

$$(1s)^2(2s)^2(2p)^2D$$

which according to the vector-addition rule can arise from the $(1s)^2(2s)^2(2p)^2$ electron configuration, differ in energy owing to the different phase relations of the $2p$ electrons in the S, P, and D states. However, the linear combinations and the resulting phase relations and energies cannot be discussed without at the same time the Pauli exclusion principle being taken into account. This principle eliminates all states which are not antisymmetrical with regard to the interchange of any pair of electrons, and for this reason not all states appear which can be obtained from the vector-addition rule. The influence of the Pauli principle, as we have seen, is further modified by the presence of the electronic spin. We shall return shortly to a brief discussion of the spin effects.

The possibility of exciting one of several electrons in an atomic spectrum together with the several ways in which the angular-momentum vectors of the electrons can be combined into a resultant atomic angular momentum accounts for the great number of atomic states in the so-called complex spectra. The possible electronic transitions increase even faster than the number of electronic states, so that the complexity, for instance, of the iron spectrum is not surprising.

One class of spectra, namely, the one-electron spectra of the alkalies is by contrast quite simple. Here all electrons except one are in a closed shell, and the visible and near ultraviolet parts of the spectra are due to transition between states of the last loosely bound electron, called the valence electron. A further simplification arises from the fact that the electrons of the core (that is all electrons except the valence electron) form a closed shell which has the total angular momentum zero and produces a spherically symmetrical field. Thus the angular momentum of the atom will be equal to the angular momentum of the valence electron. Let us consider, for instance, the sodium atom. Its lowest electron configuration is $(1s)^2(2s)^2(2p)^6(3s)$. The two electrons in $(1s)^2$ fill the K shell; the eight electrons in $(2s)^2(2p)^6$ fill the L shell. The six nonspherical wave functions of the p electrons are oriented and combined in such a way as to form a spherically symmetrical total wave function. The addition of the $3s$ electron in the M shell still leaves a zero angular momentum so that an S atomic state results. The first excited state has a $(1s)^2(2s)^2(2p)^6(3p)$ electron configuration, and corresponding to the angular momentum of the $(3p)$ valence electron a P state is obtained. The parity of the atomic states is also equal to the parity of the valence electrons. This is so because the closed shell forming the core has an even parity. Thus, for these spectra S, D, etc., states are even, and P, F, etc., states are odd. According to the parity-selection rule $P–P$, $D–D$, etc., transitions are forbidden, and the orbital angular momentum must change by ±1 in each electronic transition. This same result can be obtained by a crude intuitive method. In alkali spectra the core, being totally symmetrical and essentially unaffected by electronic transitions in the usual spectral regions, can be considered (nucleus included) as one particle. Then the structure of the alkali atom in its various states can be considered as a two-body problem. We have encountered a two-body problem in the vibration–rotation spectra of diatomic molecules. In the alkali spectra as in the infrared vibration–rotation spectrum of a diatomic molecule, changes of orbital angular momentum by ±1 occur, but no transition is found in which the angular momentum remains unchanged.

We have seen that phase relations between electrons are not provided for in the simple scheme of the Hartree model, but they have to be taken into account if energy differences are to be obtained between atomic states belonging to the same electron configuration. To describe such phase relations, the wave function must be written as a sum of products; if, for instance, we consider a state of carbon $(1s)^2(2s)^2(2p)^2$, then each term in the sum contains two factors which are $1s$ functions, two factors which are $2s$ functions, and two factors which are $2p$ functions. The wave functions obtained by limiting ourselves to these factors are approximate solutions. The exact solution can always be written as the sum of products of single-electron wave-functions, but products belonging to all electron configurations must be used; in addition to the terms of the type $(1s)^2$ $(2s)^2$ $(2p)^2$, other terms will occur such as $(1s)^2$ $(2s)$ $(2p)^2$ $(3d)$. The simplification in the Hartree model lies in the neglect of all but one of these electron configurations. In the alkali spectra this is an excellent approximation. The exact proper function of alkali atoms would include terms in which electrons of the core are shifted into higher shells. But the great energy needed for such excitation makes the contribution of such terms to the wave function insignificant. On the other hand, in the complex spectra where the excitation energy of several electrons is approximately equal, the Hartree model leads to less reliable results (compare section 3.8).

11.4 THE INFLUENCE OF SPIN The physical interaction between electron spin and electronic motion is due to magnetic forces

The effect of these forces depends on the electronic velocity and remains small as long as the electronic velocity is small compared to light velocity. For lighter atoms this is always the case, and the interaction between electron spin and electron orbits can be neglected in first approximation. The influence of the spin on the symmetry types and energies of atomic states is nevertheless great. The wave function may often be written in the absence of forces between spin and orbit as a product of wave functions depending on position and on spin alone. The atomic energy depends only on the factor containing electronic positions. But, according to the Pauli principle, the factor depending on the positions is symmetrical or antisymmetrical with regard to the interchange of two electrons according to whether the spin factor is antisymmetrical or symmetrical with regard to the same operation. It may happen that the Pauli principle is satisfied in a more complicated way in that the total wave function is a sum of spin- and position-dependent products in which no factor is completely symmetrical or antisymmetrical. Thus, while the total wave function simply changes sign whenever two electrons are interchanged, the effect of this operation on the part depending on positions alone may be more complicated. This more complicated behavior has been discussed fully in terms of group theory. Only this time the operations whose effect on the wave function is studied are not reflections and rotations but permutations of the electrons.

The result of this discussion can be summarized in two simple statements: (1) Owing to the antisymmetry of the total wave function the permutation properties of the positional factor are determined by the permutation properties of the spin factor. (2) The permutation properties of the spin factor are characterized by the value of the angular momentum resulting from a vector summation of the individual spins. Therefore we need discuss only this resultant spin momentum.

The maximum possible value of the total spin angular momentum is $\frac{1}{2}h/2\pi$ (which is the spin of one electron) times the number of electrons. Other possible values differ from the maximum value by integral multiples of $h/2\pi$. Thus the spin angular momentum of two electrons may be $h/2\pi$ or 0. For the value of this angular momentum in units of $h/2\pi$, the notation * S is used. For two electrons we have $S = 1$ and $S = 0$, and the possible values for three electrons are $S = \frac{3}{2}$ and $S = \frac{1}{2}$. For $S = 0$, the spin-dependent wave function is not degenerate. For $S = \frac{1}{2}$ there is a twofold degeneracy, for $S = 1$ a threefold degeneracy.†

* This is the same letter as is used for the symbol of a state with orbital angular momentum zero. It is easy to distinguish from the context in which sense S is used.

† In general, we have a $(2S + 1)$-fold degeneracy.

Accordingly, states with $S = 0$ are called singlet states, those with $S = \frac{1}{2}$ doublet states, those with $S = 1$ triplet states, etc. The property of a state being a singlet, doublet, etc., state is called its multiplicity. The multiplicity is indicated by an index on the upper left-hand side of the letter $(S, P, D, \cdots)$ giving the total orbital angular momentum of the electrons within the atom. For instance, the ground state of the carbon atom is a triplet; this state is written in the form $(1s)^2(2s)^2(2p)^2 \, {}^3P_g$. Actually even this symbol does not characterize the atomic state completely. The spin angular momentum S and the orbital momentum called L may still be oriented with regard to each other in an arbitrary manner giving various values to the total angular momentum J. The energy difference of states belonging to the same electron configuration, to the same S and L values but to different J values, is due to the actual physical forces acting on the spins within the atom. These energy differences are small in light elements resulting in a close multiplet of states. For hydrogen, the multiplet separations are less than 1 cm.$^{-1}$ But for heavy atoms where electrons have high velocities whenever they come close to the highly charged nucleus, multiplet separations become as great as 10,000 cm.$^{-1}$ When the multiplet separation becomes comparable to the electrostatic energies within an atom, the justification for writing the wave function as a product of positional and of spin factors falls down. Then it becomes inadmissible to assign definite values to the spin and orbital angular momenta, and the so-called L–S coupling which has been discussed previously is no longer valid. But the total angular momentum J still retains its significance. The atom still possesses a definite total angular momentum as long as the rotational symmetry of the problem as described in section 11.2, is preserved.

There exists an important connection between the multiplicity of a state and the way in which electronic orbits are filled. We shall now give a few illustrations. If the spins of two electrons form a singlet state $(S = 0)$, then the wave function changes its sign when the spins of the electrons are interchanged. It follows, according to the Pauli principle, that the orbital part of the wave function retains its sign if one exchanges the positions of the electrons. Indeed, simultaneous exchange of spin and positions is equivalent to the interchange of all properties characterizing the electrons, and, according to the Pauli principle, such interchange must invert the sign of the wave function.

When two electrons form a triplet state, their wave function is a symmetrical function of the spins; that is, interchange of the spins leaves the wave function unchanged. Then the Pauli principle demands that the wave function be antisymmetrical with respect to exchange of the positions of the two electrons.

A consequence of the previous statement is that, when two electrons are found in the same orbit, their spin state must be a singlet. Only if the two electrons occupy different orbits can their spins form a triplet. In general n electrons may add up their spins to a total value $S = n/2$. This is, however, possible only if all the n electrons occupy different orbits. One more rule is of great help in interpreting spectra. If a number of electrons form a closed shell, their spin momenta have to cancel and form a singlet state $(S = 0)$. The same holds for the n orbital momenta, and we also have $L = 0$. Thus a closed shell may always be disregarded when orbital and spin momenta of an atom are investigated.

It may be of interest to mention that in the heaviest atoms a different kind of coupling is frequently employed with success. The spin of each electron is coupled to its orbital momentum l giving the total angular momentum j of the single electron. Then the j values are coupled to give the atomic angular momentum J. Of course, whenever angular momenta are coupled, that must be done according to the rules of vector addition.

11.5 APPROXIMATE SELECTION RULES The exact selection rules given in section 11.2 refer to the parity and to the total angular momentum J. According to this rule, changes in J by two or more units are forbidden, and in addition transitions between two states $J = 0$ are also prohibited. If as assumed in the previous section the interaction between spin angular momentum S and orbital angular momentum L is weak, then less strict selection rules are valid for S and L separately.

The first of these rules is that in an electronic transition the spin angular momentum S must not change. This rule can be made plausible in the following way. The electronic spin interacts with the radiation field only through its magnetic moment, and this magnetic interaction is weak compared to the electric coupling between the radiation and the atom. At the same time it has been assumed that only small forces act on the spin within the atom. In the absence of strong forces we would not expect the spin to change. We can indeed show in quantum theory that, in the absence of forces acting on the spin, only such transitions occur in which the spin-dependent factor of the wave function remains unchanged. This means that the relative orientation of the individual spin vectors and the resultant angular momentum S do not change during the transition.

It was stated that certain permutation properties of the positional part of the wave function are associated with each spin value. Since S remains constant, it follows that the permutation properties of the positional factor of the wave function must not change in a transition. This rule is similar to the more rigorous statement requiring the total (positional and spin) wave function to remain antisymmetrical with regard to interchange of electron pairs if this antisymmetry was originally established. However, the conservation of antisymmetry and the Pauli principle is due to the identity of the electrons and is not based on the neglect of the spin forces. Thus the permanence of the Pauli principle is an exact law while the selection rule forbidding changes in S is only approximately valid.

The selection rule that the value of S, or in other words the multiplicity, must not change is very well satisfied for the lightest atoms where the forces acting on the spin are practically negligible. In helium the spins of the two electrons give rise to $S = 0$ or singlet states, or $S = 1$ or triplet states. Transitions between singlet and triplet states are so excessively weak that they remained undetected for a long time. The systems of singlet and triplet levels were thus practically independent, and they were said to belong to two different atomic species called para-helium ($S = 0$) and ortho-helium ($S = 1$). Later, evidence for a weak intercombination between the two systems was found. In heavy atoms transitions involving a change in multiplicity which are also in this case called intercombinations occur with much greater intensity. The familiar mercury line with the wavelength of 2537 Å. is due to a transition between singlet and triplet states.

The approximate selection rules for L are exactly analogous to the rigorous rules for J. Thus the possible changes in L are limited to ± 1 and to zero, and in addition no transition can occur between two S states. This rule is valid only as long as forces acting on the spins may be disregarded. Thus for heavy atoms the rule becomes less rigid.

If the Hartree model were strictly valid, further intensity rules would follow. Strong transitions could then occur only between states whose electron configuration differs only in the quantum number of one electron. The orbital angular momentum of this electron would have to change by ± 1. In transition elements where the Hartree model is often entirely inapplicable this last rule is not very useful.

11.6 THE ZEEMAN EFFECT If an electric or magnetic field is applied to atoms, the spherical symmetry on which the strict quantization of angular momentum was based is now removed. At the same time in states with J different from zero the reason for degeneracy ceases to operate. Indeed for $J \neq 0$, the state itself cannot be considered as spherical, and degeneracy arises from the equal energy of states differing in orientation only. In external fields, however, different orientations may have different energies, and the degenerate electronic levels split.*

The effect of magnetic fields on atomic spectra is more marked, easier to study, and was discovered earlier than the effect of electric fields. This may seem surprising in view of the fact that magnetic forces are v/c times smaller (v = electron velocity, c = light velocity) than electric forces. But partly because of this same fact, production of strong magnetic fields is much easier than production of strong electric fields. In the latter fields, electrical breakdown is difficult to avoid while no phenomenon of magnetic breakdown is known. There is a further reason why the magnetic effect is more readily observable. The interaction of the atom with a homogeneous field is in first approximation caused by the permanent electric or magnetic moment of the atom while induced moments cause only second-order effects. Now we have seen in section 5.2 that atoms do not have permanent electric dipoles,† while as a rule they do have permanent magnetic dipoles whenever J is different from zero. Thus magnetic fields give rise to first-order effects, whereas the effect of electric fields appears only in second approximation. We shall limit our present discussion to the magnetic or Zeeman effect, and we shall not consider the electric or Stark effect.

The splitting of degenerate levels in a magnetic field may produce rather complicated patterns in the spectra, particularly if a splitting has occurred in both the initial and final state. The number of resulting lines is, however, considerably reduced by selection rules which this time regulate the changes in the component of angular momentum about the direction of the magnetic field rather than the changes in the total angular momentum. A discussion of the selection rules will not be given here.

The reason for the complicated appearance of Zeeman patterns is the different magnetic behavior of spin angular momentum and orbital angular momentum. Both angular momenta are associated with magnetic moments but the ratio of angular momentum and magnetic moment is twice as great for the orbital motion as for the spin. Thus the orienting forces have a different effect on orbit and spin which may manifest itself in various ways in the spectrum but leads most often to a rather complicated structure. These complicated Zeeman patterns are known under the name of anomalous Zeeman effect, whereas the simple patterns which result in some special cases are called normal Zeeman effects. In each case, however, the Zeeman effect permits us

---

* In homogeneous electric fields not all the degeneracy is removed.

† There is an exception to this rule; in excited states of hydrogen, degeneracy of the s, p, and sometimes further states may give rise to an effective electric dipole.

to draw valuable conclusions about the angular momenta and also the multiplicities of the combining levels. In many cases the multiplicity is already known from the appearance of the fine structure of multiplets which in the absence of an external magnetic field are due primarily to the interaction of spin and orbital magnetic moments within the atom. With the further help of models and selection rules of which the most important ones have been treated in the previous sections, a rather detailed interpretation of almost all atomic spectra has been achieved.

11.7 ELECTRONIC STATES IN DIATOMIC MOLECULES It has been shown that the motion of particles within molecules can be described rather accurately by treating electronic and nuclear motions separately: (1) The electrons are considered as moving in the field of fixed nuclei; (2) the motion of the nuclei proceeds in the average field produced by electrons (see section 4.1). The electronic spectra of diatomic molecules may be obtained in the roughest approximation by considering the nuclear positions as fixed and allowing the electrons to move in their field. This problem is considered in the present section. We shall see later that on the electronic frequencies a vibrational and rotational structure is superimposed in a somewhat similar way as has been discussed in the infrared spectrum where rotational frequencies have modified the vibrational spectrum.

The electronic states of diatomic molecules are classified, and selection rules are obtained according to principles similar to those used for obtaining electronic states of the atoms. A part of this classification has already been described in connection with the electronic structure of ground states in diatomic molecules.

First, it is necessary to study the behavior of the electronic wave functions under the influence of the molecular symmetry. Second, we may again separate orbital and spin motion and introduce a further classification based on the properties of the wave functions, depending on the position and on the spin of the electrons. We shall discuss, for molecules, only that case where separation of spin motion and orbital motion is permissible. This simplifies the description since it is then necessary to consider the effect of molecular symmetry on the orbital motion of the electrons alone, rather than on the complete wave function depending on spins and position. In the following the electronic spins will be disregarded in discussing the effects of molecular symmetry. As in atomic spectra, this procedure is justified only as long as no heavy nuclei are present.

When comparing atomic states with states of diatomic molecules, we find that the symmetry of the problem is much higher in the former case.

Diatomic molecules possess axial rather than spherical symmetry. The lower symmetry of diatomic molecules means fewer symmetry operations and simpler transformation properties of the wave function.

The primary classification of the states is made according to behavior with respect to rotations around the molecular axis. If a rotation through the angle φ is performed around that axis, the wave function is multiplied in general by $e^{i\Lambda\varphi}$ where Λ is an appropriate constant. This behavior is analogous to that of a wave function describing the state of a particle in the absence of forces. We have seen in that case that translation through a distance x multiplies the wave function by e^{ikx}. The quantity k is related to the momentum of the particle by the equation,

$$p = k\frac{h}{2\pi}$$ 11.7(1)

Similarly, Λ is related to the component of the angular momentum around the molecular axis M by the equation,

$$M = \Lambda\frac{h}{2\pi}$$ 11.7(2)

The simple transformation property expressed by the factor e^{ikx} holds as long as no forces act on the particle in the x direction, and the momentum of the particle in that direction is therefore conserved. Similarly, the transformation law $e^{i\Lambda\varphi}$ holds as long as the potential is cylindrical, so that no tangential forces act on an electron moving around the axis. In classical mechanics angular momentum around the axis is conserved under these conditions. The number Λ is actually the angular momentum measured in units of $h/2\pi$ and is called the quantum number of that angular momentum. Because of the requirement that the wave function shall remain unchanged by a complete rotation, Λ must be a positive or negative integer or else zero. Wave functions belonging to Λ-values with opposite sign can be transformed into each other by a reflection in an appropriate plane containing the molecular axis; this is so because the plane can be chosen in such a way that the reflection turns φ, the angle of rotation around the axis, into the angle $-\varphi$. Since the two wave functions belonging to Λ and $-\Lambda$ can be interchanged by reflection, they must correspond to the same energy; that is, we have a twofold necessary degeneracy. We can visualize the reason for this degeneracy by remembering that Λ and $-\Lambda$ belong to opposite angular momenta and therefore to electronic rotations in the opposite sense. Only if $\Lambda = 0$ is the electronic state nondegenerate.

The statements in the previous paragraph are quite analogous to statements made previously about single-electron wave functions. In the case of single electrons one usually denotes the quantum number of the angular momentum around the axis by λ. For the single electrons it is easy to use the number of nodes and their connection with the momentum to visualize the connection between λ and the angular momentum.

The letters Λ and λ are chosen to emphasize the parallelism with the angular-momentum quantum numbers, L and l; these letters are used in spherical fields to denote the quantum number of the angular momentum of the whole system and the angular-momentum quantum number of a single electron. This analogy is carried further by denoting molecular states having Λ values 0, ± 1, ± 2, ± 3, $\cdots$ with the symbols Σ, Π, Δ, ϕ, $\cdots$ For single electrons, the letters σ, π, δ, φ, $\cdots$ are used. The corresponding notations for angular momenta in spherical fields have been S, P, D, F, $\cdots$ and s, p, d, f, $\cdots$.

A further classification of the Σ states is required according to their behavior with regard to reflections in planes containing the molecular axis. There are wave functions which remain unchanged under such an operation. These are called Σ^+ states. Other wave functions change their sign and are called Σ^- states. If $\Lambda \neq 0$, no such further classification exists since reflection in planes containing the molecular axis merely interchanges the wave functions corresponding to $+\Lambda$ and $-\Lambda$. It is to be noted that single-electron σ functions always have σ^+ symmetry (and for this reason, the plus sign is omitted as redundant). In fact σ wave functions are independent of the angle φ and remain unchanged if φ is replaced by $-\varphi$. The more complicated symmetry Σ^- can occur only for a molecule containing at least two electrons. In this case the wave functions of the individual electrons may depend on φ, even if the total wave function remains unchanged under rotation.

For homonuclear molecules a further classification must be introduced. These molecules have a center of symmetry and, in analogy to the case of atoms, the subscript g or u is used to show whether a wave function is even or odd, with respect to reflection in the center.

For a more detailed characterization of molecular states we can again use the Hartree model. Angular-momentum and symmetry symbols are then assigned to single electrons, and the total wave function is written as the product of the single-electron wave functions. To that product the symbol of the resulting term must be added, since a mere statement about the angular momenta of the individual electrons does not show whether these angular momenta must be added or subtracted. Thus we obtain complex symbols such as $(\sigma_g)^2 \sigma_u (\pi_u)^2 \Delta_u$. This symbol means that the molecule contains two σ_g, one σ_u, and two π_u electrons. The angular momenta of the last two add up to give a Δ state. It is to be noted that, since all angular momenta are now parallel to the axis, they must be added and subtracted like numbers (rather than like vectors as was the case in the atoms). The rule that the total state is even or odd according to whether an even or odd number of odd electrons are present is the same for homonuclear molecules and for atoms. Of course, the same restrictions must be made about the validity of the Hartree model for molecules as was made for atoms. Thus, although the angular-momentum quantum number Λ of the whole system is a well-defined quantity, the same cannot be said in general about λ. In reality, each electron moves in the field of the nuclei and the other electrons, and this instantaneous field does not possess cylindrical symmetry. In practice, the Hartree model for molecules is even less valid than for atoms for which the great energy steps between closed shells was the chief reason for the success of the approximation.

Finally one has to add to each symbol representing a molecular wave function the multiplicity which, as in atoms, corresponds to the value of the sum of the spin angular momenta of the electrons. We have singlets, doublets, triplets, and so on, denoted by the numbers 1, 2, 3, $\cdots$ in the upper left corner of the symbol of the wave function (for instance $^1\Pi$ or $^2\Delta$). Singlets, doublets, triplets, $\cdots$ correspond to total spin values of 0, $\frac{1}{2}h/2\pi$, $h/2\pi$, $\cdots$.

11.8 CO-ORDINATION SCHEMES The classification of the states in diatomic molecules as given in the previous section is not so complete as the one we have described for atoms. In the latter each electron had in addition to its designation as s, p, d, $\cdots$ a principal quantum number designating the shell to which the electron belongs. A similar simple classification is not possible with molecules. Instead we characterize molecular states by their relation to atomic states which are obtained if the molecule is dissociated and to the atomic states which would be produced if the two nuclei were pushed together to form a single nucleus of higher charge. Since in the two cases of distant and united nuclei the possible atomic states are known, we can attempt to obtain the actual molecular states by interpolation.* We shall first consider electronic states as a whole, that is, without discussing in detail the transformations suffered by the individual electronic orbits.

The co-ordination of molecular states to states of the separated and united nuclei is governed by two rules. The first is that when the atomic distance is changed, the symmetry properties of the molecular state

* This procedure has been developed by Mulliken and by Hund.

must remain unchanged. The second is that two molecular states of the same symmetry must not have the same energy for any internuclear distance. The reason for the second rule is that the mathematical requirements of degeneracy are too exacting to be satisfied merely by changing one parameter, namely, the internuclear distance. Degeneracy can, however, be established (at least in the absence of magnetic forces) by adjusting two parameters. This is of importance in discussing the behavior of polyatomic molecules and collision complexes.

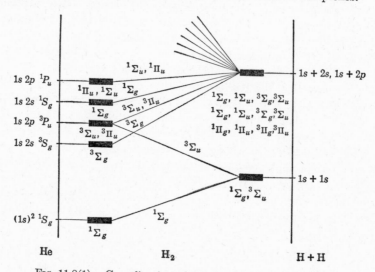

FIG. 11.8(1).   Co-ordination scheme for the hydrogen molecule.

In plotting the energy of a molecule for various internuclear distances, we always find, of course, that the energy goes to infinity when the nuclei approach each other. This is a consequence of the repulsion between the nuclei. In plotting co-ordination schemes we usually do not include the nuclear repulsion in order that this strong effect should not obscure the influence of the nuclear positions on the energy of the electrons.

The simplest example of a co-ordination scheme is obtained by comparing the energy levels of a hydrogen molecule with the energy levels of two separated hydrogen atoms and with that of a helium atom. A sketch of this co-ordination scheme is shown in Figure 11.8(1). On the left-hand side of the figure the lowest energy levels of the helium atom are marked. The electronic configurations are included. It may be seen that only such excited levels have been drawn which may be obtained by lifting one electron from the K into the L shell. The energy differences of the levels are not drawn to scale; the energy difference between the lowest level and the group of four upper levels is relatively even greater than shown in the figure. On the right-hand side of the figure we find a similar representation of the levels of two separated hydrogen atoms. Here the atomic symbols are replaced by symbols of the single hydrogen electrons. The first excited state is obtained by putting one of the hydrogen electrons in either a $2s$ or a $2p$ state. The state corresponding to two unexcited hydrogen atoms has been marked higher than the lowest state of the helium atom in order to indicate that it takes more energy to remove two electrons from a helium atom than to remove them from two hydrogen atoms. But here again the drawing is not made to scale in that the right hand of the figure should be shifted to considerably higher energies than has been done.

The first step in constructing a co-ordination scheme is to investigate what molecular-symmetry types may be obtained from the atomic-symmetry types corresponding to the two limiting cases. These symmetry types have been marked below the horizontal lines drawn next to the atomic symbols. It is simple to obtain the symmetry types on the left-hand side of the diagram; singlets give singlets, triplets give triplets, g and u states give g and u states, respectively, and the angular momentum around the molecular axis can have all values smaller than or equal to the angular momentum in the atom (for example, S gives Σ, P gives Π and $\Sigma \cdots$). The rules to be followed on the right-hand side of the diagram are more involved. Here, in addition to simple rules regulating the angular momentum, we must determine the multiplicity and the symmetry properties with regard to a center of symmetry which lies midway between the two atoms. This is done by considering the changes in the wave function brought about by an exchange of the electrons on the two atoms. We have seen in section 7.4 that two hydrogen atoms in the lowest state give a singlet and a triplet molecular state. One can show that the singlet is even and the triplet is odd. Both states are of course Σ states since the lowest hydrogen state has no angular momentum. The first excited state marked in Figure 11.8(1) gives rise to 12 different molecular states listed below the corresponding line. All the Σ levels indicated are Σ^+ levels, and so for simplicity the plus sign is omitted.

The energy levels for the hydrogen molecule are shown in the middle of the figure by the lines connecting the levels at the two ends. The abscissa corresponds to (but does not serve as a quantitative measure of) the internuclear distance. The method of construction is that one connects the lowest $^1\Sigma_g$ state on the left side with the lowest $^1\Sigma_g$ state on the right side. Then one connects the next $^1\Sigma_g$ state on both sides and so on for the various symmetry types. By this method intersections between unlike symmetry types can often not be avoided, and, in fact, there is no rule forbidding such intersections. One such intersection is seen on the left-hand side of the diagram, where the $^3\Sigma_g$ and the $^3\Sigma_u$ levels cross. Of course, since the lines are obtained by simple interpolation, the results cannot be quantitatively correct. For instance the $^1\Sigma_u$ and the $^1\Pi_u$ lines at the top of the figure have been drawn as coinciding simply because they are interpolated between the same levels. In reality these states will have different energies in H_2. The figure indicates why the lowest $^1\Sigma_g$ level is attractive while the lowest $^3\Sigma_u$ is repulsive. The former leads to a much more firmly bound helium level than the latter. The following four levels shown in the figure seem to be attractive since they behave similarly to $^1\Sigma_g$ in connecting hydrogen and helium levels of like degree of excitation. Further levels indicated on the upper right side of the diagram but not continued through to the helium side must lead to high helium states and are probably repulsive.

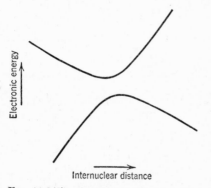

Fig. 11.8(2). Avoidance of intersection of two potential curves.

We may attempt to obtain a more detailed description of the molecular states by applying to each electron separately the same reasoning which has just been carried out for the molecule as a whole. The same rules can be applied for setting up electronic orbits in the two limiting cases and for interpolating between them. Again states of like symmetry must be connected, and again intersections of curves of like symmetry must be avoided. But it must be noted that these rules hold for individual electrons only approximately, because, as has been stated in the previous section, the symmetry classification for individual electrons is not rigorous. It may happen that through consideration of electronic orbits we are led to conclude that two molecular states of the same symmetry cross for a certain internuclear distance. In such cases the two energy levels in question usually approach each other but the intersection is avoided by a more or less sudden turn of the curves in which each curve approaches the continuation of the other one, Figure 11.8(2).

In Figure 11.8(3) the states of an electron in the field of two protons are obtained by interpolation. On the left-hand side the states of the He^+ ion are indicated, whereas on the right-hand side we have the states of the hydrogen atom which in this limiting case are uninfluenced by the distant H^+ ion. Near these extreme cases the symbols of the corresponding molecular symmetries appear. Near the limiting case of united nuclei the electronic symbol for the united atom is put down in front of the molecular symbol (for example, $1s\sigma_g$). This symbol is often used for a more complete characterization of an electronic orbit in the molecule. Less frequently the electronic state is characterized by the molecular-symmetry symbol which is followed by the symbol of the

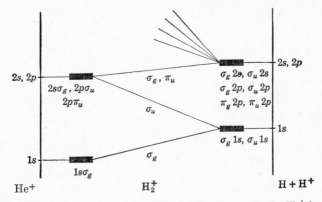

FIG. 11.8(3). Co-ordination scheme for the electron in the H_2^+ ion.

atomic orbit obtained by dissociation. This notation is shown close to the right side of the diagram.

We shall use the more common notation (including the electronic symbol for united nuclei) in discussing the energy levels of the hydrogen molecule in terms of the individual electronic levels shown in Figure 11.8(3). For a low energy-level, one electron will be always in the lowest, that is, $1s\sigma$ state. For the lowest level of the molecule we find the configuration $(1s\sigma)^2 \, {}^1\Sigma_g$. The configuration gives the singlet state because of the Pauli principle. Next we may put one electron into the $1s\sigma_g$ state and a second one into the $2p\sigma_u$ orbit. This configuration gives a $(1s\sigma_g)(2p\sigma_u)^3\Sigma_u$ and a $(1s\sigma_g)(2p\sigma_u)^1\Sigma_u$ state. The former is easily identified with the ${}^3\Sigma_u$ repulsive state of Figure 11.8(1). The second must be the ${}^1\Sigma_u$ level appearing on the top of the same figure. We see that the two methods of obtaining this ${}^1\Sigma_u$ level lead to rather different energy values for this level. Figure 11.8(1) shows conclusively that the state must dissociate into a hydrogen atom in the ground state and into one in the first excited state. Figure 11.8(3) cannot be used to obtain the dissociation products, because the method of independent electron orbits does not take into account the fact that for great interatomic distances the electrons tend to distribute themselves onto the two dissociation products in a definite manner—in the present case so as to give two neutral atoms rather than a positive and a negative ion. In fact, in the Hartree approximation which is the same as the molecular-orbital approximation of Chapter 7, each electron moves independently of the instantaneous position of the other electron, and so it may be easily seen that this method must break down for great internuclear distances. On the other hand, Figure 11.8(3) brings out the fact that

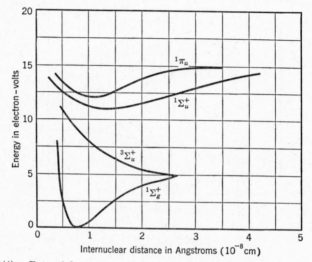

Fig. 11.8(4). Potential energy curves for hydrogen. The repulsion between the protons is included.

the curves of $^3\Sigma_u$ and $^1\Sigma_u$ are closely related to each other. This leads us to suspect that the $^1\Sigma_u$ curve lies considerably lower than the $^1\Pi_u$ curve with which it coincides in Figure 11.8(1). According to Figure 11.8(3), the latter state may be obtained from the electron configuration $(1s\sigma_g)(2p\pi_u)$ which contains the higher π_u electron. Experimentally both the $^1\Sigma_u$ and the $^1\Pi_u$ curves are known. They are shown in Figure 11.8(4), together with the curve of the ground state $^1\Sigma_g$ and that of the repulsive state $^3\Sigma_u$. Corresponding to our expectation, the state $^1\Sigma_u$ lies lower than $^1\Pi_u$. At somewhat greater internuclear separations the $^1\Sigma_u$ curve starts to rise, indicating the point where the Hartree approximation breaks down, and the energy level, instead of continuing along the energy curve of σ_u in Figure 11.8(3), turns toward the higher dissociation products shown by the termination on the right-hand side of the $^1\Sigma_u$ curve in Figure 11.8(1). This example shows that co-ordination schemes of individual electrons and of molecular states are both needed if we wish to represent the experimental results in even a qualitatively satisfactory manner.

The complexity of the methods just outlined increases considerably when applied to heavier molecules. But a classification of molecular levels seems hopeless without such a procedure. This classification has the same importance for an understanding of the chemical bond as the classification of atomic states has for an understanding of the periodic system. In the latter case information about excited atomic states leads to the prediction of the lowest states of the following atoms. For molecules, on the other hand, information about excited electronic states permits us to predict the appearance of bonding or antibonding electrons in the ground state of molecules carrying one or several additional electrons. It can actually be shown that σ_g, π_u, δ_g, $\cdots$ electrons are bonding whereas σ_u, π_g, δ_u, $\cdots$ electrons are antibonding. In this way, facts of spectroscopy and chemical binding are interrelated.

11.9 SELECTION RULES IN DIATOMIC MOLECULES

As in the previous sections we shall consider here only the rules valid for L–S coupling.

The same rule holds for the spin in molecules as in atoms. Transitions with strong intensity occur only between levels of the same spin value, that is, the same multiplicity. Transitions between levels of different multiplicity are weak—for the lightest molecules extremely weak. Such transitions are again called intercombinations.

In the allowed bands, simple selection rules hold for the angular momentum Λ. For atomic spectra it has been stated that the angular momentum L may change in transitions by the amounts 0, ± 1. The same rule holds for essentially the same reason for Λ. If the change in Λ is zero, then the initial and final wave functions have the same symmetry with regard to rotations about the molecular axis. In this case transition can occur only if the vibrating electric dipole responsible for the transitions does not disturb the axial symmetry, that is, if the dipole is parallel to the molecular axis. Such transitions are therefore called parallel transitions. On the other hand, transitions with $\Lambda = \pm 1$ occur between levels which have different symmetry with regard to rotations. To make such a transition possible, the radiating or absorbing dipole must disturb the axial symmetry, and one can show that it must be perpendicular to the axis. The corresponding bands are called perpendicular bands. We shall see later that parallel and perpendicular bands can be experimentally distinguished from each other because of the difference in their rotational structure.

For diatomic molecules consisting of two different kinds of atoms the only additional selection rule is that Σ^+ and Σ^- levels do not combine. For homonuclear molecules only transitions between g and u states are allowed, those between g and g states and u and u states are forbidden.

Among the permitted transitions we can make a further selection of those combinations which are apt to occur with greatest intensity. As in atoms we will expect above all such transitions in which only one electron changes its orbit and where the selection rules applied to the symmetry character of this one electron are not violated. (For instance $\sigma_g - \pi_u$ transitions are allowed but $\sigma_u - \delta_g$ or $\pi_g - \pi_g$ transitions are forbidden.) One kind of transition which is apt to occur with particularly great intensity is one in which the electronic configuration remains unchanged except that a bonding electron goes over into the corresponding antibonding state or vice versa. In such a transition the electronic wave functions in the initial and final states differ essentially in the same manner as the two lowest functions of a two-minimum problem (see section 7.9) differ from one another. Thus the electron transition corresponds to a vibration of the electron between the two minima or, specifically, between the two atoms. This vibration gives a large radiating dipole and consequently a strong transition probability.

11.10 VIBRATIONAL STRUCTURE OF ELECTRONIC TRANSITIONS Transition between two electronic states may be accompanied by various changes of the vibrational quantum number. As is seen later, a definite electronic and vibrational transition further consists of a number of rotational lines which, except in the H_2 spectrum, are spaced closely enough so as to give at low resolutions the appearance of a band. (Hence the name of band spectra for molecular spectra.) Bands belonging to the same electronic transition but to different vibrational transitions form a band system. The classification of the molecular spectral lines into bands and band systems is a natural one because electronic energies are great compared to vibrational energies, and these in turn are great compared to rotational energies.

For vibrational transitions in electronic spectra no such simple and stringent rules hold as for pure vibrational transitions. In the latter only changes by one quantum number occur with great intensity. In an electronic spectrum, on the other hand, the most intensive vibrational transition may be one in which the vibrational quantum number has remained unchanged or one in which a change of many quanta has occurred. At the same time many vibrational transitions may occur for the same electronic transition; that is, a band system may contain many bands. The reason for the difference between the electronic-vibrational transitions and the pure vibrational transitions is that in the latter the nuclei move in the same potential in the initial and in the final states, whereas in the former the average potential due to the electronic motion has changed during the transition so that the nuclei are subjected to different forces before and after the transition.

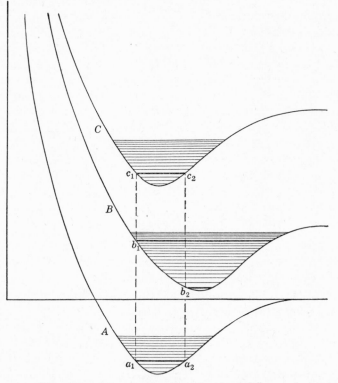

FIG. 11.10(1).   Transitions between vibrational levels of different electronic states in a diatomic molecule.   (Franck–Condon principle.)

The changes of vibrational energies occurring in electronic transitions can be systematized by the simple rule that during an electronic transition neither the positions nor the momenta of the vibrating nuclei have time to undergo an appreciable change.   This statement was first made by Franck on an intuitive basis and then proved by Condon on the basis of quantum mechanics (Franck–Condon principle).

The curves in Figure 11.10(1) show the potential energy of the nuclei as a function of the internuclear distance r.   As has been stated before, this potential energy is due to the repulsion of the nuclei and to the average action of the electrons in their orbits. The curves A, B, and C correspond to three electronic states, and the difference in potential energies is due to the different average action of the electrons. The vibrational levels are indicated by horizontal lines in the potential curves.

We shall consider a molecule in the third excited vibrational state of the lowest curve, indicated by a heavier line. According to the laws of classical mechanics the vibrating molecule will spend a relatively long time near the turning points of the vibration where the vibrational velocity becomes equal to zero, so that if the vibrating particles are observed at a given instant we are apt to find them close to the maximum or minimum r value. The same is true in the quantum treatment of the vibration; except for the zero-point vibration the absolute maxima of the probability function $|\psi|^2$ occur close to the turning points, in our special case, the points a_1 and a_2 in Figure 11.10(1). In an electronic transition the nuclear position remains essentially unchanged. If by absorption of light the molecule is lifted from curve A to curve B, and if the nuclei are caught near the position a_1, they will land near the same position, that is, near b_1 on curve B. Near a_1 the vibrational velocity was close to zero, and therefore the vibration near b_1 will start with the relative velocity of the two nuclei practically equal to zero. We conclude that the molecule is lifted by the absorption into a vibrational state whose energy level crosses curve B near b_1. This state is indicated in the figure by a heavy line. It is the fourteenth excited level rather than the third, so that a considerable change in vibrational quantum number has occurred. The electronic transition can occur with practically equal probability from the point a_2. Then the molecule arrives at the point b_2. The zero'th vibrational level which is reached in this way is again represented by a heavier line.

One often finds that transitions occur from a single initial vibrational state into a long sequence of final vibrational states. This is to be expected if the potential curve in the final electronic state is steep near one of the turning points of the initial vibrational state. In this case the turning points of several final vibrational states will lie close to the turning point of the initial vibrational state, and transitions to all these states may become strong. It is furthermore not certain that the transition will start from a point near a_1 or a_2. If the transition occurs near the minimum of curve A, the vibrational velocity in the initial state will be greater, and the nuclei will arrive in the curve B with a relatively high velocity. In this way additional transitions to levels of curve B can occur.

An actual calculation of the transition probabilities involves the detailed vibrational wave functions. These more complicated calculations explain characteristic fluctuations in the band intensities. Thus it may happen that transition to a vibrational level occurs with high intensity; the band carrying one more vibrational quantum in the excited state may be quite weak, and the band carrying one additional quantum may be again strong. The simple consideration just given is a qualitative but nevertheless useful guide which allows us to find the approximate changes in vibrational quantum number occurring with the highest intensity.

In an electronic transition from curve A to curve C the vibrations behave in an entirely different manner. The curves A and C differ from each other only by a constant shift in energy. Both the shapes of the curves and the r values for which the minima occur are the same. The same simple construction being used as previously, transition from points a_1 and a_2 lead to the points c_1 and c_2 which are the terminal points of the third excited vibrational level in the C curve. In fact, every detail of the vibration in the third level of the A curve is the same as in the third level of the C curve, and the vibrational wave functions are also the same. Under these specialized conditions only such transitions occur in which the vibrational quantum number remains unchanged during the transitions.* In the case just discussed no vibrational structure would appear at all since the vibrational energies in the initial and final state are the same, and therefore the transition between the two zero'th levels has the same frequency as the transition between the two first levels, between the two second levels, and so on. This is of course an idealized case in that the two potential curves are assumed to be exactly equal. A case frequently encountered in absorption or emission spectra is one in which the two combining curves have minima at closely equal r values but have different shapes. In general, the vibrational frequencies will be different in the upper and lower curves, and so the bands corresponding to the $0-0$, $1-1$, $2-2$, $\cdots$ vibrational transitions do not coincide. But the band system will still preserve the simple appearance of a relatively closely spaced group of bands as long as the equilibrium positions in the initial and final states do not differ greatly.

11.11 DISSOCIATION ENERGIES Although the facts mentioned in the previous section permit inferences about the shapes of the potential curves and the positions of their minima, even more important results may be obtained from the spectrum concerning the behavior of the potential energy curves at very great r values. As soon as r is sufficiently great, the molecule may be said to have separated into two

---

* This rule is strictly valid except for the usually weak influence of the internuclear distance on the electronic transition probability.

atoms. Thus at great distances the energy becomes equal to the sum of the energies of the two separate atoms. The difference between the asymptotic value which the energy approaches as r approaches infinity and the energy of the minimum of the potential curve is the dissociation energy. The most direct method of obtaining information about dissociation energies from molecular spectra is to study the appearance of

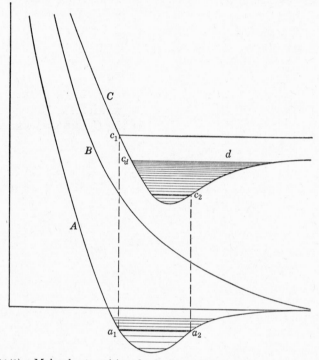

FIG. 11.11(1). Molecular transitions leading to a discrete state and to dissociation.

continua in the spectra. In the potential curve C of Figure 11.11(1) a number of vibrational levels are shown, the highest one of which lies very close to the dissociation energy. Above the dissociation energy indicated by the letter d the nuclear motion may possess any amount of energy. Strong transitions from the third vibrational level of curve A (drawn as a heavy line) lead to the second vibrational level of curve C and also to a level within the continuum adjoining the vibrational levels of C. (This final energy state is also drawn as a heavy line.) Of course, transitions are possible from the neighborhood of a_1 into the neighborhood of c_1, and so a finite portion of the continuum appears in the spectrum. If the transition leads to a repulsive curve, the spectrum is always continuous. Such would be the case in a transition from curve A to curve B in Figure 11.11(1).

From the presence of a continuum we can merely conclude that absorption of light led to dissociation. It is of further interest whether the atoms obtained in this process are in their ground states or in an excited state; we may ask furthermore, how much kinetic energy do the atoms carry as they fly apart? The state of excitation of the dissociating atoms must be decided by a more extensive study of the spectrum and possibly by using co-ordination schemes. The question concerning the kinetic energy may be answered by direct observation if a transition in the spectrum leads to the region of c_d in Figure 11.11(1)

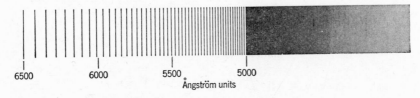

Ångström units

FIG. 11.11(2).   Drawing showing an absorption limit in the iodine spectrum. The black lines represent the absorption bands.

where the C curve and the dissociation energy d intersect. Then transitions will occur to discrete vibrational states below the level d and also into the continuum above d.

From the onset of the continuum the dissociation energy can be determined in a direct way. In Figure 11.11(2) a portion of the I_2 absorption spectrum is shown where the onset of the continuum is visible at a wavelength of 4990 Å. which corresponds to 2.472 electron volts. The molecule dissociates at this point into an iodine atom in its ground state and another one with the known excitation energy of 0.937 electron volt. While these dissociation products are obtained from the potential curve in the upper electronic state, the lower electronic state can be shown to dissociate into atoms in the ground state. The dissociation energy in this state can be obtained as a difference of the energy corresponding to the frequency of the limit of continuous absorption and the excitation energy of the iodine atom obtained in the dissociation. The former energy is 2.472 volts which gives with the excitation energy of 0.937 volt the dissociation energy of 1.535 volts. In Figure 11.11(3) the magnitudes just mentioned are shown. The energy corresponding to the continuous limit is F, the excitation energy is E, and their difference, the dissociation energy, is D. The dissociation energy is counted from the zero'th vibrational level; the corresponding dissociation energy is D_0. This value differs somewhat from D_e which is counted from the bottom of the potential curve but the relevant quantity in spectra as well as in thermochemistry is D_0. However, when molecules containing isotopes are compared, the vibrational frequency and with it D_0 will be different while D_e remains unchanged.

We can determine dissociation energies by a more indirect and a less accurate method (the Birge–Sponer method) which, however, has the

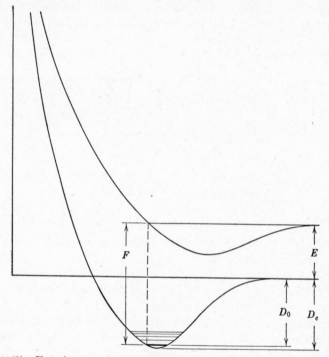

FIG. 11.11(3). Energies occurring in the spectroscopic determination of a dissociation energy.

advantage of much wider applicability. This method is based on the change in spacing of the vibrational levels. In Figure 11.11(4) a potential curve is shown with its vibrational energy levels. For the sake of clarity the total number of vibrational levels has been kept small. It may be seen that the spacing of the vibrational levels becomes closer as the energy increases. This behavior is the rule for diatomic molecules. It can be understood by remembering that the energy difference of two consecutive levels corresponds to the vibrational frequency, and the frequencies of higher-amplitude vibrations are lower because they penetrate into the flat region of the potential curve. As the vibrational energy approaches the dissociation level, the frequency and also the energy difference between two neighboring levels approach zero. The dissociation energy can be obtained if a sufficiently great number of vibrational levels are known to permit extrapolation to the point where the energy difference of two consecutive levels vanishes. Results of this method are of course all the more reliable, the greater the number of vibrational levels that are known experimentally and the greater the regularity shown by their spacing. The extrapolation is greatly

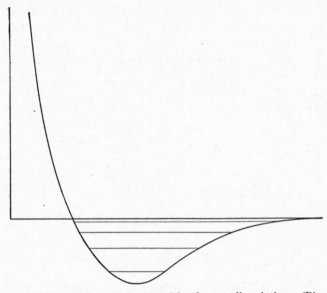

FIG. 11.11(4).   Convergence of vibrational levels near dissociation.   (Birge–Sponer method.)

facilitated by the fact that the number of vibrational levels in most of the potential curves is finite. It can be shown that, if the potential curve behaved as $1/r$ at great distances, infinitely many vibrational levels would be obtained in analogy to the infinitely many electronic levels in the $1/r$ potential of the hydrogen atom. In this case extrapolation to the dissociation energy is more difficult. But this happens only if the dissociation products are ions.* If the molecule dissociates into neutral atoms, the potential curve approaches the dissociation energy more rapidly, and only a finite number of vibrational levels are found.

* More accurately an infinite number of vibrational levels is found if the curve approaches the dissociation energy less rapidly than $h^2/32\pi^2\mu r^2$ (where μ is the reduced mass), and a finite number of levels is found if the dissociation energy is approached more rapidly.

In that case it is easier to obtain the dissociation energy by extrapolation.

11.12 THE ROTATIONAL STRUCTURE IN DIATOMIC MOLECULES

The rotational structure superposed on the electronic and vibrational frequencies differs from the rotational structure in infrared spectra in one important respect. In the latter spectrum the moment of inertia is closely similar in the initial and final states. In a spectral transition the angular momentum does not change greatly. Therefore the rotational velocity in infrared spectra is similar in the initial and final states. This rotational velocity can be pictured as a classical rotation, and the shape if not the fine structure of the infrared rotational and vibrational–rotational bands can be obtained from classical considerations. In the electronic spectra the equilibrium distances and therefore the average moments of inertia differ often greatly in the initial and the final states. The angular momentum remains again almost the same, so that this time the angular velocities may be considerably different in the two combining states. Therefore we cannot select a single angular velocity which can be used to give a classical description of the influence of the rotation on the spectrum. The rotational structure must be discussed in terms of energy levels, selection rules, and transition probabilities.

The rotational energies of a diatomic molecule are *

$$\frac{h^2 J(J + 1)}{8\pi^2 \mu} \frac{\bar{1}}{r^2} \qquad \text{11.12(1)}$$

Here J, the rotational quantum number, can be any positive integer or zero, μ is the reduced mass of the molecule, h is Planck's constant, and $\dfrac{\bar{1}}{r^2}$ is the inverse square of the interatomic distance averaged over the vibration. This average value is in general different for the initial and the final states. In the following discussion we shall write the rotational energy as

$$hBJ(J + 1) \qquad \text{11.12(2)}$$

where B stands for the factor $\dfrac{h}{8\pi^2 \mu} \dfrac{\bar{1}}{r^2}$ in equation 11.12(1). The quantities B and J for the upper and lower electronic states in an electronic transition are distinguished by using a single and a double prime.

The selection rules for J are essentially the same as the selection rules for the total angular-momentum quantum number of an atom. The

---

* In this expression the influence of the electronic angular momentum is neglected.

permitted changes in J are $+1$, 0, and -1. In addition, the transition is forbidden if $J' = J'' = 0$. While these selection rules are of general validity, further approximately valid rules are useful in obtaining information about the symmetries of the electronic functions of the combining states. It has been stated in section 11.9 that electronic transitions are permitted only if Λ, the electronic orbital angular momentum about the molecular axis, changes by $+1$, 0, or -1. Now whenever Λ remains unchanged the transitions with $J' - J'' = 0$ are much less intense than the transitions with $J' - J'' = \pm 1$. In the terminology introduced in section 10.9 the P and R branches are much more intense than the Q branch. If Λ is zero in both the combining states ($\Sigma - \Sigma$ transition) the Q branch is completely absent. ($J' - J'' = 0$ is forbidden.) This behavior is essentially the same as found in the infrared vibrations of diatomic molecules where the electronic dipole vibrates in a direction parallel to the molecular axis. It was stated in section 11.9 that in the $\Sigma-\Sigma$, $\Pi-\Pi$, $\Delta-\Delta$, $\cdots$ transitions the vibrating electronic-dipole moment is parallel to the molecular axis (parallel bands). Thus a similarity of rotational selection-rules is not surprising. In those transitions in which Λ changes by ± 1 the vibrating electronic dipole is perpendicular to the molecular axis (perpendicular bands, see section 11.9). In this case P, Q, and R branches ($J' - J'' = 0$, ± 1) appear with comparable intensities in close analogy to the appearance of these branches in the vibration–rotation bands of linear polyatomic molecules in which the vibrating dipole is perpendicular to the axis.

In order to find the position of the rotational lines relative to the frequency due to the electronic and vibrational motions, we subtract $hB''J''(J'' + 1)$ from $hB'J'(J' + 1)$ and divide by h. For the P branch in which $J'' = J' + 1$ we obtain for the rotational frequencies

$$B'J'(J' + 1) - B''J''(J'' + 1) = B'J'(J' + 1) - B''(J' + 1)(J' + 2)$$

$$= (B' - B'')J'^2 - (3B'' - B')J' - 2B'' \quad 11.12(3)$$

For the R branch where $J'' = J' - 1$, we have

$$B'J'(J' + 1) - B''J''(J'' + 1) = (B' - B'')J'^2 + (B' + B'')J' \quad 11.12(4)$$

and the frequencies for the Q branch, where $J'' = J'$, are

$$B'J'(J' + 1) - B''J''(J'' + 1) = (B' - B'')J'^2 + (B' - B'')J' \quad 11.12(5)$$

In all three branches the frequencies for high J values increase (or decrease) as J^2. If the equilibrium distance in the upper electronic state is greater than in the lower electronic state, then $\dfrac{1}{r^2}$ in equation 11.12(1) is likely to be smaller for the upper electronic state, and B' is smaller than B''. In this case the rotation for high J values gives a negative contribution to the frequency, and the corresponding rotational lines extend toward the red end of the spectrum. The bands are said to be shaded off toward the red. If, on the other hand, the equilibrium distance is smaller in the upper electronic state, then B' is greater than B'', the rotational lines extend towards the short wavelengths, and the bands are said to be shaded off toward the violet.

The appearance of the bands actually shows this fading out toward the red and toward the violet. But in the opposite frequency direction the bands terminate sharply; this end of the band is referred to as the head. The occurrence of a head can be understood from the foregoing equations. Let us suppose that B'' is greater than B'. Then the rotational contributions in the R branch are positive for low J' values and become negative only for high J' values. Thus the beginning of the R branch proceeds toward the violet. At the approximate value $J' \cong \dfrac{B'' + B'}{2(B'' - B')}$ a maximum shift toward the violet is reached. For higher J' values the lines proceed toward the red. Near the violet end, where the direction in which the lines proceed is reversed, there is an accumulation of lines which brings about the phenomenon of a sharp head.

The band heads are striking and easily measurable, but investigation of other regions in the band yields more useful information about the molecule. Near the head the lines are most crowded and most difficult to resolve. But resolution of the lines is needed to calculate the moment of inertia and the average distance of nuclei in the two electronic states. These quantities not only are interesting in themselves but also help in recognizing a common electronic state occurring in two different band systems.

In the analysis of the rotational structure one of the most important points is to locate the pure electronic vibrational frequency, the so-called zero line, and to investigate the rotational lines close to the zero line. It can be shown that, depending on the electronic angular-momentum quantum numbers of the combining states, a certain number of rotational lines are missing in the neighborhood of the zero line. In Σ–Σ transitions of the simplest type one line is missing (namely the zero line itself), in Σ–Π two lines, in Π–Π transitions three lines, and so on. This peculiarity can be derived from the fact that the total angular-momentum quantum number J of the molecule can never be smaller than the electronic quantum number Λ. It may be seen that not only can perpendicular and parallel bands be distinguished on the grounds of the presence or absence of a strong Q branch, but also the specific kind of electronic transition may be determined by a close study of the neighborhood of the zero line.

The rotational structure described in the foregoing is the one obtained for most molecules in the singlet state. We have omitted in the discussion the interaction energy between the rotation of the electrons around the molecular axis and the rotation of the molecule as a whole. If this interaction is taken into account and if the total electronic spin is different from zero, that is, if we are dealing with a doublet, triplet, etc., state, further complications arise in the rotational structure. The spin may be coupled to the electronic orbital angular momentum Λ (Hund's case a), or through gyroscopic effects to the total angular momentum J (Hund's case b). If the spin is coupled to Λ, doublet, triplet $\cdots$ systems will have the appearance of 2, 3, $\cdots$ bands with 2, 3, $\cdots$ zero lines and 2, 3, $\cdots$ heads. If, on the other hand, the spin is coupled to J, one band appears with double, triple, $\cdots$ branches all originating closely from the same zero line. Further complications arise sometimes from the fact that for low J values the spin may be coupled to Λ, whereas, following a region of transition, for high J values the spin is coupled to J.

These coupling cases are but a few among several possibilities. However, the theory appears to be relatively simple when we consider the number and complexity of spectra explained. And the method is fully justified by the body of reliable data obtained about diatomic molecules including those stable in the ordinary chemical sense as well as those unobservable by other than spectroscopic means.

11.13   ELECTRONIC SPECTRA OF POLYATOMIC MOLECULES

Though the same general rules apply to the spectra of polyatomic molecules as to the spectra of diatomic molecules and atoms, yet for practical reasons these spectra must be treated in a rather different manner. One of the significant differences is that a polyatomic molecule can dissociate in several ways, and for this reason dissociation continua are much more frequent in these spectra. For the same reason emission spectra cannot be produced so easily in an electric discharge since the conditions in the discharge are apt to destroy the molecule. Therefore most available information concerns absorption and sometimes fluorescence spectra of chemically stable molecules.

The possible symmetries of polyatomic molecules are very great in number. They range from the axial symmetry of linear molecules through molecules containing reflection planes and rotation axes in various arrangements to the highly symmetrical compounds of tetrahedral and octahedral symmetry. It is possible to systematize these symmetries and derive electronic selection-rules for each symmetry type, but we shall limit ourselves here to a few general statements and to a few examples. The arbitrariness in selecting these examples is not very great, because there are only a few polyatomic spectra where a fairly complete analysis has been made.

The vibrations have a more thorough influence in polyatomic spectra than in diatomic spectra. The reason is that the vibration of a diatomic molecule never changes the symmetry of the molecule whereas in every polyatomic molecule there exist vibrations, the nontotally symmetrical vibrations, which change the symmetry. Such vibrations may cause a violation of selection rules for electronic transitions which are based on the molecular symmetry or to be more exact on the symmetry of the equilibrium configuration.

The rotations too have a different influence on spectra in polyatomic molecules. The greater moments of inertia of these molecules have the consequence that the rotational frequencies are smaller and the rotational structures are less extended and more difficult to resolve. The difficulties of resolution are increased by the great number of frequencies occurring in the complicated rotation of asymmetric top molecules. Nevertheless rotational structures of triatomic molecules have been analyzed successfully.

11.14 SYMMETRY OF ELECTRONIC FUNCTIONS AND SELECTION RULES
In this section we shall describe a few symmetry types of electronic wave functions, and we shall mention a few selection rules applicable to a relatively great variety of molecular symmetries.

In polyatomic molecules as in diatomic molecules and atoms, transitions between states of different multiplicity are forbidden. This rule is violated to an increasing extent if the electron or electrons involved in the transition get close to a nucleus of high charge.

We call electronic proper functions totally symmetrical if the wave function remains unchanged in all possible symmetry operations. One selection rule is that a transition from a totally symmetrical state into another totally symmetrical state is forbidden if the symmetry of the molecule is incompatible with a permanent electric dipole.

Electronic states in molecules having a center of symmetry are called even or odd according to whether they retain or change their sign on reflection in the center. A selection rule essentially similar to rules about even and odd functions given in previous sections forbids transitions between even and even states and also transitions between odd and odd states.

There are in polyatomic molecules degenerate electronic states; that is, several wave functions may belong to the same energy, and symmetry operations change these wave functions into each other or into linear combinations of each other. Electronic degeneracy occurs only if the molecule possesses at least one threefold- or higher-symmetry axis. If only one such symmetry axis exists, no degeneracies higher than twofold exist. In such molecules we call the axis of high symmetry the figure axis. Molecules of higher symmetry such as tetrahedral or octahedral symmetry possess twofold and threefold degenerate states. We shall mention as an example one selection rule for these highly symmetrical molecules which permits an electronic transition only if at least one of the two combining states is threefold degenerate.

Electronic transitions in polyatomic molecules may differ with regard to the orientation of the vibrating electronic dipole relative to the molecule. This is a phenomenon analogous to the parallel and perpendicular transitions in diatomic molecules. As an example we may mention that in $\begin{matrix} H \\ H \end{matrix}\!\!\!>\!\!C\!=\!O$ the vibrating dipole may be parallel to the C–O direction, parallel to the H–H direction, or finally, perpendicular to both these directions. A molecule possessing a figure axis may have parallel bands, that is, bands with the vibrating dipole parallel to the figure axis, and perpendicular bands with the dipole perpendicular to the figure axis. A selection rule states that in parallel bands either both the combining states must be nondegenerate or both must be degenerate; in perpendicular bands at least one of the combining states must be degenerate.

The previous classifications and rules may serve as a sample of the theoretical results on polyatomic spectra. Those rules are derived and systematized by group theory which is the appropriate method of discussing the connection between different symmetries and the effect of the symmetry operations on wave functions and dipole moments.

11.15 STABILITY OF SYMMETRICAL POLYATOMIC MOLECULES

A great number of molecules with high symmetry are known, and we would almost be led to the conclusion that, if the arrangement of atoms and valence bonds is compatible with a symmetrical configuration in a polyatomic molecule, the symmetrical configuration corresponds to the equilibrium position of the nuclei.

Now it can indeed be shown for nondegenerate electronic states of polyatomic molecules that the symmetrical configurations correspond to equilibria though not necessarily to stable equilibria. More explicitly, the symmetrical configuration corresponds to a minimum or a maximum of the potential. Actually it occurs frequently that the potential is a maximum, and the most symmetrical configuration is not a stable one. This is, for instance, the case for the linear symmetrical arrangement in H_2O. But in a very large number of examples the potential has a minimum in the symmetrical configuration, and that configuration is stable.

For degenerate electronic states, on the other hand, it does not follow that the symmetrical configuration corresponds to an equilibrium. Degeneracy of the orbital motion of the electrons is due to the symmetry of the field in which the electrons move. Displacements which destroy the molecular symmetry split the orbital degeneracy. Thus near the symmetrical configuration we shall find two or more potential surfaces representing the potential energy of the nuclei as a function of their con-

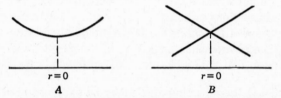

FIG. 11.15(1). Behavior of potential curves near a symmetrical configuration. *A*. Case of a nondegenerate wave function. *B*. Case of a degenerate wave function.

figuration; these potential surfaces coincide in the symmetrical configuration but get separated in the regions near the symmetrical configurations. This picture of potential surfaces must remain unchanged under all symmetry operations. For nondegenerate orbits it follows that the derivative of the potential surface vanishes in the symmetrical configuration and a maximum or minimum results. But for degenerate electronic functions we can only conclude that the picture of interpenetrating surfaces shall be symmetrically arranged. As a qualitative example we may consider Figure 11.15(1). In *A* a potential curve is given as function of the displacement r. Symmetry around a point $r = 0$ requires that at $r = 0$ the derivative should vanish. On the other hand *B* shows two potential curves which intersect at $r = 0$ so that at this point degeneracy is established. Symmetry around $r = 0$ may be satisfied without a minimum occurring at that point simply by the assumption that interchanging positive and negative values of r interchanges the two potential curves.

It may happen even for degenerate electronic states that symmetrical nuclear configurations correspond to stable equilibria. In particular, it can be shown that for a configuration where all atoms lie on a straight line all potential-energy curves have zero derivatives with regard to all nontotally symmetrical displacements. Thus linear molecules may be stable even though the electronic state is degenerate. But in all other types of molecules it can be shown that in the symmetrical configuration potential surfaces will intersect each other at finite angles so that the nuclei are not at equilibrium in the symmetrical configuration. It is of course possible that the angle at which the surfaces intersect is small, and the actual equilibrium might occur in special cases close to the symmetrical configuration. But we cannot expect that the equilibrium configuration should coincide exactly with the symmetrical one.

A consequence of this theorem is that orbital-electronic degeneracy cannot persist in the equilibrium position of the molecule except if all atoms lie on a straight line. Indeed, degeneracy is to be expected only for symmetrical configurations, and it has been stated that for degenerate states symmetrical configurations are unstable.

Symmetrical configurations seem frequently to be stable even though the electronic orbits are degenerate. This is the case in many rare-earth salts where a rare-earth ion is found in a symmetrical surrounding in a crystal in spite of the fact that electronic degeneracy is present in the incomplete f shell. Symmetrical equilibrium configurations are found also for degenerate electronic states in excited molecules in which the degenerate electronic orbit is at a rather great distance from those nuclei whose asymmetrical displacements may cause a splitting of the degeneracy. In all these cases it is reasonable to assume that the coupling between the degenerate electrons and the nontotally symmetrical vibrations is small. Thus the equilibrium configuration may be separated from the symmetrial configuration by a very small displacement. If this displacement is smaller than the amplitude of the zero-point vibration, then the molecule will be symmetrical for all practical purposes.

Degeneracy due to electronic spin affects the equilibrium configuration to a varying extent according to the strength of the spin-orbit coupling. For weak coupling, that is, in the absence of heavy nuclei, the influence of the spin will be unimportant. But in the presence of heavy nuclei the coupling may become strong, and in this case spin degeneracy has a similar effect on the equilibrium positions as orbital degeneracy. There is one exception to this rule. If the number of electrons is odd, then twofold degeneracies are not split by any electric fields or by any displacements of nuclei. Such twofold degeneracies, therefore, do not make the symmetrical configuration unstable. Actually such twofold degeneracies may be removed only by magnetic interactions. This peculiar behavior is due to the symmetry with regard to reversal of time direction (that is, the differential equations describing the motion of particles remains unchanged if t is replaced by $-t$). The twofold spin degeneracy is independent of the spacial symmetry of the molecule and persists if the molecule is distorted.

In linear molecules electronic degeneracy does not make the symmetrical configuration unstable. But the splitting of energy levels by asymmetric displacements makes the molecular vibrations and the vibrational structure of the electronic bands very complicated. The electronic states into which a degenerate state is split by the displacement of the nuclei have small energy differences. The usual simple scheme of separating the molecular energy into electronic, vibrational, and rotational energies is based on the different orders of magnitude of these energies. In the present case electronic- and vibrational-energy differences are similar and can no longer be separated. Thus a rather complicated scheme of electronic–vibrational levels results.

11.16 VIBRATIONAL SELECTION RULES The vibrational structure of electronic bands in polyatomic spectra can be obtained from the same Franck–Condon principle which governs the vibrational structure of diatomic molecules. During the electronic transition no great change of the positions or velocities of the nuclei can take place. The consequences of this rule are simplest for allowed electronic absorption bands. For sufficiently low temperatures we may assume that the molecule in the lower electronic state does not possess any vibrations. Absorption of light will throw the molecule into the higher electronic state with the nuclei still possessing the equilibrium configuration of the original electronic state. A vibrational motion will result, carrying the nuclei from the old equilibrium configuration toward the new one. This motion will have to be resolved into a number of normal vibrations. The excitation of each normal vibration depends on the question of how greatly the two equilibrium configurations differ with respect to the displacement of the normal vibration in question. If, in particular, the equilibrium configurations in the two combining states possess the same symmetry, then the vibration carrying the molecule from the old toward the new equilibrium configuration may be decomposed into totally symmetrical normal vibrations. In fact, there is no reason for the molecule to deviate from its original symmetry at any time during the vibration. The initial and final states do not differ in any nontotally symmetrical displacement, and such vibrations are therefore not excited.

From a single initial state transitions may occur—in polyatomic molecules as in diatomic ones—to a whole sequence of vibrational states. In fact, the vibrational structure may be analyzed in general into as many sequences as there are normal vibrations affected by the electronic transition. If the symmetry of the equilibrium configurations are the same in the two combining states, then the number of sequences cannot exceed the number of totally symmetrical normal vibrations.

The sequences just described include only the strongest vibrational transitions. Considerably weaker vibrational bands may be attributed to changes in quantum numbers in nontotally symmetrical vibrations. They occur if the form or frequency of these latter vibrations differ in the initial and final states. A more detailed consideration of the vibrational wave functions leads to the conclusion that in the simplest cases transitions in which only one nontotally symmetrical vibration is changed by one quantum number are forbidden.

The effect of vibrations on the electronic transitions is important, because nontotally symmetrical deformations may remove electronic selection rules based upon molecular symmetry. We might suspect that if the molecule has an asymmetric equilibrium configuration in the final state the selection rules based on the symmetry of the initial state may cease to operate. This is, however, not so. According to the Franck–Condon principle, we can think of the electronic transition as occurring in the initial configuration of the nuclei, and therefore the initial configuration is the relevant one for the selection rules. Actual violation of selection rules may occur weakly owing to thermal excitation of an appropriate nontotally symmetrical vibration. Even the zero-point amplitude of such a vibration causes forbidden electronic transitions to appear with very small intensity.

Forbidden transitions brought out weakly by a nontotally symmetrical vibration differ in their vibrational structure from allowed transitions. In the latter changes of nontotally symmetrical vibrations by one quantum number are forbidden, whereas in forbidden electronic transitions the specific nontotally symmetrical vibration which causes the breakdown of the selection rule must change by one quantum number. As an example we may consider the weak electronic-band system in benzene having a frequency of approximately 40,000 cm.$^{-1}$ This transition might be interpreted as a vibration of the electrons between the two Kekulé structures. In quantum language the transition occurs between the ground state, the wave function of which can be symbolically written

$$11.16(1)$$

and an excited state with the wave function,

$$11.16(2)$$

Just as in the case of the two-minimum problem discussed in Chapter 7, the transition between the sum and difference function corresponds to the oscillation of the electrons between the two configurations whose sum and difference enter in the wave functions. It may easily be seen that owing to the high symmetry of benzene this electronic vibration does not produce any dipole. But, if by a nuclear vibration the regular hexagon of benzene is deformed into an elongated hexagon, then the electronic oscillation does produce a small dipole. An analysis of the vibrational structure of the 40,000-cm.$^{-1}$ benzene band shows that in all strong vibrational bands the nontotally symmetrical vibration of approximately 600 cm.$^{-1}$ which causes an elongation of the hexagon changes its quantum number by ± 1. This fact is in agreement with our conclusions, and it can be used as supporting evidence that the upper electronic state of the 40,000-cm.$^{-1}$ band system actually has the electronic symmetry to be expected for the wave function 11.16(2). It may be seen that a vibrational analysis leads to conclusions about symmetries of electronic functions. The same purpose was achieved for diatomic molecules by an analysis of the rotational structure.

11.17 COLOR AND RESONANCE The absorption spectra of most stable compounds lie in the ultraviolet. In fact, stability implies that no electron is easily removable and also that the molecule has no empty electron orbits of low energy which would cause the compound to have a high electron affinity. Thus much energy is needed to lift one of the firmly bound electrons into one of the loosely bound excited states.

Most of the substances that absorb in the visible either are to some extent unsaturated or contain an atom with an incomplete inner shell. The latter is the case for inorganic salts containing colored ions like chromium. In this case the relatively small energy differences giving rise to the color are due to a regrouping of the electrons in the inner incomplete shell. Because of their shielded positions these electrons do not participate strongly in the chemical binding, and so a high degree of chemical stability is compatible with the presence of low excitation levels. In these transitions the excited level belongs to the same electron configuration as the ground state. The difference lies only in the coupling between the electrons, most frequently in the resultant angular momentum of the ion. In such a case it is easy to show that the two states in question have the same parity (they are both even or both odd). Therefore transitions between these states are forbidden. Nevertheless, the transitions occur though they have a small intensity. This may be due to the asymmetric surroundings of the ion which removes the symmetry center. However, the effect of such external fields on the electrons of internal shells is not strong. The transition may also be a quadrupole transition for which even–even and odd–odd transitions are allowed.

An absolute measure of the intensity is provided by the so-called f value of the transition. The quantity f gives the ratio of the intensity of the transition to the intensity which would be observed if the transition were due to a harmonically vibrating electron. The f values for colored metal ions are often about 10^{-4}. But even such weak absorptions are capable of giving rise to very strong colors in the condensed state.

Another extensive class of colored substances is that of the organic dyes. Here as in the case of benzene the color is often due to a transition between two states resulting from the resonance of two or more electronic configurations. As in benzene a classical picture of the light-absorption process can be obtained by considering the electron distribution as fluctuating between the resonating states. In benzene the transition lies in the ultraviolet and is furthermore forbidden. There are, however, many cases where a transition lies in the visible region and is allowed. This explains the extremely intense coloring of some organic dyes.

As an example we shall consider the organic cyanine ion. The lowest electronic state can be written as a superposition of two electronic configurations:

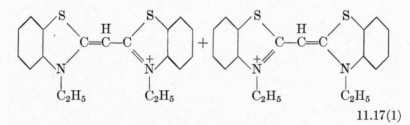

$$11.17(1)$$

The + sign between the two formulae means as usual that the wave function is a sum of the two wave functions crudely represented by the two valence pictures. An excited electronic state may be obtained by superposing the two wave functions with the − sign. A transition between the lower and higher electronic states draws its intensity from a dipole that can be pictured as a fluctuation of charge from one of the two chemical formulae to the other. Actually the empirical fact that organic dyes frequently can be equally or almost equally represented by two structural formulae has been known for a long time. Quantum mechanics has shown that in such cases it is best to symbolize the ground state of the molecule as well as the upper state in the absorption process by a superposition of at least two structural formulae. As has been stated in Chapter 7, the energy of the lowest state is lowered by this resonance between two configurations of equal or not too widely different energies. This is due to the uncertainty principle according to which the average momentum and kinetic energy of the electrons may be lowered if their spacial distribution becomes less sharply defined. This lowering takes place, however, only if the electronic wave functions corresponding to the different structural formulae are superposed with appropriate phases. Actually the energy of the upper state in the characteristic absorption of dyes is increased rather than lowered by resonance.

According to the correspondence principle, the strong absorption of light in case of resonance is due to the oscillation of the charge between the two resonating configurations. The frequency of this oscillation is as a rule lower if the two electron configurations between which the oscillation takes place differ strongly from each other. In this case a longer time is needed for the more thorough regrouping of the electrons. As an example we may mention the next member in the homologous series of cyanine ions, the formula of which, in the ground state, may be written as

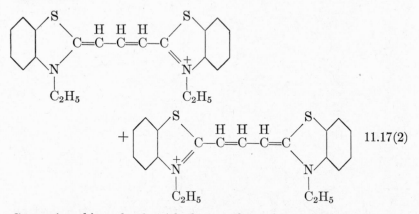

$$11.17(2)$$

Comparing this molecule with the one shown in equation 11.17(1), we see that with the lengthening of the carbon chain the charge is shifted during the resonance over a greater distance and that within the chain additional rearrangements are necessary as new carbon atoms are added. Actually the absorption of the bigger molecule lies farther towards the red, the center of absorption of the larger and smaller molecules being, respectively, 18,000 cm.$^{-1}$ and 24,000 cm.$^{-1}$

There is a second difference between the ions of the dye molecules shown in equations 11.17(1) and 11.17(2). The second molecule which contains the longer chain has an appreciably stronger absorption spectrum than the smaller molecule. The reason is that a bigger oscillating dipole is associated with the longer chain.

The chain in the cyanine dyes may be lengthened by the insertion of additional $\begin{smallmatrix} H & H \\ | & | \\ —C{=}C— \end{smallmatrix}$ groups. Each added group causes a decrease in absorption frequency. Actually the frequency is inversely proportional to the length of the chain and seems to decrease toward zero with increasing chain length. At the same time an increase in absorption strength is observed. All this is in good agreement with our qualitative expectations. The time needed for the exchange of charges between the terminal groups should increase in proportion to the intervening substituents, and the frequency should decrease in inverse proportion. The length of the vibrating dipole and the strength of the absorption increase with the separation of the end groups between which the charge oscillates.

Further support for the resonance picture is obtained if one considers ions in which the terminal groups are different. We consider the ion,

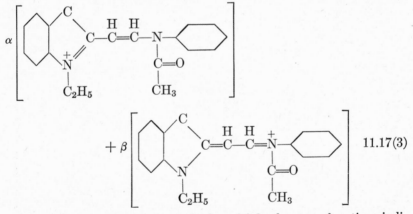

$$11.17(3)$$

Here α and β are two numbers which multiply the wave functions indicated by the chemical symbols. Because of the lack of symmetry, it is no longer true that the two configurations occur with equal probability, and therefore α and β are different. The excited state will be obtained by replacing, in equation 11.17(3), α by β and β by $-\alpha$.

Insertion of further $\begin{smallmatrix} H & H \\ | & | \\ —C{=}C— \end{smallmatrix}$ groups causes a decrease in frequency, but, as the chain becomes longer, the frequency seems to approach 20,000 cm. $^{-1}$ rather than zero. This is easy to understand. For long chains resonance causes a small energy difference, but in case of different terminal groups, as shown in equation 11.17(3), there remains an energy difference between the ground state and the first excited state which is due to the fact that a different energy is obtained if the charge of the ion attaches itself to one or the other of the end groups. Mathematically the decreasing importance of the resonance is expressed by stating that, of the two quantities α and β, one will vanish as the length of the molecule increases. Thus in the limiting case, the absorption corresponds to a transition from a state described by one of the chemical formulae given in equation 11.17(3) to a state characterized by the other formula.

It is, of course, possible that two different terminal groups may attract the charge of the ion with approximately equal strength. Then the ion behaves as though the end groups were equal. The frequency approaches zero as the chain is lengthened, and in the wave function describing the lowest state of the ion we have $\alpha = \beta$. This seems actually to happen when, in the ion shown in equation 11.17(3), the $N-CO-CH_3$ group is replaced by NH.

Any attempt to work out the quantitative theory of these resonating ions results in finding that the explanation of light absorption by dyes as previously given is oversimplified. It is not sufficient to consider just two valence formulae in describing the electronic states of the molecule. According to the previous simple representation it would be, for instance, impossible to understand why a charge resonating between two very distant points still gives rise to a fairly high visible frequency. If, as implied by the simple picture used here, the energy would be considerably higher whenever the charge is in between the two positions indicated by the two valence pictures, then the resonance would require the tunneling of the charge through a broad potential barrier. With the broadening of the barrier, the frequency of the transition should soon shift into the infrared and should approach zero much more rapidly than is actually the case. The tendency of organic dyes to give rise to fairly high frequencies requires that intermediate positions of the charge and in general partial regroupings of the electrons leading from one of the resonating states to the other shall not have much higher energies than the two resonating states considered in the beginning. Rather than being forced to consider a whole series of resonating states, it is often better to represent such molecules by the molecular-orbital picture. According to the latter description, electrons can move more or less unhindered through the whole molecule. It is interesting to point out in this connection that resonance between two regions of a bigger molecule requires as a rule that these two regions shall be connected through an uninterrupted chain of conjugated double bonds. An interruption in such a chain would mean from the point of view of resonance that in regrouping the electrons an intermediate state of considerably higher energy will occur or else that we have to consider a direct interaction between states of strongly differing electron configurations.

We arrive at the same conclusion if we consider the problem from the point of view of the molecular-orbital approximation. It must be remembered that this approximation is best adapted to the more loosely bound double-bond electrons. A saturated carbon atom which interrupts a chain of conjugated double bonds acts as a potential barrier on the molecular orbits of the double-bond electrons. This is so because near a saturated atom all the low-lying orbits are already occupied by single-bond orbital functions which are best considered as localized. Thus an intermediate saturated link in an unsaturated chain might greatly reduce the effects of resonance so that only small energy differences and small absorption frequencies are obtained.

The properties and the absorption of resonating organic ions can be considerably influenced by solvation effects. Solvation energies are in general not simply proportional to the average charge on the solvated ion. In fact, solvation energies for positive and negative ions have the same sign, and one should, therefore, expect that solvation energies are proportional to the square of the charge [compare equation 6.8(1)]. In the molecule represented by equation 11.17(1) the average charge on each of the two N atoms is one half of the elementary charge. In the absence of resonance one of the N atoms would have one charge, and the other would be neutral. The hydration energy in this latter case is different, most probably higher than the hydration energy in the resonating state. Thus solvation may stabilize one of the two resonating structures.

The theory of acid-base indicators is closely related to the effects of solvation on resonance. But in the case of indicators the resonating ion interacts with another ion in the solution and this ionic interaction is as a rule considerably stronger than the effects of solvation. Let us consider the two positions in the resonating ion which compete for the charge of the ion. If an ion of the opposite charge approaches one of these positions, the charge of the dye ion gets localized near the charge of the approaching ion, resonance is removed, and the color of the compound is changed. As an example we consider the phenolphthalein ion in alkaline solution.

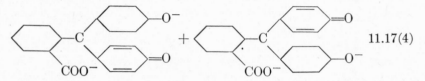

$$11.17(4)$$

Presence of H^+ ions may destroy the resonance between the two structures shown in equation 11.17(4). Indeed, as an H^+ ion attaches itself to the organic ion, a ⟨◯⟩—OH group and a ⟨◯⟩=O group are obtained which no longer resonate.

11.18 PREDISSOCIATION, RADIATIONLESS TRANSITIONS

It has been observed in spectra of diatomic molecules that in certain regions the rotational lines become diffuse rather suddenly. The broadening of the lines very often obliterates the rotational structure. Even the band as a whole often broadens until the vibrational structure is also submerged, and a continuous absorption is obtained. Very frequently broadening appears as the energy of the final electronic state in the transition increases toward a certain value. At energies higher than the critical energy a continuum due to dissociation of the molecule may exist. The broadening which precedes the true dissociation continuum is called predissociation.* In some cases it is observed that, when the energy in the final state increases beyond the critical state, the lines become again sharper, and the diffuseness of the spectrum may thus be restricted to a more or less narrow spectral region.

The phenomenon of predissociation is explained by actual dissociation of the molecule. But, whereas in a dissociation producing a structureless continuum the time required for the dissociation is just the time needed for the atoms to move apart, in predissociation the molecule stays together for several periods of vibration and sometimes even for several of the much longer periods of rotation. The breadth of the lines is due to a "breadth" of the dissociating levels. The latter is equal according to the uncertainty principle to $h/2\pi\tau$ where τ is the average time needed for dissociation. If τ becomes short compared with the period of a rotation, then the breadth of the lines becomes great compared to the distance between rotational lines, and the rotational struc-

---

* The expression predissociation was introduced by Victor Henri who discovered the phenomenon and investigated it. Originally the name predissociation carried with it the suggestion of a process different from simple dissociation. As we shall see subsequently, no essentially new process need be introduced to explain predissociation.

ture vanishes. If τ becomes shorter even than the period of a vibration, then the breadth exceeds even the distance between vibrational bands, and a structureless continuum is obtained. Actually the minimum time needed for the atoms to get apart cannot be expected to be much shorter than the vibrational period.

One necessary condition for predissociation to occur is for the molecule to have sufficient energy to dissociate. For this reason upper limits for dissociation energies may be obtained from observation on predissocia-

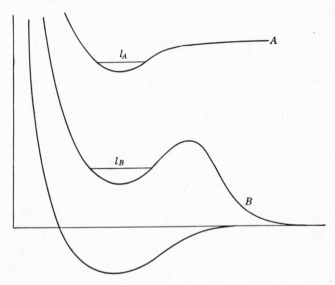

Fig. 11.18(1). Stable molecular energy levels possessing energy in excess of the dissociation energy.

tion. But the energy of a state may be above the dissociation limit, and yet predissociation may fail to occur. In Figure 11.18(1) the vibrational level l_A on the potential curve A has a considerably higher energy than two separate atoms in the ground state whose energy has been chosen as the zero of the ordinate. But the level l_A lies on a potential curve which does not dissociate into two atoms in the ground state. As long as the electronic motion proceeds in the instantaneous field of the nuclei and the nuclear motion in the average field of the electrons, an unperturbed molecule behaves as though no other potential curve existed except the one in which the molecule happens to be found. Thus no dissociation or predissociation is to be expected from the vibrational level l_A. If the molecule is found on the potential curve B, it may dissociate into atoms in the ground state. From the vibrational level l_B

predissociation might occur, because this level lies higher than the dissociation energy belonging to the curve B. Curve B has been assumed to have a somewhat unusual shape in that the potential goes through a maximum. If, as has been shown in the figure, l_B lies far below the maximum of the curve, the nuclei must pass through a considerable barrier before dissociation can occur. This requires a tunnel effect which takes a long time and leads to an unobservably small broadening.

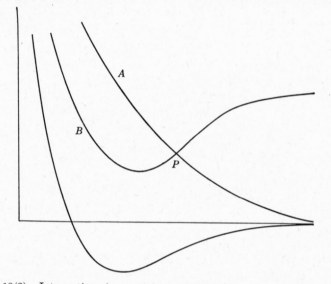

Fig. 11.18(2). Intersection of potential curves illustrating a possible reason for predissociation.

Only if the vibrational level lies immediately below the maximum, can we expect that the tunneling has a sufficiently high probability to cause a perceptible broadening. If then the energy is increased by a further small amount, the dissociation may occur over the top of the barrier rather than through the barrier. Then dissociation occurs within one vibrational period, and a true structureless continuum arises. In the case just discussed, the continuum will persist in the curve B for all vibrational energies high enough to carry the molecule over the maximum.

A different behavior of the potential curves must be assumed in order to explain predissociation restricted to a certain spectral region with sharp lines of the same band system occurring at both lower and higher frequencies. In Figure 11.18(2) are shown two potential curves A and B which cross at point P. An electronic transition leading into curve A

gives rise to a continuum. A transition leading to curve B gives rise to a discrete spectrum in which, however, some lines may be broadened, owing to the fact that at point P the molecule may go over from curve B to curve A. Then dissociation will take place. The rule that a molecule must not change from one potential curve to another is actually derived from the separation of the molecular motion into an electronic and a nuclear part (compare Chapter 4), and this is justified only as long as the frequency of the nuclear motion remains small compared to the frequency of the electrons. If two potential curves intersect, an electronic energy difference, and with it an electronic frequency, becomes equal to zero. Therefore in the region of the intersection, nuclear and electronic motions can no longer be separated, and a transition from one potential curve to the other becomes possible.

In discussing co-ordination schemes we have seen that as a rule two potential curves in which the electronic wave functions have the same symmetry and in which the total electron spin (multiplicity) is the same do not intersect. On the other hand, the interaction between two electronic states of different symmetry or of different spin is in first approximation zero. An interaction has to be established in order that a transition from the potential curve B to the potential curve A may occur. Such an interaction may be caused for curves belonging to different multiplicities by the spin–orbit coupling, and for some states differing in symmetry properties by the interaction of molecular rotation and electronic motion. The interaction can be represented by changing the potential curves in such a way as to avoid an actual intersection. In Figure 11.18(3) the behavior of the potential curves near the point of intersection P is shown in detail. The original curves A and B are shown by the broken lines together with the adjoining parts of the solid lines. The sharply bent parts of the solid lines near P represent parts of the potential curve which are strongly affected by the interaction between the original unperturbed curves A and B. On the left-hand side of the upper curve, the electronic-wave function is the one characteristic of curve A. On the right-hand side of the upper curve, the electronic-wave function is the one belonging to B. The reverse statements can be made about the left and right sides of the lower curve. When the solid upper curve approaches P, its electronic wave function changes to a superposition of the wave functions characteristic of A and characteristic of B, and the wave function for the lower solid curve in this region is a different superposition of the same original functions.

If during the molecular oscillation the molecule passes through the neighborhood of point P very slowly, then the molecules follow the solid potential curves. In this case transition from an A-like portion to a

B-like portion is a certainty. If on the other hand the internuclear distance changes rapidly, the electronic wave function cannot change over from the B state to the A state sufficiently rapidly, and the molecule will follow the broken curve. Which of the two paths will be taken with greater probability depends on the ratio of two time intervals: the time spent by the molecule in one transition near P and the period of the electronic vibration at P. The former time is d/v where d, as shown in Figure 11.18(3), is the distance throughout which the two curves are

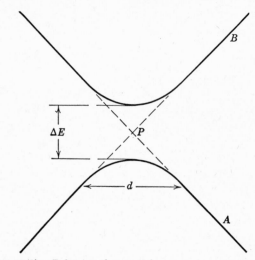

Fig. 11.18(3).   Behavior of potential curves near an intersection.

close to each other, and v is the relative velocity of the two nuclei. The period of electronic vibration at P is $h/(2\pi\,\Delta E)$ where ΔE is the minimum energy difference between the two curves. If the time of transition is the longer one, the molecules remain on the potential curves indicated by the full lines, and the situation is the same as though the potential curves were far apart. If the period of the electronic vibration is greater, the molecule behaves as though ΔE were zero and as though the curves actually crossed. If the two times are comparable, either path can occur with the probabilities depending on the actual ratio of the two times.

The foregoing discussion explains the peculiar fact of predissociation restricted to a certain special region. If in Figure 11.18(2) the vibration in curve B has just enough energy to reach point P, then the interatomic distance will change slowly near that point, and a transition to the repulsive curve can occur with great ease. Thus predissociation is to be expected. For lower energies P is not reached, and no predissociation occurs. For higher energies the atoms move fast through P, and a transition into curve A is improbable. Thus sharper bands are obtained for increasing vibrational energies.

An example of one type of reaction of two atoms in which transitions between two curves should be considered is the reaction between an alkali atom and a halogen atom. The potential curves for this reaction are shown in Figure 11.18(4). The curves in the figure approach, on

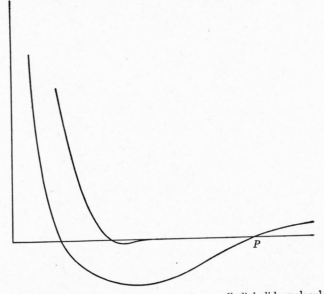

Fig. 11.18(4).   Lowest potential curves for an alkali–halide molecule.

the right side, the energy of the dissociation products. The lower level corresponds to two neutral atoms while the upper lever represents the energy of a positively charged alkali and a negatively charged halogen ion. The order of the two curves at great distances corresponds to the actual situation for all alkali halides excepting caesium fluoride for which case a separated Cs^+ and F^- ion have a lower potential energy than the two separated neutral atoms. As the interatomic distance decreases, we proceed from the extreme right of the figure toward the left. In the ionic state the long-range attraction between the ions causes a lowering of the upper curve while the lower curve still runs practically horizontally. At the point P the curves cross. The ionic curve continues to fall as a result of the coulomb interaction until finally at small distances repulsion sets in so that a stable minimum is formed. The atomic curve continues to be almost horizontal until the two atoms touch and commence to repel each other. The main features here described are supported by spectroscopic evidence.

Both curves in Figure 11.18(4) can be shown to correspond to $^1\Sigma^+$ states. According to the general statements made previously, the two curves should not cross. However, two curves will come very close to crossing each other, not only if the two electronic states differ in their symmetry properties or in their spin, but also if the two electronic states differ sufficiently strongly in another characteristic such as the position of an electron. In the present instance the ionic and atomic states differ from each other mainly in the position of one electron, and, as long as the two atoms are far apart, the difference in the electronic position is great. Thus we cannot expect that a crossing of the two curves is avoided to an appreciable extent if the crossing point lies at a great value of the abscissa. In fact, it is plausible to assume that the ionic curve is not greatly affected at the point P by the circumstance that a state of the same energy can be formed by detaching an electron from the negative ion and transferring this electron to the distant positive ion. Actually at point P a resonance exists between the ionic and atomic states, but the influence of this resonance is small since it can be established only by a tunneling of the electron between two distant positions. Thus the two curves will actually avoid each other at P, but their closest approach ΔE is equal to $h/2\pi t$ where t is the long time required for the tunneling of the electron from the one atom to the other.

It will be interesting to reconsider from our present point of view the concept of an ionic molecule. If we start from the equilibrium configuration of an alkali halide and separate the two atoms very slowly, we shall obtain not two ions but two neutral atoms as dissociation products. This is so because at P the two curves avoid each other just as has been shown in Figure 11.18(3), and, approaching on the lower curve, we always will leave the region of P on the lower curve. We might argue therefore that the alkali halides are atomic molecules because with the exception of caesium fluoride they dissociate into atoms. But in order to obtain atoms as dissociation products, we must pass the point P at a sufficiently low speed to allow sufficient time for the tunneling of an electron from one atom to another. In most actual experiments the speed of the atoms will not be slow enough to allow the tunnel effect to take place, and in this case the dissociation will proceed further along the ionic curve. It seems therefore more reasonable to talk about ionic molecules whenever the lower state remains an ionic state for internuclear distances greater than the sum of the ionic radii and if a possible radiationless transition to an atomic curve can only occur at a great interatomic distance. But this definition, though more reasonable, is less clear-cut since the question remains open what internuclear distance shall be considered as great.

In the spectra of polyatomic molecules predissociation is even more frequent than in diatomic molecules. Some of the reasons are: The great number of potential surfaces which may intersect each other in a variety of ways, the operation of selection rules for symmetrical configurations and their modification for asymmetric positions, and finally the fact that a polyatomic molecule has often several possible ways of dissociating. It is possible that two electronic states of a polyatomic molecule have different symmetry properties and may therefore intersect each other as long as the molecule is symmetrical. For a symmetrical configuration the two potential surfaces would cross without interacting. On the other hand, an asymmetric displacement of the nuclei causes interaction between the potential surfaces but at the same time tends to prevent an interpenetration of the surfaces. For a slight asymmetric displacement all conditions for predissociation may easily be fulfilled. For the neighboring symmetrical configuration actual crossing of the surfaces may occur while the small asymmetric displacement provides an interaction between the surfaces.

There is an additional reason why interpenetration of potential surfaces and radiationless transitions are more likely for polyatomic molecules than intersection of potential curves in diatomic molecules. Diatomic potential curves belonging to states of the same kind do not intersect because variation of just one parameter, namely the internuclear distance, is as a rule insufficient to establish degeneracy at the point of intersection. In polyatomic molecules the nuclear configuration is described by several parameters, and variation of two parameters is sufficient to establish degeneracy.* Potential surfaces depending on two parameters can be represented as ordinary two-dimensional surfaces in three-dimensional space. Since variation of one parameter is insufficient to cause degeneracy, the two surfaces will not intersect along a curve, but they may interpenetrate at a point in the same way as the two halves of a double cone do. Such an interpenetration if occurring at an appropriate point may enable the molecule to get from one potential surface to another, transforming in the process the original potential energy into kinetic energy of the nuclei. As an example of this process we may mention the chlorophyll molecule. This molecule absorbs red and blue light, the two absorptions apparently leading to two different excited electronic states. But the light re-emitted by chlorophyll, that is, the fluorescence of the molecule, lies in the red region of the spectrum and corresponds to the lower of the two excited states. This is true

* In the presence of magnetic forces variation of three parameters is needed.

both if the irradiated light was in the red or the blue region. Apparently excitation of the higher excited state by light is followed by a radiationless transition to the lower one of the two excited states, and this state is the initial state in the fluorescence. Similar radiationless transitions may be responsible for quenching of fluorescence by collisions in which at least three atoms take part. In photochemical processes the same rearrangement of atoms within a polyatomic molecule may be due to excitation of different electronic states; it is plausible to assume that any excess excitation energy is dissipated by a radiationless transition.

In one important respect the appearance of predissociation in polyatomic molecules differs from predissociation in diatomic molecules. In the latter molecules predissociation sets in fairly suddenly. In polyatomic molecules predissociation may start with an almost imperceptible diffuseness of the lines; this diffuseness then slowly increases over a spectral region often extending over several hundred angstroms until the bands merge into a continuum. The reason for this phenomenon is that dissociation in a polyatomic molecule may often occur only from certain regions of the potential surface, and the molecule may have to perform many oscillations before it finds the region in question. With increasing oscillation energy a wider region becomes accessible from which dissociation can take place, and thus for high oscillation energy dissociation occurs in a shorter time.

In the discussion of photochemical processes it is often of importance to know whether or not predissociation has occurred. Actually whenever predissociation is observed, we can conclude that the time needed for atomic rearrangement is quite short, and this process has become much more likely than the loss of energy by radiation. It is, however, difficult to say whether we are dealing with an internal rearrangement or whether actual predissociation is taking place. Radiationless transition leading to an internal rearrangement of a polyatomic molecule might cause an apparent broadening which we cannot readily distinguish from the broadening due to radiationless transition into a dissociated state.

If predissociation is indicated by no broadening, it is nevertheless not permissible to conclude that no dissociation has taken place. The time needed for reradiation of an absorbed quantum is equal to or greater than about 10^{-8} sec. If the time needed for dissociation is 10^{-9} sec., the broadening caused by this weak predissociation is only $\frac{1}{30}$ of a wave number and is therefore practically imperceptible. If no collisions with other molecules interfere, dissociation will occur with a quantum efficiency close to one, a fact which cannot be deduced from the appearance of the bands. Such cases of weak predissociation may be indicated by the absence of fluorescence, though the absence might be due to other causes such as quenching of the fluorescence by collisions.

11.19 ELECTRONIC EXCITATION OF A CRYSTAL LATTICE

A crystal lattice differs from a large molecule in that it possesses an additional type of symmetry—the symmetry of translation. In an ideal lattice, each cell is identical with each other cell. The simplest way to visualize a higher electronic state of a crystal would be to localize excitation in one of the lattice cells. This picture leads us to expect highly degenerate excited states. In fact, different excited states could be obtained by exciting different cells, and on account of the translational symmetry all of these states would have the same energy.

Actually it may be preferable to consider excited states of the crystal in which excitation is not localized to the neighborhood of a definite lattice point. Even if at a given time the excitation were localized, there is no reason why it should stay linked to that point; at a later time we might find the originally excited lattice cell back in its lowest state while another one of the cells is excited instead. This wandering of the excitation is caused by the coupling of neighboring lattice cells, and the time required for interchange of excitation between two neighboring points may be as short as the time of the revolution of an electron in its orbit. We might expect that the excitation moves along in the lattice according to the rules of diffusion. This would indeed be the case if transfer of the excitation from a lattice cell to a neighboring cell were independent of the previous "path" of the excitation. But it can be shown that, whenever the transfer of the excitation occurs rapidly, the excitation has a tendency to be propagated in a straight line. This behavior is analogous to that of the motion of electrons in conductors. There too a diffusion of the electrons was expected, and a rectilinear motion was found.

Mathematically, the propagation of excitation in a crystal can be described by an expression analogous to the wave function of an electron in a metal. Let ψ_j be the wave function describing the lattice in which the jth cell is excited. Then the function,

$$\psi = \Sigma_j \, \psi_j e^{i(k_x x_j + k_y y_j + k_z z_j)} \qquad\qquad 11.19(1)$$

corresponds to a wave of excitation passing through the lattice. The summation in equation 11.19(1) is to be taken over all lattice cells j. The co-ordinates x_j, y_j, and z_j in the exponent specify the position of the jth lattice cell. The wave numbers k_x, k_y, and k_z describe the wave process; the wavelengths and the direction of propagation of the wave can be obtained from these quantities. We can associate momenta with the wave numbers:

$$p_x = hk_x$$

$$p_y = hk_y$$ 11.19(2)

$$p_z = hk_z$$

These momenta have a similar significance and are subject to restrictions like those affecting the analogous quantities for an electron which moves in a strong periodic field. The energy of excitation depends on these momenta. If the time required for the exchange of excitation between two neighboring lattice points is short, the energy of excitation can be shown to depend sensitively on the k values. If, on the other hand, a long time is required for the transfer of the excitation between neighboring cells, then all excitation waves will have nearly the same energy. The plane waves given by equation 11.19(1) describe excitations which are not localized at all. By superposing such plane waves we may obtain wave packets corresponding to excitations localized to a varying extent. The resulting wave packet travels in a straight line. Its velocity is connected with the momentum vector, hk_x, hk_y, hk_z, by a law which depends on the relation between the momentum of the wave process and the energy of the excitation.

Statements of the previous paragraph can be summarized in a simpler way by associating with the excitation an imaginary particle which has been called by Frenkel, the exciton. The momentum vector described previously is the momentum of the exciton. The difference between the excitation energy for a given momentum and the excitation energy for a zero momentum can be called the kinetic energy of the exciton. The velocity of the exciton can be obtained from its momentum and from the mass of the exciton, the mass being determined by the connection between momentum and kinetic energy. In particular, if the kinetic energy depends sensitively on the momentum, the mass is small, and excitons will have high velocities. If the energy is practically independent of the momentum, the exciton velocities will be small, corresponding to a sluggish exchange of excitation between neighbors.

This simple description of the exciton becomes more complicated on detailed consideration. To describe the dependence of energy on momentum, it is necessary to assume that the mass depends both on the magnitude and direction of the momentum. It may happen that the state with $k_x = k_y = k_z = 0$ has the highest energy, in which case the kinetic energy of the exciton is always negative, and we must therefore endow this particle with a negative mass. But other simple statements about particles would continue to remain true. Thus a particle with momentum zero always has zero velocity.

If light is absorbed by an ideal crystal and if crystal vibrations may be disregarded, then the exciton which is created must have the same wavelength as the light which was absorbed. As a rule this wavelength is very long compared to the lattice period so that the wave number and the momentum of the exciton are negligibly small. We find that light absorption creates excitons which have a velocity zero and are not localized.* One practical consequence is that in absorption processes excitons are created with no kinetic energy. Thus, even if the possible excitation energies cover a considerable energy region, the absorption of a crystal should still remain a sharp line. Of course, different kinds of excitation should give rise to different kinds of excitons with a corresponding number of regions of excitation. But in the spectrum merely a number of sharp lines should appear.

Such sharp lines are, experimentally, the exception rather than the rule. Usually, more or less broad bands of absorption appear. Broad bands are actually to be expected when absorption leads to ionization (internal photoeffect) rather than to excitation. Broadening may also be due to interaction with crystal vibrations. The vibrations frequently continue to influence the spectrum even at very low temperatures. But it is to be expected that more sharp absorption lines in solids will appear at low temperatures.

11.20 INTERACTION OF LATTICE EXCITATION AND VIBRATION Excitation waves are not the only processes in a lattice which may be usefully described by a particle picture. The same description may be applied to lattice vibrations. A quantum of such a vibration is often called a sound quantum or phonon. The energy of a phonon is h times the vibrational frequency, and its momentum is h times the wave number. A complex lattice has several kinds of phonons corresponding to the several normal vibrations in a lattice cell. They can be studied with the help of infrared and Raman spectra just as the normal vibrations of a molecule. With regard to the behavior of wave packets and peculiarities of the dependence of mass on energy, similar statements can be made about the phonons to those which have been made in the previous section about the excitons. In simple lattices only such phonons are present which correspond to compression and shear waves in the lattice. They differ from other phonons in that their velocity approaches the velocity of sound rather than the velocity zero,

---

* A certain amount of localization near the surface of the crystal is to be expected since the intensity of light decreases as it penetrates into the crystal.

if the wave number becomes very small. This special class of phonons often called acoustic vibrations is responsible for the specific heat of solids at low temperatures. Phonons may be pictured as particles which are independent of each other as long as normal vibrations are independent of each other, namely, as long as the restoring forces are strictly harmonic. As soon as anharmonic terms are taken into consideration, it is found that phonons interact and collide with each other. Heat conductivity in an insulator is best described by the diffusion of the phonons which are scattered by each other and by lattice irregularities.

Phonons may also interact with excitons. This is the case if the excitation energy depends on the position of the nuclei. Such an interaction may have two consequences. One is that absorption of light instead of producing a simple excitation will simultaneously give rise to an exciton and a phonon. If the coupling between the exciton and the crystal vibrations is particularly strong, it may even happen that several phonons are created together with the exciton. The second consequence of the coupling is that an exciton after having been created may collide with phonons. Such collisons may involve a change in the number of particles participating; that is, it may happen that phonons or excitons may appear or disappear in collisions, passing on their energy and momentum to each other.

The simultaneous creation of an exciton and one or more phonons in a light-absorption process is analogous to those absorption processes in a molecule in which vibrational quanta are excited by an electronic transition. But in solids a continuous distribution of normal vibrations is available, or in other words a phonon of any momentum might be created along with the exciton. Thus a continuous absorption band is to be expected. There is a further difference between absorption spectra of molecules and of solids. In the former the energy differences between vibrational bands may be interpreted in terms of the vibrational frequencies of the initial and final electronic states. In solids a new quantity enters into the energy balance: the kinetic energy of the exciton. We have seen in the previous section that, if light absorption results in the creation of just an exciton, the momentum of this exciton is zero. If, on the other hand, an exciton and a phonon appear together, all we can say is that the sum of the momenta of these two particles is zero. Therefore, excitons with varying kinetic energies may be obtained by the absorption process, and the breadth of the absorption band may be more strongly influenced by the kinetic energy of the exciton than by the vibrational energy, that is, the kinetic energy of the phonon. From the preceding argument it may be seen that the actual absorption spectrum might reduce to a sharp line with no phonons created; or, if phonons appear with a small probability, we may still obtain a sharp line with a weaker continuum accompanying it; or, finally, if the coupling with vibrations is strong, the sharp line may have disappeared completely. Which of these cases occurs depends on the strength of the coupling between the vibrations and the electronic excitation and also on the vibrational amplitudes found in the lattice previous to the absorption of light.

Collisions between excitons and phonons change the rectilinear motion of the excitons into diffusion. Collision processes in which excitons disappear can be classified under radiationless transitions discussed in section 11.18.

Strong interaction between an exciton and phonons may have a peculiar consequence: the trapping of the exciton. As a result of this process, the lattice is distorted within and around a certain cell, and this same cell carries the excitation energy. The distortion is such as to lower the energy of the particular state in which that lattice cell is excited. For instance, an electronic orbit may have obtained a greater radius owing to the excitation; then in the trapped state the lattice is distorted in such a way as to give a greater volume to the excited cell. In the trapping process, phonons carry away the energy that is liberated by the lattice distortion. A trapped exciton corresponds to a degenerate state of the crystal since the trapping can occur at any cell with equal energy. But in order to transfer excitation energy from one trapped position to another, it is not sufficient to change the electron configuration, but nuclei must be moved as well. The nuclei have a minimum energy for the trapped configuration, and in order to get into another trapped state they must pass a potential barrier. Thus propagation of the excitation is now linked with a tunnel effect which, as a rule, takes a very long time. Therefore in such crystal excitations in which trapping occurs as a rule, the possibility of exchange of excitation between cells is of no practical importance. The absorption process itself leads in such cases to trapped states. Such crystal spectra can be treated more nearly as molecular spectra. The distorted crystal cell can be considered as the molecule. The remainder of the crystal serves merely as a medium carrying away phonons emitted during the process of light absorption. The emission of these phonons broadens the absorption lines.

11.21 PHOTOCONDUCTIVITY, PHOSPHORESCENCE Not all electronic absorption processes in a crystal can be described with the help of excitons and phonons. Absorption of light in certain frequency regions makes a crystal conducting for the period of the illumination and for a small fraction of a second following the illumination. This conductivity is due to the internal photoeffect which consists in tearing an electron loose so that this electron can now move in an empty Brillouin zone as a conduction electron. At the same time a hole appears in a filled Brillouin zone. This hole behaves like an electron of positive charge and contributes to the conductivity. Other absorption processes are not connected with an internal photoeffect. In such processes, the excited electron remains linked to the region of its original position in the lattice. The excitation may still travel in the lattice, but positive and negative charges travel together so that no current results. This case is analogous to the excitation of atoms or molecules while the internal photoeffect corresponds to a photo-ionization.

The fact that photoconductivity persists only for a very short time after illumination has ceased, calls for an explanation. The easiest interpretation would be that the freely moving electrons have found the holes from which they have been lifted by the original radiation and that the crystal has reverted to its original state. But this explanation though perhaps partly true in some cases often fails to explain the brief persistence of photoconductivity and is completely inadequate in those cases where a field applied during illumination has separated geometrically the mobile electrons and holes from each other. In addition, there is direct experimental evidence in a number of cases that, though conductivity has disappeared, the crystal has not returned to its original state. After the decay of conductivity, new absorption bands may appear in the visible or in the infrared, and irradiation by some of these bands may restore the conductivity. The same effect may be produced by merely heating the crystal. It seems that the electrons which have been made mobile by the original absorption have been trapped in the lattice sufficiently firmly to prevent their following an electrostatic field. But a light quantum of smaller energy or even elevated temperature may suffice to set them free again.

The nature of these trapped states might be explained in different ways. One explanation is that the lattice gets distorted around an electron. This lowers the energy so that the electron cannot move away without a readjustment of the lattice. This readjustment requires a tunnel effect of the nuclei and is therefore slow. The similarity between this process and the trapping of an exciton is evident. Details of the extensive experimental evidence on alkali halide crystals seem to require a different explanation. The photoelectrons are trapped at lattice irregularities which are present in every crystal however carefully prepared. It is assumed in particular that some lattice points on which an ion should be present are vacant. Electrons will then be trapped preferably at points where a negative ion is missing and which region therefore is deficient in negative charge. The presence of such vacancies in crystals formed at high temperatures can be understood readily. The vacancies correspond to the statistical equilibrium state at elevated temperatures at which the crystal has formed, whereas at lower temperatures the mobility of ions becomes so small that the vacancies cannot be eliminated.

The striking fact of very long-lived metastable electronic states in crystals brought out by the experiments on photoconductivity is also of importance in connection with the phenomenon of phosphorescence. It is common knowledge that crystals can absorb light energy and re-emit the light after a considerable time interval. This reradiation can be stimulated by various methods, for instance, by heating. Phosphorescent substances are usually crystals containing slight amounts of impurities. One explanation of phosphorescence is that the original irradiation ionizes the impurity atom. The photoelectrons get trapped by some mechanism, and reradiation occurs when the electrons find their way back to the ionized impurity atoms. It is not astonishing that the properties of phosphorescent crystals depend greatly on the way in which they have been prepared. The evenness of the distribution of the impurities, the sizes and imperfections of the crystals are all factors which can influence the process. By changing these conditions we may influence the length of time during which a phosphorescent substance retains its excitation energy, and we may obtain crystals which will reradiate this energy under various conditions. We may even produce crystals in which the electrons return to their original state by a radiationless process.

11.22 SPECTRA OF CONDUCTORS Insulators are the only solids the spectra of which show, or can be expected to show, any details. Conductors and even semiconductors have continuous spectra. The absorption coefficient may become smaller in certain spectral regions and may, in principle, even vanish. But as a rule materials which show any electronic conductivity are opaque.

The general reason for this fact is easily found. A necessary condition for conductivity is that a Brillouin zone should not be completely closed and that therefore electrons should be present which are capable of taking up arbitrarily small amounts of energy. These electrons which can be accelerated freely under the influence of an electric field and which can lose their energy by collision with lattice vibrations account for absorption in the infrared, and in fact absorption extends as a rule into the visible.

There is one conspicuous difference between the appearance of metals and semiconductors. The former are shiny; the latter are black. This can be explained by considering the conductivities. The high conductivity of metals has the consequence that in their interior the electromagnetic fields must satisfy equations which are quite different from those that hold outside the metal. As a result the electromagnetic equations can be satisfied only if but a small fraction of the electromagnetic radiation enters the metal; the rest is reflected. In semiconductors, on the other hand, a considerable fraction of the light penetrates since for these substances the conductivity is small and does not cause so sudden a change of the optical properties on the surface. But the conductivity is still great enough to absorb the light that does enter.

In general, extended absorption in the visible shows that a considerable number of low energy levels are present. Apart from conductors and semiconductors, extended absorption is also shown by insulators in which resonance occurs. Thus crystals, in which ions of the same atom but of different valency occupy equivalent lattice points, are as a rule opaque. As an example Fe_3O_4 may be mentioned.

Sufficiently thin sheets of metals transmit a certain amount of light, and moreover the transmitted light is colored, showing a variation of the absorption coefficient with frequency. In fact, the absorption coefficients of some metals show marked dips usually at rather short wavelengths. For higher frequencies it is in fact not justified to consider the electrons as free, and it is clear that, if the frequency of light becomes comparable to the frequency of electronic motion about a lattice point, resonances are bound to occur even in metals. The behavior of electrons in metals under the influence of ultraviolet light can be understood in greater detail if the Brillouin zones are considered. An absorption process can lift an electron from one Brillouin zone to another. Because electrons of varying energies are present in the filled and partly filled Brillouin zones and broad bands of unfilled states are available as final states of the electrons, we might expect continuous absorption and little variation in the absorption coefficient. But the same reason which gave rise to the concept of zero-momentum excitons in a simple absorption process imposes limitations on electronic transitions between Brillouin zones. In particular, an electron must not change its momentum when an absorption process transfers it from one Brillouin zone to another, or, if the notation of section 8.14 is employed, the quantity k must change in such a transition by a multiple of $2\pi/a$. Thus each electron can go into but one state of a given Brillouin zone. Because of the continuous distribution of electrons in the filled and partly filled zones and because each electron will absorb a different frequency, we still must expect continuous regions of absorption. But it is no longer surprising to find frequencies which happen not to be absorbed by any electron of the metal and for which the metal is practically transparent.

12. NUCLEAR CHEMISTRY

12.1 SIZE OF ATOMIC NUCLEI The great; similarity of the chemical and physical properties of isotopes gives a strong indication that the atomic nucleus is much smaller than the atom. Since two isotopes differ only in their nuclei, we would expect that any appreciable size of the nucleus or any long-range force that is not the same for the nuclei of the various isotopes would cause a difference in their chemical behavior, whereas actually such a difference is absent to a very high degree of approximation.

As it is, the only long-range force emanating from the nucleus is the coulomb force due to its positive charge Ze, where Z is the atomic number and e is the absolute value of the charge on the electron; Z being the same for isotopes, the long-range forces are the same. Chemical experiments on isotopes, even if carried out with very great accuracy, do not reveal any difference in properties that could not be explained merely by the difference of the mass of the nuclei. More detailed information about the forces acting between nuclei can be obtained by observing the deflections that a nucleus of high speed suffers when passing through various kinds of materials. The first experiments of this kind were carried out by Rutherford who observed the scattering of alpha particles by thin foils. The alpha particles are helium nuclei of high speed (about $\frac{1}{20}$ of the velocity of light) which have been emitted from some radioactive source. It was found that most alpha particles pass through a sufficiently thin foil without any noticeable change of direction, but a few suffer deflections through various angles. Very few are deflected through great angles. The law according to which these angles are distributed is in most cases in quantitative agreement with the idea that the deflections are due to the electrostatic field of the nuclei which are subjected to the alpha-particle bombardment. The resulting law of the distribution of deflections is called the Rutherford law.

The greatest possible deflection, that is 180°, will be obtained in a straight head-on collision. At the moment of closest approach in a head-on collision all the available kinetic energy is converted into potential energy. Thus the two nuclei get closer to each other in a head-on collision than in any other kind of collision. The minimum distance of approach r_{min} is obtained by setting the potential and kinetic energies equal to each other. This gives

$$r_{min} = \frac{Z_1 Z_2 e^2}{E_{kin}} \qquad 12.1(1)$$

where Z_1 is the charge of the bombarded nucleus and $Z_2 = 2$ is the charge of the alpha particle. Using high-energy alpha particles and not too heavily charged scattering centers we can obtain r_{min} values more than 10,000 times smaller than atomic dimensions. In this way it has been verified that the coulomb law holds, down to a distance of 10^{-12} cm.

By using light nuclei and fast alpha particles, deviations from the Rutherford law have been found. These deviations can be described by stating that more particles are scattered at great angles than are predicted by Rutherford's formula. This "anomalous" scattering indicates a deviation from the coulomb law for close distances of approach, and this kind of scattering can be roughly explained by assuming that at small distances a repulsion sets in that is much stronger than the coulomb repulsion. Actually the assumption of elastic spheres would give rise to an isotropic scattering and therefore to more scattering at great angles than is found in the normal Rutherford scattering. The distance at which the deviations from the coulomb law set in can be assumed to be approximately equal to the sum of the radii of the two colliding nuclei. From this assumption and also from other sources, the size of the nuclei may be estimated; our present knowledge may be summarized by stating that the nuclear radii are approximately proportional to the cube root of the nuclear mass. Or, numerically,

$$r_{nuclear} = 1.5 \times 10^{-13} \sqrt[3]{\frac{M}{M_p}} \qquad 12.1(2)$$

where M is the mass of the nucleus and M_p is the mass of the proton. Actually the nuclear radii range from 2×10^{-13} to 10×10^{-13} cm. It may be noted that the preceding law for r_{nuclei} implies that in the different nuclei the density of matter ρ is the same, namely,

$$\rho = 10^{14} \text{ grams per cubic centimeter} \qquad 12.1(3)$$

This high density is descriptive of the great concentration of mass within the small radius of the nucleus.

The repulsive forces which we have assumed when two nuclei touch, can be considered as the analogue of the van der Waals repulsion for atoms, of course, with the significant differences that the forces are much greater and extend over a much smaller region. The reason for such repulsive forces might be, however, essentially the same as for atoms. The Pauli principle does not permit increase in density over that obtained for the lowest quantum state of the particles without a rather big increase in energy.

12.2   THE NEUTRON   One characteristic of the atomic nuclei is their relatively great mass. There is only one known particle of a comparable mass which is not an atomic nucleus, namely, the neutron. Its mass is closely equal to the mass of the proton. (Actually the neutron is about 0.1 per cent heavier than the proton.) The property that sets the neutron apart from the atomic nuclei is that it does not carry any charge and therefore does not attract electrons and does not surround itself with an electronic shell. Neutrons are produced in some close nuclear collisions, that is, in collisions in which nuclei get into contact with each other.

The only interaction of neutrons with atomic nuclei is one of short range which is of the same type as the forces giving rise to anomalous alpha-particle scattering. Thus a neutron must as a general rule get to the surface of a nucleus in order that it should be deflected. The only established interaction of neutrons with electrons is a weak force of the magnetic type. Further short-range interactions do not exist or are extremely small. It can be shown that owing to the small mass of the electrons these weak forces are particularly ineffective in the interaction of free electrons with neutrons. The probability of electronic excitation by neutron impact is very small. But electrons in atomic orbits can influence the path of a neutron with higher probability if during a collision the electrons do not become excited. In this case the electrons act as parts of the atom and can be said to possess effectively the mass of the whole atom. In such collisions the weak magnetic interaction was detected. All interactions of neutrons with electrons seem, however, to be of small importance in our discussion.

The most important interaction of neutrons with matter remains the collisions with atomic nuclei. According to a geometrical picture these collisions ought to have a cross section of the order of 10^{-24} cm.^{2} (or one barn *). This would lead to a mean free path of a neutron in a solid which may be longer than a centimeter. As a general rule neutrons do penetrate solids as easily as is suggested by this long free path. This fact is a very direct illustration of the small extension of nuclear particles.

* The unit barn $= 10^{-24}$ cm.^{2} was introduced into nuclear physics because in some types of nuclear reactions the cross section 10^{-24} cm.^{2} may be considered "as big as a barn."

12.3 CONSTITUENTS OF ATOMIC NUCLEI It has been mentioned already that in nuclear collisions neutrons may be emitted. In other collisions fast protons are obtained. We shall call such transformations of nuclei nuclear reactions. Nuclei are usually considered as consisting of neutrons and protons. This view is supported not only by the fact that neutrons and protons are knocked out of the nuclei in many reactions but also by the mass of the nuclei. All nuclear masses are close to simple multiples of the protonic mass which is to be expected if they are built from the almost equally heavy protons and neutrons. Actually the nuclear masses are about 1 per cent smaller than would be expected by adding the masses of an appropriate number of protons and neutrons. This is explained by the binding energy of nuclei.

As may be seen by the great energies sometimes consumed and sometimes liberated in endothermic and exothermic nuclear reactions, the energies holding the nuclear constituents together are approximately a million times greater than chemical binding energies. Thus in building up a nucleus from free neutrons and protons a great amount of energy is emitted. Emission of energy causes, according to the theory of relativity, a decrease in mass which is calculated by dividing the energy by the square of the velocity of light. On the average, the binding energy per proton has turned out to be about 8×10^6 volts which corresponds to 0.008 part of the protonic mass. This explains why the isotopic masses are close to integer numbers if the units are so chosen that the mass * of the hydrogen atom is approximately 1.008. Nuclear reactions can be investigated more simply than chemical reactions in one respect; by measuring the mass of the nucleus (with the help of a mass spectrograph) the total binding energy of that nucleus can be obtained. Differences of these energy contents show up as kinetic energy liberated or absorbed in nuclear reactions. The relations so obtained always check, except when some of the nuclei are produced in an excited state. In principle, it would be possible to obtain energy contents of molecules by simple measurement of their masses and from these to calculate energies of reactions. Unfortunately, the energy changes in chemical reactions give rise to changes in mass which are too small to be observed. Thus, if water is formed from hydrogen and oxygen and the energy of reaction is radiated or conducted away, there will be a decrease in mass of one part in 6×10^9.

A nucleus is characterized by two integers, its charge number Z and its mass number M. The first number is equal to the number of protons in the nucleus; the second is equal to the sum of the number of protons and neutrons. To characterize a nuclear species we add the mass num-

* More exactly, the mass of the hydrogen atom in conventional units is 1.00812.

ber as an index in the upper right-hand corner of the atomic symbol and the charge number in the lower left-hand corner. Thus the abundant isotope of neon is written $_{10}\text{Ne}^{20}$. The charge number is often omitted. The atomic symbol actually makes it redundant.

Nuclei of the same charge number are called isotopes. Nuclei of the same mass number are referred to as isobars.

12.4 SPIN AND STATISTICS, PARA- AND ORTHO-HYDRO-GEN

Protons and neutrons are similar to electrons in two respects. They have a spin of $\frac{1}{2}$; that is, there is attached to both of them an angular momentum of the magnitude $h/4\pi$ which can orient itself only in two ways, namely, either parallel or opposite to any given field. The other similarity between protons and neutrons on the one hand and electrons on the other hand is that all these particles obey the Pauli exclusion principle. This means that two particles of the same kind never can occupy exactly the same quantum state, or, speaking in the more general terms of wave mechanics, the wave function must be anti-symmetrical with regard to an interchange of two particles of the same kind.

The spins of both proton and neutron give rise to magnetic moments attached to these particles. In the case of the neutron this seems somewhat surprising since the particle itself does not carry a total charge. A direct demonstration of the spins of the neutron and proton is made possible by the associated magnetic moments. Studies of the deflection of atomic amd molecular hydrogen have given precise information about the magnetic moment of the proton. The neutron magnetic moment has been measured by its interaction with electrons; this interaction leads to observable effects if the neutrons penetrate a magnetized sheet of a ferromagnetic substance. In such a sheet there is an excess of electron spins in one direction which produces an over-all effect in being more transparent to neutrons of one spin direction than to neutrons of the opposite spin direction.

That protons obey the Pauli principle is shown by the behavior of two hydrogen modifications known as ortho- and para-hydrogen. Para-hydrogen consists of hydrogen molecules in which the molecular rotation has an angular momentum of 0, 2, 4, etc., times $h/2\pi$. In the ortho-hydrogen the angular momentum of the rotation is 1, 3, 5, etc., times $h/2\pi$. It can be shown that, if the two protons not only were absolutely alike but also could not be distinguished from each other by any internal characteristics such as the spin, then any collision a hydrogen molecule makes or any other action on the hydrogen molecule could change the rotational angular momentum only by even multiples of $h/2\pi$. Actually the spins are only very weakly coupled with the motion of the hydrogen nuclei, and for this reason the molecules behave during collisions very nearly as though the spins were absent so that change of rotational momenta by an odd multiple of $h/2\pi$ is rare. Thus conversion of the ortho and para molecules into each other will be slow. There are only two ways in which such a conversion can be effected, namely either by a strongly inhomogeneous magnetic field or by dissociation and recombination. An inhomogeneous magnetic field exercises forces on the magnetic moments of the protons and in this way establishes a coupling between the spin of the proton and its orbital motion. Inhomogeneities which occur in macroscopic magnetic fields are far too small to act effectively on the minute nuclear magnets. More strongly inhomogeneous magnetic fields are produced locally by paramagnetic molecules; collisions with such molecules, for instance with O_2 or NO, give rise to the ortho–para transformation in conveniently measurable times. The other type of conversion does not rely on the spin–orbit coupling; if the hydrogen molecules are dissociated and protons coming from different molecules are reunited, there is no rule prohibiting the atoms from forming an ortho or a para molecule.

Experimentally pure para-hydrogen can be produced at low temperatures at which according to the Maxwell distribution only molecules in the rotational state with zero angular momentum (nonrotating molecules) are present in appreciable quantity. Para conversion will be completed if an appropriate catalyst is introduced which may act with the help of inhomogeneous magnetic fields or else by dissociating some of the hydrogen molecules. If this para-hydrogen is heated in the absence of a catalyst, no conversion takes place. Subsequent conversion by added catalyst can be used to get information about reaction mechanisms involving hydrogen or to show the magnetic nature of the catalyst. The conversion can be followed with the help of the difference of the thermal and spectroscopic properties of the two modifications.

In thermal equilibrium at high temperatures there are three times as many ortho as para molecules. This remarkable preference of the hydrogen molecules for an odd rotational angular momentum can be explained by assuming the validity of Pauli's exclusion principle for the protons. In fact the ortho–para ratio at high temperatures is the best proof for the exclusion principle. The connection between the abundance of ortho- and para-hydrogen and the Pauli principle are outlined in the following paragraphs.

If a hydrogen molecule is rotated by $180°$, the electronic structure gets back into exactly the same spatial position as originally, and the only alteration effected is the exchange of the two protons. The rotational wave functions have the property of remaining unchanged by rotation through the angle 180° if the angular momentum is an even multiple of $h/2\pi$ and of changing their sign if the angular momentum is an odd multiple of $h/2\pi$. A similar statement holds for the motion of an electron in the hydrogen atom. Rotation by 180° changes the sign of the wave function for odd values of l and leaves the wave function unchanged for even values of l. This can be verified by inspecting Figure 2.8(1).

Now, if the Pauli principle is assumed, the wave function should change sign when both the positions and the spins of the two protons are exchanged. In even-rotational states, rotation by 180° interchanges the positions of the nuclei and leaves the wave function unchanged. Therefore interchange of the spins should cause a change in sign. This is possible only if the spins point in opposite directions, which amounts to the old rule that, if there is symmetry in the wave functions, the spins cannot be in the same state. Actually the two spins will have to form one well-defined state called a singlet state in which their angular momenta and magnetic moments compensate (see section 11.4). This is the same kind of a spin state as formed by two electrons occupying one orbit such as the wave function of a K shell or the bonding orbital function in the H_2 molecule.

In odd rotational states, when nuclei are interchanged by rotation through 180°, the rotational wave function changes sign. Therefore exchange of spins should leave the wave function unaltered. This can be accomplished by allowing both spins to point in one definite direction, that is, by letting them occupy the same spin state. There exist three independent spin states for which symmetry with regard to the interchange of spins is established. These three states have practically identical energies because the spins interact very weakly with each other and with other degrees of freedom. The three states together form a triplet state.

According to the laws of quantum statistics the a priori probability for any state to be occupied is the same, and therefore it is three times more probable to find a hydrogen molecule in an odd-rotational state which in reality is a triplet (that is a collection of three states as far as spin is concerned) than to find the molecule in an even-rotational state which stands for a single definite spin state. Thus ortho-hydrogen will be three times more abundant than para-hydrogen. This is essentially due to the fact that there is just one way in which an antisymmetrical spin function can be constructed but three ways in which a symmetrical spin function can be obtained, and the Pauli principle links the para-hydrogen state with antisymmetrical spin functions and ortho-hydrogen states with symmetrical spin functions.

If in the hydrogen molecule one of the two protons is replaced by a deuteron,* the HD molecule so obtained will be able to change its rotational quantum number by even or odd multiples of $h/2\pi$ with approximately equal ease. In fact, the reason why a change by odd rotational quantum numbers was practically ruled out for hydrogen was that any kind of force could act in almost exactly the same way on the two atoms of the molecule. In the rotation of the HD molecule, the H atom is farther from the center of mass which is also the center of rotation and for this reason the H atom and the D atom will act differently in a collision. Thus transitions between odd and even rotational states will become possible, and the reason for a distinction between para and ortho modifications disappears.

The two kinds of modifications will regain their importance in the D_2 molecule in which again both atoms act in an exactly similar manner as long as the influence of spins is disregarded. In the case of deuterium, it is usual to designate the even and odd rotational states as ortho-deuterium and para-deuterium, respectively. Thus the prefixes ortho- and para- are associated with different rotational states in H_2 and D_2. The even rotational states, or ortho-deuterium states, can be produced by similar methods as the para-hydrogen states, and also their conversion into odd rotational states or para-deuterium states is effected by the same kind of magnetic or dissociating catalyst. There is, however, this difference between hydrogen and deuterium molecules; in equilibrium at high temperatures para hydrogen is three times less abundant than ortho-hydrogen whereas under the same conditions para-deuterium is less abundant by a factor of two.

The behavior of ortho- and para-deuterium can be explained by making an assumption about the exchange of deuterium nuclei, opposite to the one we made about the exchange of protons: we assume that the wave function remains completely unchanged when both positions and spins of the deuterons are exchanged. This links the para-deuterium states with antisymmetrical spin functions which can be constructed in smaller number than the symmetrical spin functions associated with the ortho-deuterium states. The fact that the numerical ratio between symmetrical and antisymmetrical spin states is now $2:1$ instead of $3:1$ can be explained by endowing the deuteron with an internal angular momentum $h/2\pi$ rather than $h/4\pi$ found for the proton. A count of the possible spin states then gives the experimental result.

* The deuteron, denoted by D, is a hydrogen isotope containing a proton and a neutron.

The difference in spin and statistical properties between protons and deuterons can be easily understood if the deuteron is considered as composed of a proton and a neutron. If both of these component particles carry the angular momentum $h/4\pi$, it is not strange that the nucleus which they form should have an angular momentum $h/2\pi$. To explain why wave functions are symmetrical with regard to exchange of deuterons, we shall have to consider the application of the Pauli principle to neutrons as well as to protons. In fact, since direct interactions of neutrons are experimentally almost impossible to observe, the study of the behavior of the deuterons is the simplest method through which the application of the Pauli principle to neutrons can be verified.

We assumed that a wave function changes sign if positions and spins of two protons are interchanged, and we now assume the same thing for the neutrons. If we interchange spins and positions of two deuterons, then we have effectively interchanged spins and positions of a pair of protons and a pair of neutrons. The wave function therefore must have suffered two changes of sign; that is, the wave function finally returns to the same value that it had before the exchange of the deuterons. This is the same behavior which we had to postulate in order to explain that the abundance of ortho-deuterium is greater than the abundance of para-deuterium.

Similar considerations apply to other diatomic molecules in which the two nuclei are the same isotopes. For instance the existence of a para- and ortho-nitrogen modification has been effectively proved by the alternating intensities of rotational lines in the nitrogen spectrum. A chemical separation has not been possible up to now. If it were attempted by similar methods to those used for hydrogen, the lower energy of rotational quanta in nitrogen would necessitate a cooling of nitrogen to lower temperatures (about 1° K.) at which nitrogen is solid * and the use of any kind of catalyst extremely difficult.

Spectroscopic observations on diatomic molecules yielded values for angular momenta of a few nuclei, and it has also shown whether or not a change in sign is caused by the interchange of the two nuclei. It has been found that a change in sign occurs if the mass number of the nucleus is odd, and a change in sign does not occur if the mass number of the nucleus is even. This is in agreement with the assumptions that the nuclei are composed of protons and neutrons and that the protons and neutrons behave according to Pauli's exclusion principle.

An interesting situation arises if the nucleus does not possess any spin, that is, if its internal angular momentum is zero. This is the case

---

* Potential barriers occurring in the solid state are likely further to reduce the energy difference between ortho- and para-nitrogen.

for the predominant isotopes of oxygen or of carbon. The foregoing rules show that, for instance, exchange of two O^{16} nuclei will leave the wave function unchanged. Since no spins are present, this imposes a strict symmetry condition on the exchange of the two oxygen positions, and we obtain the result that only every second rotational level of oxygen is actually realizable. Thus only one oxygen modification exists.

In the pursuit of the chemical separation of modifications similar to ortho- and para-hydrogen we need not be confined to diatomic molecules. Such modifications must be expected whenever rotation can result in the exchange of similar atoms. For instance, we would expect two water modifications and three different methane modifications.

The behavior of the nuclei in changing or retaining signs when interchanged corresponds closely to the behavior of electrons. In discussing the Pauli principle for electrons we were led to the conclusion that electrons are indistinguishable. The same line of reasoning leads to the result that protons are identical in their properties and that there is no difference between neutrons.

12.5 BETA RADIOACTIVITY It has been assumed in the early speculations about nuclear structure that the nucleus contains electrons. Experimentally this idea is supported by the fact that some nuclei emit electrons and are transformed into isobaric nuclei of practically the same weight and one more charge. The fast electrons emitted by nuclei are known by the designation of beta rays and the spontaneous nuclear transformations giving rise to these rays as beta radioactivities.

It has proved impossible to obtain a consistent theory of nuclear structure in which electrons occur as nuclear constituents. The main reason why attempts at such a theory must fail is the uncertainty principle. We have seen that a particle can be localized with high precision only if wide tolerance is allowed in the accuracy of the momentum. When an electron is confined to the small volume of the nucleus, the electronic momentum will assume high values with considerable probability. High momentum means, for a light particle, high kinetic energies, and we find that we cannot have an electron within the nucleus without giving it a kinetic energy that is great compared with the binding energies of the nucleus, so that an electron even if present in a nucleus cannot be held there.

The mere argument that, if an electron comes out of a nucleus, it must have been within the nucleus previously is not more convincing than the statement that, if a light quantum is emitted by an excited atom, this atom must have bodily contained the light quantum previous to the emission.

The argument about the presence of electrons in nuclei was further influenced by the discovery of the positron beta activity. Although all the known naturally beta-active elements emit electrons, it was found possible to produce by nuclear collisions, a number of elements which showed an activity similar to the beta activity in all respects save the one, namely, that they emitted positrons rather than electrons. Such positron activity results in the transformation of the element into an isobar of one less charge. Would it then be necessary to assume the presence of both electrons and positrons in the nucleus? Such an hypothesis would put into the nucleus two kinds of particles which outside the nucleus are known mutually to destroy each other. The only reason why in atomic reactions electrons are conserved and thus act as indestructible particles is that the appearance or disappearance of an electron–positron pair is accompanied by an energy change of 10^6 electron volts, that is more than 10^5 times the energy available in a chemical reaction.

The electron and positron activities which are both called beta-activities have been systematized by the assumption that transformations of this kind can take place for the simplest nuclear particles, that is, for protons and neutrons. Actually a neutron has a slightly greater mass than a proton plus an electron, and it is assumed that a neutron is in reality beta-active and can transform into a proton and an electron. In this process the excess mass of the neutron would be transformed into the kinetic energy of the radioactive products. From the knowledge of the available energy and from the experimental fact that the periods of beta transformations decrease rapidly with the energy of transformation, we can estimate that the lifetime of the neutron is of the order of one hour. Direct verification of this is still lacking.

Conversely, we may consider the possibility of the transformation of a proton into a neutron and a positron. This process actually does not occur since the proton is lighter than a neutron plus a positron, and so this nuclear transformation is "endothermic." But, if a proton happens to be within a nucleus in such a state that its transformation into a neutron would sufficiently increase the binding energy, the originally endothermic, proton → neutron + positron, transformation can be changed into an exothermic one, and the positron activity may proceed.

It may be noticed that, according to the picture that is presented here, protons and neutrons cannot be considered as two really different elementary particles. Nor is it very clear whether the designation "elementary particle" is descriptive for entities which can suffer transformations.

12.6 THE NEUTRINO HYPOTHESIS The electrons (or positrons) ejected in a definite beta transformation emerge from the nucleus with varying energies. This fact is remarkable because in a beta transformation a nucleus starting from a definite initial state is as a general rule transformed into a definite isobaric end state, and so the nucleus should lose in the transformation a definite amount of energy. There seem to be only two ways in which to explain the varying kinetic energies of the ejected electrons. We must assume that in the beta process either energy is not conserved or leaves the nucleus in some other form. Nonconservation of energy would necessitate far-reaching changes in many branches of physical theory and would meet with great difficulties in the theory of gravitation. The second assumption is preferred; in fact, as we shall see presently, there are further indications that in a beta process the electron (or the positron) is not the only particle ejected.

This can be illustrated in connection with the assumed beta transformation of neutrons into protons. Let us consider two neutrons just before the beta transformation. The wave function of these neutrons is antisymmetrical with regard to their exchange. Now let us assume that the two neutrons undergo beta transformations. If they have been sufficiently far apart, and if the two transformations occurred in a sufficiently short time interval, then immediately after the transformation there will be two electron–proton pairs near the original positions of the two neutrons, and these pairs are far apart compared to the distance between members of one pair. Exchanging the two pairs, we find that the wave function must undergo two changes of sign, one because of the exchange of the protons, another because of the exchange of the electrons. Thus, after the transformations the wave function is symmetrical with regard to the exchange of pairs, whereas before the transformations the wave function was antisymmetrical with regard to the exchange of the neutrons. This would mean a change in the long-range behavior of the wave function caused by spontaneous local processes. Such long-range effects seem unlikely and actually cannot be incorporated in the present formalism of atomic physics.

It is assumed therefore that a further particle, a neutrino, is emitted simultaneously with the electron (or the positron) in the beta process. The wave function for neutrinos is supposed to be antisymmetrical with regard to their exchange, and thus the difficulty described in the previous paragraph is avoided. It is also assumed that the neutrinos carry an amount of kinetic energy which added to the kinetic energy of the electron gives a constant energy emitted in every individual process of a definite beta disintegration. If we furthermore endow the neutrinos with the internal angular momentum $h/4\pi$, we may account for the spin changes accompanying beta transformations which changes would otherwise present as great a difficulty as the apparent nonconservation of energy and of the symmetry with regard to exchange.

The existence of neutrinos has not been proved by any direct experiment. An attempt has been made to measure the total energy liberated in a beta transformation by calorimetry. The amount of heat obtained corresponds to the integrated energy of the ejected electrons. The energy supposedly carried by the neutrinos must have escaped through the walls of the calorimeter.

The neutrino is a particle devoid of charge (its emission does not cause change of charge), devoid of rest mass (details of beta disintegration are best explained by the assumption that all or almost all the energy or mass carried by the neutrino is carried as kinetic energy), and also devoid of noticeable interaction with other particles. We hope, however, that the neutrino is not devoid of existence since it is needed as the carrier of energy, angular momentum, and symmetry properties which seem to disappear in beta transformations. There is no definite proof that only one such unobserved particle accompanies the emission of a beta ray, but the assumption of more than one particle of this kind seems only to give rise to unnecessary complications. The assumption of the emission of one neutrino not only accounts for the qualitative changes taking place during the beta process but also gives a good quantitative explanation of the energy distribution of the observed beta rays and of the connection between disintegration energy and lifetime of the radioactive substance.

12.7 ENERGY–PERIOD RELATION IN THE BETA DECAY

One characteristic constant is attached to each radioactive transformation: the decay constant. Given at an instant a radioactive nucleus, that is one which can undergo a radioactive transformation, the decay constant is the probability that the nucleus will disintegrate in the next second. Apparently this probability statement is the only prediction that we can make about an impending disintegration. There is nothing in the nucleus that would indicate that the time of occurrence of the process is near.

From this probability law we can obtain the law of survival of radioactive nuclei. If we have initially N such nuclei, then after a time t, there will remain $Ne^{-\frac{t}{\tau}}$ unchanged nuclei. Here $1/\tau$ is the decay constant and τ is the average life of a nucleus. The number of disintegration processes occurring in unit time is proportional to the number of unchanged atoms. Thus, if there is no fresh supply of radioactive atoms, the number of disintegration processes will change proportionately to $e^{-\frac{t}{\tau}}$. We can therefore determine the lifetime τ by counting the decay processes over a time not short compared to τ.

The decay time will in general be different not only for different species of radioactive atoms but also for two radioactive isotopes. There are even cases of radioactive excited nuclei which stay in the excited state for a sufficiently long time to be studied separately. Such nuclei are called isomers; they differ only in their energy content and not in their charge or mass number. Each isomer has its own characteristic decay constant and lifetime.

The known decay periods range from a fraction of a second to time intervals comparable with the usually assumed age of the universe (a few times 10^9 years). The latter periods are of course based not on any observation of the change of radioactivity with time but rather on an actual count of decay processes in a given mass of the faintly radioactive material. There is no clear-cut rule which would allow us to calculate the periods, but some regularities can be detected. As a general rule, the lifetime will be the shorter, the more energy the beta particles carry. A quantitative relation has been suggested between the decay energy and the lifetime. Here the decay energy is defined as the energy of the fastest beta particles that leave the nucleus. This upper limit can be determined fairly sharply; it is assumed that, if an electron is emitted with an energy close to the upper limit, only the small difference between the upper limit and the electron energy is left over for the kinetic energy of the neutrino. If the number of emitted electrons are plotted against their energy, we find that this number tends to zero as the upper limit is approached. This behavior is to be expected on the basis of the neutrino hypothesis, and in fact the energy-distribution curve of electrons can be obtained from the hypothesis by making very simple assumptions about the emission probabilities of electron–neutrino pairs. If the neutrino does not possess any mass, the whole change in energy and mass accompanying a beta decay is given by the maximum energy carried by the beta particle.

According to the empirical data, the lifetime changes roughly as the fifth power of the decay energy. This relation holds approximately if series of "similar" beta transformations are considered. In Table 12.7(1) a few artificially radioactive (positron-emitting) elements are listed which are similar in that they all contain one more proton than neutron, and they all transform into an element with one more neutron than proton. It may be seen in the last column that the decay period times the fifth power of the decay energy does not change much throughout the series.

The increase of decay probability with the fifth power of the decay energy can be understood on the basis of the neutrino hypothesis. The reason briefly is that, if more energy is available, there are more possibilities of dividing up this energy between the electron and the neutrino and a greater range of momenta can be given to the two particles. The same simple assumption which explains the energy distribution of the beta rays also leads to the observed fifth-power relation at least

TABLE 12.7(1)

ENERGY-LIFETIME RELATION FOR SOME POSITRON-EMITTING ELEMENTS

β Activity	Maximum Energy in 10^6 Volts	Average Lifetime in Minutes	Lifetime $\times$ (Energy)^5
$C^{11} \rightarrow B^{11}$	1.17	30.2	66.2
$N^{13} \rightarrow C^{13}$	1.25	14.3	43.5
$O^{15} \rightarrow N^{15}$	1.70	3.02	42.8

for decay energies higher than a million volts. For low decay energies the lifetime should vary less rapidly with the energy.

The fifth-power law here discussed holds only very roughly when applied to nonsimilar nuclei. It seems that besides the decay energy the lifetime depends on another factor which can be interpreted as the necessary rearrangement of nuclear constituents which accompanies the beta decay. The more unlike the initial and final nuclear configurations are, the less probable is the decay. In particular, transformations may become very improbable when the nucleus has a greatly different angular momentum before and after the disintegration. This is illustrated in the beta decay of Rb^{87} into Sr^{87}; the decay energy is 1.26 MeV. If rubidium were a member of the series given in Table 12.7(1) it would probably have a lifetime of a quarter of an hour whereas actually the lifetime is 0.27×10^{12} years. The angular momenta of the rubidium and strontium isotopes are $\dfrac{3}{2} \dfrac{h}{2\pi}$ and $\dfrac{9}{2} \dfrac{h}{2\pi}$, respectively. It may be seen that the rubidium activity is very closely analogous to a forbidden transition in spectroscopy.

Among the radioactive elements there are a few that do not emit positive or negative beta rays. We shall use the element Be^7 as an example. If the Be^7 nucleus had more energy than the Li^7 + positron, transformation into Li^7 could occur by emission of a positron, and in fact Be^7 would then be a member of the family given in Table 12.7(1). Actually there is not enough energy available for this transformation. The Li^7 nucleus in turn cannot transform into the Be^7 nucleus, because the Li^7 nucleus is lighter than the Be^7 nucleus. But a transformation of Be^7 into Li^7 is possible if Be^7 captures one of its own electrons. The Be^7 atom is heavier and has more energy than the Li^7 atom, and so, energetically, the transformation is feasible. It follows from the theory of the positrons that it is no more difficult to absorb an electron and create a hole in an inner shell of an atom than it is to emit a positron, that is, to create a hole in the omnipresent (and unobservable) sea of electrons with negative energy. In the Be^7–Li^7 transformation only the neutrino is emitted immediately. Subsequently electromagnetic gamma radiation may be emitted by the nucleus if it happened to transform into an excited state of Li^7. Radiation will be necessarily emitted by electrons falling into the hole that was created during the transformation. This latter radiation consists of well-known X rays of the product nucleus. In the case of the Be^7 + electron $\rightarrow$ Li^7, the gamma- and X-ray activities are the only experimental indications of the transformation.

If there are two isobaric elements, the charges of which differ by one, then according to the preceding argument it should be always possible for one of these isobars to transform into the other. If the atom with the smaller Z value is heavier, then the weight of its nucleus must exceed the weight of the isobaric nucleus by more than the mass of an electron, and the element with the smaller Z may therefore emit an electron. If the atom with the higher nuclear charge is heavier, then its nucleus can capture an electron and transform into the other isobar even though the nuclear mass should have to increase in the transformation. This argument of course presupposes that there is no fixed amount of mass or energy that has to be carried away in a beta transformation. In particular, the argument is not valid if we assume that the mass of the neutrino is different from zero. According to experimental evidence, the neutrino mass is not more than a small fraction of the electronic mass, but it has not been demonstrated that the mass of the neutrino actually vanishes.

Several isobaric pairs with charge numbers differing by unity are known. For instance Cd^{113} and In^{113} both seem to be stable isotopes. It is possible, however, that one of them is actually beta-active but that the activity is so weak that it has not been observed. Such exceedingly weak activity may be due to the smallness of the available decay energy or to a strong selection rule or to both.

12.8 NUCLEAR STABILITY If it were not for the possibility of beta decay, the number of stable isotopes would be very much greater than it is. As has been stated in the previous section, an atomic species is usually unstable if one of the neighboring isobars in the periodic table (that is, an element with the same mass number but with one more or one less nuclear charge) has a smaller mass. Among all possible isobars of a given mass number there must of course be one which has the lowest mass, and this isobar alone is absolutely stable with regard to beta decay. It is, however, quite frequently found that isobars differing by two charges exist while the intermediate isobar is missing. This can be explained by assuming that the intermediate isobar has a greater mass than either of its neighbors so that it could disintegrate into either of them. Of the two stable isobars one will in general have a greater mass, and its "exothermic" transformation into the other stable isobar is possible in principle, but such transformation would require as a first step the change into the intermediate isobar which is energetically impossible. We might assume that two beta processes take place simultaneously and that the charge number jumps by two units. The beta transformation is, however, a very improbable process since it takes, even in the most favorable cases, a much longer time than the periods with which particles inside the nucleus are supposed to move, approximately 10^{-21} sec. There is at present no known theoretical reason why particles in the nucleus take much longer to emit an electron than to change their positions and why the beta process is on the nuclear scale of time so slow. The improbability of beta transformations is an empirical fact which enters into the present beta theory in the form of a constant, the value of which is unexplained. If a beta process takes a time equivalent to 10^{23} nuclear vibrations, then it will be necessary to wait for 10^{46} vibrations for two such transformations to occur "simultaneously." The period for a double decay is therefore estimated as 10^{+46} nuclear time units which is about 10^{18} years. A transformation of this period would not be observable.

It is interesting from the point of view of nuclear structure that all stable isobaric pairs, the charge number of which differ by two, have even mass numbers and even charge numbers. This means that they have an even number of protons and an even number of neutrons. On the other hand, stable nuclei with an odd number of protons and an odd number of neutrons are found only in the beginning of the periodic system (H^2, Li^6, B^{10}, N^{14}). No stable nucleus of this kind heavier than N^{14} is known. It seems that, if the total number of particles is even, the neutrons and protons have a marked tendency to occur in pairs which is in simple and significant analogy to the fact that very few stable chemical compounds possess an odd number of electrons.

Another tendency particularly strongly noticeable for the light elements is that the number of neutrons and protons are approximately equal so that the mass number is approximately twice the charge number. This fact can be qualitatively explained by assuming that the orbits in which neutrons and protons can move within the nucleus are similar to each other. If for the stable nucleus the lowest available orbits are to be filled up successively, we find that each neutron orbit will be capable of holding two neutrons, and there will be a proton orbit of similar energy capable of holding two protons. Thus the filling up of neutron and proton orbits will progress in a roughly parallel way.

The absence of heavier nuclei with an odd number of protons and an odd number of neutrons is explained most easily by assuming that the presence of two neutrons or two protons in the same orbit is energetically favorable. This makes elements with an odd proton and an odd neutron unstable, because energy may be gained by transforming the odd neutron into a proton and putting it into the same orbit with the odd proton already present; or else it should be possible to transform the odd proton into a neutron and pair it off with the neutron which is alone in its orbit. However, the existence of light odd–odd nuclei shows that these qualitative considerations do not suffice to systematize our knowledge of nuclear stability. It seems that a neutron–proton interaction leads to a lower energy than a neutron–neutron or a proton–proton interaction provided that the interacting neutron and proton occupy practically identical orbits. One can show that this last condition can be fulfilled only for light elements.

The stability relations for isobars with an even mass number are represented in Figure 12.8(1). The figure refers to nuclei of a given even mass number. These nuclei differ in their charge, that is, in the number of their protons, and this number is plotted as the abscissa. The ordinate is the energy content of the nuclei which are represented by various kinds of circles. The nuclei containing an even number of protons and an even number of neutrons fall on one curve in this figure, whereas the nuclei with an odd number of protons and an odd number of neutrons have their positions along a roughly parallel line of higher energy. Somewhere in the region of equal numbers of neutrons and protons both curves will have a minimum.

The atom of lowest energy is the only really stable nucleus of the isobaric set. It is represented in the figure by a full circle. Two other nuclei on the lower curve indicated by empty circles are metastable since no exothermic transformation into a neighboring isobar is possible.

The other nuclei, indicated by circles containing a cross, are unstable and emit electrons or positrons or both. Arrows in the figure indicate possible beta transformations. The figure illustrates the reason for the instability of the odd–odd nuclei and also the possibility for several even–even isobars which cannot undergo single beta disintegrations. It also shows that, if an even–even isobar is too far removed from the most favorable neutron–proton ratio, it becomes unstable, thus explaining

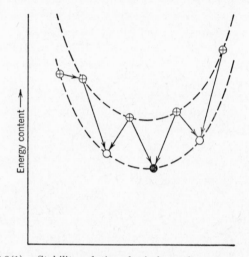

Fig. 12.8(1).   Stability relations for isobars of even mass number.

     ●   Stable nucleus.
     ○   Metastable nuclei.
     ⊕   Unstable nuclei.

why all known isobars of any mass number are found within a relatively narrow range of charges.

For nuclei with an odd mass number it does not seem to make much difference whether the odd particle is a neutron or a proton. Thus a diagram similar to Figure 12.8(1) would reduce essentially to one curve in which beside radioactive elements only one stable nucleus is to be expected. There is no reason for the occurrence of metastable nuclei. Actually among the nuclei with odd mass numbers only a few neighboring stable isobaric pairs are known. As has been said, the reason for their stability is uncertain.

In reality, nuclear energies will probably not lie on such smooth curves as indicated in the figure, but the usefulness of this representation in understanding the stability of isobars shows that the distinction indicated by the two separate curves in Fig. 12.8(1) is not without point.

It may happen that all nuclei of a certain charge number are unstable. Thus we would expect from the proton–neutron ratios of the neighboring elements that the element with the charge 43 would have a mass number in the neighborhood of 98. But the element with the charge 42, that is, molybdenum, has isotopes with the masses 92, 94, 95, 96, 97, 98, and 100. The nucleus with the charge 44, that is ruthenium, has isotopes with masses 96, 99, 100, 101, 102, and 104. Thus, if the element 43 is to have a mass number different from its neighbors, this mass number must be as low as 93 (which happens to be the mass number of the element 41), or as high as 103 (which happens to be the mass number of the element 45, that is, rhodium). It seems therefore likely that none of the conceivable nuclei with the charge 43 are stable and that no stable element 43 exists. An unstable element of this charge has, however, been produced by nuclear reactions. This artificial element is valuable in rounding out the systematic chemical knowledge incorporated in the periodic table. It has been named technetium. In the same way the element 61 may fail to appear in a stable form since all mass numbers which we may expect associated with this charge actually occur in the neighboring elements.

12.9   THE INFLUENCE OF COULOMB FORCES, THE END OF THE PERIODIC SYSTEM In light nuclei the number of neutrons and the number of protons are frequently equal and are always nearly equal; yet a dissymmetry between neutrons and protons is noticeable. There are only two stable nuclei, the proton and He^3 in which the number of protons exceeds the number of neutrons, and for higher mass numbers the number of neutrons becomes markedly greater than the number of protons. For instance, the most abundant isotope of krypton has 36 protons and 48 neutrons, whereas the most abundant isotope of lead has 82 protons and 126 neutrons. This is due to the effect of the coulomb forces.

For light nuclei the coulomb forces are rather unimportant. For heavier nuclei, however, they become more significant. The reason for this is that the nuclear forces have a short range and act practically only between neighbors, whereas the coulomb forces have a longer range and act effectively over the whole nucleus. Thus whereas the binding energy of a nucleus, owing to the short-range nuclear forces, increases proportionally to the number of particles within the nucleus, the coulomb interaction increases as the number of pairs of protons, that is, as the square of the number of protons. Though the increase of nuclear radius cuts down in heavier nuclei the coulomb effect, its relative importance continues to increase.

The behavior of light nuclei indicates that the optimum neutron–proton ratio, as far as the short-range nuclear forces are concerned, is one to one. As the coulomb effect becomes important, however, energy can be gained by converting some protons into neutrons. Though this is somewhat disadvantageous for the close-range forces, the lowering of coulomb repulsion overcompensates the loss.

Another important consequence of the coulomb forces is that they make the heaviest nuclei unstable in that it becomes energetically favorable for them to split into smaller parts. Though such splitting or fission causes an increase in the surface of nuclear matter and therefore an increase of the potential energy of the short-range forces, this increase is overcome by the decrease of potential energy occurring when two charged particles separate.

It actually has been observed that, if uranium or thorium is excited by a few million volts, these nuclei can undergo fission and separate into particles of approximately equal size, liberating about 200 million volts in the process. The original excitation by a few million volts must be considered as an activation energy.

Such activation energy does not seem to be required for a disintegration of the heaviest nuclei into strongly dissimilar parts, that is, for the emission of alpha particles. Alpha particles are helium nuclei of the mass number 4 and the charge number 2, the particular stability of which is discussed in the next section. This stability makes emission of alpha particles energetically favorable.

It is not certain what delimits the periodic system toward the higher elements. It is possible that all elements beyond uranium will show a too fast alpha decay. It is possible that the chief reason for the instability is fission; but, whichever of the two is the case, these highly charged nuclei are essentially unstable because of the coulomb forces acting on the positive charges crowded into the nucleus. Radioactive elements following uranium, that is, with the charge 93, 94, 95, and 96, have been produced and studied. They are called neptunium, plutonium, americium, and curium. Of these plutonium is best known as a fissionable element which can be used in releasing nuclear energy in an explosive or in a steady and controlled manner.

12.10 THE ALPHA-PARTICLE MODEL, BINDING ENERGIES IN NUCLEI The alpha particle has played a particularly important part in the development of nuclear physics. These particles are ejected from heavy radioactive elements, and many very stable light nuclei (such as C^{12}, O^{16}, Ne^{20}, Mg^{24}, Si^{28}, S^{32}, and A^{40}) may be considered as composed of alpha particles. It has been therefore assumed that alpha particles are among the constituents of nuclei.

From our present viewpoint this statement has a rather limited validity. The alpha particle is actually the first closed shell that can be built from neutrons and protons. It contains two neutrons with opposite spins and likewise two protons, and its position as the first closed shell explains its great stability. Light nuclei may be considered as built from alpha particles, but this is valid only in the same sense in which a solid crystal may be considered as being built up from molecules. Such a picture is significant only as long as the binding energy within the molecule is great compared to the binding between different molecules. It is true that in light nuclei the binding energy within an alpha particle is somewhat greater than the energy binding the alpha particles together, but the difference of these energies does not justify far-reaching conclusions.

Actually the particular stability of the elements C^{12} to Ca^{40} can be equally easily summarized by postulating as has been done previously that nuclei with equal and even numbers of neutrons and protons are more stable. The alpha-particle picture may be considered as a particular illustration of a system in which this more general postulate is fulfilled.

It is, however, significant that among light nuclei very little and sometimes no binding energy is gained if a neutron or proton is added to one of the pure alpha-particle nuclei. On the other hand, a particularly great amount of binding energy is obtained if a particle is added to a nucleus and an alpha particle is thereby completed. Thus, the last neutron in C^{13} is but lightly bound, and He^4 is not at all capable of binding a further neutron and forming He^5. On the other hand, a great amount of energy is liberated if Li^7 or B^{11} captures a proton. The most direct and simple explanation of this phenomenon is given by the alpha-particle model, though other explanations are possible.

In heavier nuclei the energies liberated on attaching neutrons or protons do not show such marked fluctuations. On the average one fourth of the binding energy of an alpha particle is liberated when a proton or neutron is attached to a nucleus, giving thus a binding energy of about 8,000,000 volts for either. For the heaviest nuclei this figure is reduced: the protons are less strongly bound because of the coulomb repulsion, and the neutrons are also held less tightly because their excessive number forces the least strongly bound neutrons into higher orbits.

12.11 ALPHA RADIOACTIVITY By tearing out an alpha particle from the nucleus, the short-range forces that hold the protons and neutrons together are not greatly decreased, since it is a closed "molecule" that left the nucleus. The long-range coulomb potentials are, however, greatly changed by removal of the twice-charged alpha particle, particularly if the charge of the nucleus is high. Thus emission of an alpha particle is an exothermic reaction for the highly charged nuclei. Such nuclei actually show alpha activity. Emission of a proton or neutron is always endothermic on account of the strong potentials that hold the nucleus together.

The alpha disintegration is similar to the beta decay in that it shows a definite lifetime and also in that this lifetime though varying greatly from nucleus to nucleus is extremely long compared to the short period of 10^{-21} sec. with which particles within the nucleus move.

The long life of alpha-active elements has been explained by the quantum-mechanical tunnel effect. If an alpha particle is being separated from a nucleus, the first effect is an increase of potential energy due to the action of the short-range nuclear forces. When the distance of the alpha particle from the nucleus is increased, a decrease of potential energy follows because of the coulomb repulsion. The repulsion eventually overcompensates the initial attraction and makes the reaction exothermic. Thus the alpha particle must penetrate a potential barrier in order to leave the nucleus. According to classical theory this would be impossible.

When discussing the wave function of one electron in the field of two distant protons (Chapter 7), we have seen that the wave function penetrates the region between the two protons into which, according to classical mechanics, the electron cannot enter. We also have seen that the penetration probability decreases exponentially with the distance between the two protons. If the electron originally is placed near one of the protons, it does get over to the other proton, but the time required for the penetration of the intervening barrier increases exponentially with the distance between the two protons. In a similar way the alpha particle can get through the barrier and leave the nucleus, but the time needed to do so increases exponentially with the thickness and also with the height of the barrier. In first very rough approximation, the time of disintegration is given by the Gamow formula

$$t_{\text{decay}} = t_0 \exp. \left(-\frac{8\pi^2 e^2 Z}{hv} + \sqrt{Z\frac{r_0}{r_\alpha}} \right) \qquad 12.11(1)$$

Here t_0 is the nuclear time unit, about 10^{-21} sec., v is the velocity of the alpha particle leaving the nucleus, and Z is the charge of the residual nucleus. The radius of the nucleus is r_0, and r_α is a length associated with the alpha particle. Its value is

$$r_\alpha = \frac{h^2}{256\pi^2 e^2 M} = 1.15 \times 10^{-14} \text{ cm.} \qquad 12.11(2)$$

where M is the mass of the alpha particle. It is to be noted that r_α has no connection with the radius of the alpha particle. This formula does not take into account the details of the way in which the alpha particle separates from the nucleus. Apart from the nuclear time unit t_0, it includes only the penetration factor. The first term in the exponent of this factor gives, in rough approximation, the effect of the coulomb repulsion, if it is assumed that the alpha particle starts out from $r = 0$. The second term takes into account that the alpha particle when beginning to penetrate the barrier is on the surface of the nucleus and so is already the distance r_0 away from the center.

The detailed formula in spite of its rough nature explains qualitatively in a satisfactory manner the relation between the decay energy and the lifetime of alpha activities (Geiger–Nuttal relation). The decay energy appears as the kinetic energy of the alpha particle and is therefore related to the velocity v, appearing in the penetration factor, by the formula $E = \frac{1}{2}Mv^2$. The validity of the expression which is based on the tunnel effect is shown by the fact that it remains in reasonably good agreement with the experimental lifetimes of radioactive elements when the latter vary from about 10^{10} years (thorium, uranium) to 10^{-4} sec. (radium C′). This variation is caused by a corresponding increase of the disintegration energy from 4,000,000 to a little less than 8,000,000 electron volts.

12.12 NUCLEAR FISSION Uranium may disintegrate spontaneously by emitting alpha particles and also by splitting into two approximately equal fragments. We have already referred to the latter process. It is designated as fission.

Spontaneous fission of uranium is a much less probable process than alpha decay. This is due to the fact that in the alpha disintegration only the relatively small mass of an alpha particle need pass through a potential barrier, whereas in a spontaneous fission process practically all of the nuclear matter must participate in the tunnel effect. Fission becomes a much more probable process when the nucleus is given an activation energy of a few million volts. Then the initial distortion can proceed without a tunnel effect.

The distortion which leads to fission is a stretching of the nucleus into the shape of an elongated ellipsoid. This distortion is favored by the coulomb forces, but it is opposed by a force which is analogous to surface tension. During the initial displacement this second stabilizing force is the more powerful one. But, after a certain elongation has been attained, the effect of the electrostatic repulsion becomes predominant, the nucleus is stretched at an accelerated rate, and it breaks into two fission fragments which separate, carrying an energy of nearly 2×10^8 volts.

The great energy release in the fission process is not the most important feature of this phenomenon. It is more important to note that the fission fragments also carry considerable amounts of internal energy as a result of which they emit several neutrons as a sequel to the fission. These neutrons may enter further fissionable nuclei. Thus a chain reaction starts which makes it possible to utilize the energy of nuclei on a macroscopic scale.

As we have noted before, the ratio of neutrons to protons in uranium is considerably greater than in lighter elements. When fission separates uranium into two fragments of smaller mass number, these fragments still have the high neutron-to-proton ratio characteristic of uranium. Thus the fission fragments must undergo several consecutive beta-decay processes to adjust their neutron–proton ratio to the value which for their mass number corresponds to a maximum binding energy. These beta decays have been observed. Many new beta-active substances have been discovered in this manner.

12.13 ALPHA-PARTICLE REACTIONS The alpha and beta decays are analogous to unimolecular reactions. In the last two decades "bimolecular" nuclear reactions have been studied to an increasing extent. The chief difficulty with this type of reaction is that all nuclear particles save the neutron are positively charged and do not undergo transformations unless brought to within a nuclear radius of each other. To obtain a nuclear reaction we must either start from particles of very high kinetic energy which are capable of overcoming the coulomb repulsion, or else neutrons must be used. The latter particles, however, were themselves produced by some sort of nuclear reaction, and in the last analysis we are therefore always reduced to the necessity of using high energies to initiate a nuclear reaction. Only the chain reaction opened up the way to copious neutron sources and to abundant nuclear reactions.

The first nuclear reactions have been studied by using the high-energy alpha particles emitted by alpha-radioactive elements. As has been said in discussing the Rutherford scattering (section 12.1), such alpha particles can approach lighter nuclei to within a nuclear radius, and it has been found that collisions of alpha particles with light nuclei do produce nuclear transformations. Thus nitrogen bombarded with alpha particles emits protons according to the reaction:

$$\text{He}^4 + \text{N}^{14} \rightarrow \text{H}^1 + \text{O}^{17} \qquad 12.13(1)$$

This finding was all the more remarkable since at the time it was made no other evidence of an O^{17} isotope was available. Later evidence of a stable O^{17} isotope was found in the spectrum of O_2.

The bombardment of beryllium with alpha particles led to the discovery of neutrons which were formed according to the reaction:

$$Be^9 + He^4 \rightarrow C^{12} + n^1 \qquad 12.13(2)$$

Whenever a steady fast-neutron source of not too high intensity is required, it is still one of the best procedures to bring beryllium under the action of an alpha emitter.

12.14 ARTIFICIAL SOURCES Great impetus was given to research in nuclear reactions by the various devices which made it possible to accelerate strongly charged particles and to give them kinetic energies which often exceed the energies of natural radioactive products. Many different kinds of such apparatus have been developed. The first operates by throwing several ordinary high-voltage apparatus for a short period in series (Cockroft machine). The second is a simple enlargement both in scale and in voltage of the ordinary electrostatic generator (Van de Graaff generator). The third, the cyclotron, involves the following ingenious trick. Charged particles moving in a magnetic field in a plane perpendicular to the field have a rotational period which is independent of the velocity of the particles. If these charged particles are now subjected to an electric field which is perpendicular to the magnetic field and which oscillates in phase with the motion of the charged particles in the magnetic field, the electric field will accelerate the charged particles during their whole motion. Through this resonance effect the same electric field acts repeatedly and finally speeds up the charged particles to a high velocity. More modern variations of the cyclotron permit an adjustment of the oscillating electric frequency during the acceleration of the particles. This permits acceleration of the particles to much higher velocities. A similar apparatus is the synchrotron in which the magnetic field, rather than the frequency, is adjusted. In a machine now under construction called the linear accelerator the electric field is forced to travel along with the particles, and thus high energies are reached without the establishing at any time of a great potential difference in the apparatus. Finally the betatron utilizes the circular electric field produced by a varying magnetic flux. The strongest and most extended sources of neutrons are now obtained from the controlled chain-reacting systems called piles.

The chief advantages of artificially produced particles over the natural sources is that they can be obtained in much greater quantities, they can reach higher energies, and these energies can be regulated

The natural sources, on the other hand, possess the advantage of the maximum possible steadiness. The Cockroft machine is perhaps the least difficult to construct, but the existing machines of this type give particles of only a few hundred thousand volts. The van de Graaff generator is capable of giving a few million volts and has the advantage that its voltage can be easily varied and measured. The cyclotron has been developed technically to a higher degree and gives high voltages and great particle currents. In this apparatus heavy particles can be accelerated to several hundred million volts. The same can be done to electrons by betatrons. There is definite expectation that machines now under construction, such as the linear accelerator, will give particles beyond the 10^9 volt limit. If such particles are used, nuclei and their constituents are likely to react in novel ways which at the present time have been studied insufficiently in cosmic-ray observations.

The great intensities given by the energy-producing piles permit the use of arrangements which give fine beams of neutrons, so that we can now start to explore neutron optics. The extremely great amounts of neutrons available in these structures make it possible to produce new isotopes and new elements in macroscopic quantities.

Even the atomic bomb could be used as an instantaneous source of neutrons, beta rays, and gamma rays. The extremely great intensity of this source and its short time of action would permit a number of experiments which are more difficult if conventional apparatus is used.

12.15 PENETRATION FACTOR IN NUCLEAR REACTIONS

Nuclear reactions can be produced by accelerated particles of energies much smaller than those necessary, according to classical mechanics, to bring two nuclei into actual contact. According to quantum mechanics, such contact can be established by the tunnel effect, and once contact is established there may be a considerable probability of an exothermic reaction. The probability of sufficiently close contact can be approximately described by a collision cross section equal to

$$\lambda^2 \exp.\left(\frac{-4\pi^2 e^2 Z_1 Z_2}{hv} + \sqrt{\frac{128\pi^2 e^2 Z_1 Z_2 m r_0}{h^2}}\right) \qquad 12.15(1)$$

The first factor contains the de Broglie wavelength λ characteristic of the collision which is equal to h divided by the momentum of the relative motion of the two colliding particles. The cross section λ^2 is often much greater than the geometrical cross section of the nuclei. The actual collision cross section, however, will be much smaller than the geometrical nuclear cross section owing to the exponential penetration factor. The fact that the actual cross section is proportional to the wave-mechanical magnitude λ^2 rather than to a classical geometrical cross section is due to the essentially wave-theoretical character of the tunnel effect. The actual cross section must be proportional to a quantity characteristic of the state of incipient penetration, and, when the penetration starts, the particle cannot "know" yet to what radius it has to intrude until it meets the other nucleus.

The penetration factor is similar to the exponential factor appearing in the alpha-decay formula. Z_1 and Z_2 are the charges of the colliding nuclei, v is their relative velocity, m their reduced mass (which for rather different masses is practically equal to the smaller mass), and r_0 is the distance at which the two nuclei begin to undergo an internal rearrangement. The formula as has been said is rather rough, and its validity is restricted to small penetration probabilities. In particular, it becomes invalid if it yields cross sections greater than the geometrical nuclear cross section. If the energy of the colliding particles becomes sufficiently large to surmount the coulomb repulsion, the reaction cross section will be given in order of magnitude by the geometrical cross section of the nucleus. The penetration formula for nuclear reactions has been tested in many cases by observing the dependence of the yield on the bombarding energy, and the formula has been found in good qualitative agreement with experiment.

12.16 REACTIONS WITH ACCELERATED PARTICLES The reactions which can be performed most easily (that is at lowest voltage) with artificially accelerated particles are reactions involving the lightest nuclei and therefore the smallest charges. In fact, nuclear reactions in deuteron–deuteron collisions can be observed, even if the impinging deuterons have only a kinetic energy of about 10,000 volts. If heavy water is bombarded with such deuterons, only very few of the bombarding particles will come close enough to the deuteron nuclei in the target to produce nuclear reactions. Those which do can produce one of the two reactions,

$$H^2 + H^2 \rightarrow He^3 + n^1$$
$$H^2 + H^2 \rightarrow H^3 + H^1$$

$$12.16(1)$$

Both these reactions are exothermic by a few million volts, and the particles produced even if small in number are easily observed over the background of the slower bombarding particles.

Another reaction which proceeds at rather low bombarding energies is

$$H^1 + Li^7 \rightarrow He^4 + He^4 \qquad 12.16(2)$$

This reaction was the first one to be observed by using accelerated particles.

With more strongly accelerated particles it is possible to obtain reactions among protons, deuterons, and alpha particles on the one hand and heavier elements on the other. Heavier nuclei could also be used as bombarding particles, particularly if the corresponding atoms were accelerated in a high state of ionization. In this way a sufficiently great energy could be imparted to the heavy nucleus.

For the deuterons there exists a special mechanism of reaction by which nuclear transformations can occur, even if the deuteron does not have enough energy to penetrate the coulomb barrier with a sufficiently high probability. This mechanism is made possible by the rather small binding energy of the deuteron, the dissociation of which into a neutron and a proton requires only 2×10^6 volts. It may therefore happen that the deuteron does not penetrate all the way to the surface of the other nucleus, but before crossing the region of strongest repulsion it dissociates into a proton and a neutron. On the last part of the way to the other nucleus, the neutron may travel alone unopposed by electric forces. The net effect is that a deuteron enters, a proton leaves, and there remains the originally bombarded nucleus plus a neutron.

12.17 NUCLEAR RESONANCE, THE COMPOUND NUCLEUS

It has been mentioned that, when Li^7 is bombarded with protons, the reaction complex breaks up into two alpha particles. These particles carry away with them the rather high reaction energy of 16,000,000 volts. If the bombarding energy of the protons is around 440 kv., we find in addition to the fast alpha particles numerous alpha particles of much smaller energy. It seems that there is a possibility of forming a reaction complex which because of some selection rule cannot break up into alpha particles immediately but must first go over into some other state by emitting gamma rays in doing so. The alpha particles eventually obtained have an energy that is diminished by the amount carried away by the gamma rays.

This phenomenon has been observed in a rather restricted energy region of bombarding particles. If the proton energy deviates by more than a few thousand volts from the optimum value, the effect disappears. Actually the yield is proportional to

$$\frac{1}{(E - E_0)^2 + \Delta E^2} \qquad 12.17(1)$$

Here E is the energy of the bombarding particles, E_0 is the optimum or resonance energy and ΔE can be called the breadth of the resonance. In fact, the yield decreases rapidly when the difference between bombarding and resonance energies becomes greater than ΔE. The formula is analogous to the dispersion formula in optics, E_0 corresponding to an absorption frequency, E to the incident frequency, and ΔE finds its counterpart in the breadth of the spectral line. The analogy is not purely formal; in order to explain what happens in spectra near an absorption line we must consider an excited state of the atom, and the breadth of the spectral line corresponds to the lifetime of the excited state; a broad line indicates a brief life. In a similar way nuclear resonance is explained by a more or less stable intermediate state called the compound nucleus (it is compounded of the reaction partners). The time $h/\Delta E$ is connected, according to the uncertainty principle, with the energy breadth of the resonance and is the lifetime of the compound nucleus. The compound nucleus may decay either by going back into the original reacting partners or into other reaction products, or, finally, by emitting gamma radiation.

Resonance phenomena are not at all uncommon in nuclear reactions. Only when the reaction complex can break up into some reaction products within the short time 10^{-21} sec. appropriate for nuclear rearrangements of the simplest kind, does the resonance breadth ΔE become great enough (approximately 10^6 volts) to wipe out any apparent selectivity in energies. Then the reaction is better described by a straightforward rearrangement than by a more or less unstable intermediate compound. There are several reasons why nuclear reactions may take times long compared to 10^{-21} sec. and may thus necessitate the introduction of an intermediate compound. The transformation of the compound nucleus into the resulting product may involve penetrations through potential barriers. Or the transformation may be improbable by itself such as the emission of gamma rays which as a general rule takes times upward from 100,000 times longer than 10^{-21} sec. Or the disintegration may involve violation of a selection rule. Finally the disintegration may require rearrangement of many particles or redistribution of energies which may take, relatively speaking, as long a time as the untangling of one of the more familiar mechanical puzzles by mere shaking. Here as there, it is necessary that the constituents should occupy rather narrowly defined positions before decomposition can take place.

12.18 PRODUCTION OF NEUTRONS Neutrons can be produced in a great variety of ways. The general procedure is to bombard appropriate nuclei with protons, deuterons, or alpha particles. If in the ensuing nuclear reactions charged fragments are produced in addition to neutrons, the former can be eliminated by the use of any kind of absorbing material. The neutrons penetrate this material with practically no loss in intensity. Although it is a little more difficult to separate the neutrons from gamma rays, this separation is possible, because gamma rays primarily interact with electrons and neutrons interact with nuclei. Thus heavy elements such as lead which contain many electrons and relatively few nuclei will stop gamma rays more effectively than neutrons.

Among the reactions which can produce neutrons, we may mention

$$H^2 + H^2 \rightarrow He^3 + n^1$$

$$Be^9 + He^4 \rightarrow C^{12} + n^1 \qquad 12.18(1)$$

$$Li^7 + H^1 \rightarrow Be^7 + n^1$$

The first of these reactions proceeds at the lowest voltage since only singly charged nuclei are involved. It also gives neutrons of a well-defined although not too high energy, the reaction being exothermic by 3.18×10^6 volts. If the deuterons are accelerated in a high-voltage van de Graaff machine, the energy of the neutrons can be conveniently increased within certain limits by increasing the energy of the impinging deuterons.

The beryllium-plus-alpha-particle reaction has the advantage that it can be applied if only naturally radioactive sources are available. One reason for using natural radioactive sources is that the output of neutrons is free from the variations which always result when artificial sources are employed. The alpha-particle-plus-beryllium reaction gives high-energy neutrons, the fastest of which have energies in the neighborhood of 10^7 volts, but the neutrons obtained are not homogeneous in energy.

The $Li^7 + H^1$ reaction is endothermic by 1.7×10^6 volts. The reaction can be used to produce neutrons of definite energies around and below 10^6 volts. For energies higher than 2,000,000 volts neutrons obtained from the deuteron–deuteron reaction may be used instead.

Another way to obtain neutrons is by photodissociation. If a gamma ray of sufficiently high energy is absorbed by a nucleus, a neutron may be emitted in a way similar to the ejection of an electron from an atom by ultraviolet radiations. Such photoneutrons can be obtained from any substance but particularly easily from nuclei like deuteron or beryllium which contain a rather loosely bound neutron. In the case of the deuteron nucleus, the energy of the photoneutron is always homogeneous when monochromatic radiation is used. The photoprocess may be produced by natural gamma rays or by gamma rays emitted by the fast electrons of a betatron. The natural-gamma-plus-beryllium source has the advantage over the alpha-particle-plus-beryllium process that the radioactive substance need not be mixed with the neutron emitter.

Recently neutrons of about 10^8 volts have been obtained by collisions of very fast (2×10^8 volts) deuterons with nuclei. When such a deuteron passes near another nucleus, the deuteron is exposed to the rapidly varying field of the nucleus. The neutron continues its flight with approximately the same velocity it had when it was inside the deuteron.

Finally neutrons may be obtained from the fission process. These neutrons do not have so high or so sharply defined energies as those which we can get from some other processes. If, in particular, neutrons are obtained from energy-producing piles, these neutrons usually collide with nuclei of the pile material and thus emerge with modified energy. Piles are, however, by far the most copious sources of neutrons.

In the preceding discussion some attention was paid to the energy and particularly to the homogeneous or inhomogeneous nature of the neutrons produced. Homogeneity is often more essential in neutron sources than in sources of charged particles, because, if charged particles are inhomogeneous, we always can select a homogeneous group by deflection in a magnetic or electric field; for neutrons this is impracticable.

The neutrons discussed so far are usually termed fast neutrons. If a neutron collides elastically with a nucleus, some of its energy is converted into kinetic energy of that nucleus, and the converted fraction will be considerable if the mass of the collision partner is not great compared to the mass of the neutron. Collisions with protons are most effective. After collision with a proton, the energy is shared on the average equally between the two collision partners. In this way about 20 collisions are sufficient to slow down the fast neutrons to thermal velocities. The thermal or slow neutrons react often rather differently from the fast neutrons. They are the only known particles which can enter into nuclear reactions even though their energy is small. The reason, of course, is that they are not repelled by the nuclei. The same would hold for electrons too but the only known reaction involving electrons and nuclei is the beta process which has an exceedingly small probability. Of course, stable nuclei do not react with slow electrons at all. They are constantly surrounded by such electrons, and, if they could react with them, they would not be stable.

Although neutrons can be slowed down very efficiently in hydrogen-containing substances, they are also absorbed in such media. After an average of 140 collisions with protons, a neutron will unite with the proton to form a deuteron nucleus, and the binding energy of 2.2×10^6 volts is emitted in the form of gamma radiation. This is the reverse of the photoneutron process previously discussed.

If neutrons are slowed down in paraffin, we actually obtain a mixture of fast and slow neutrons. This is due to the relatively rapid capture of slow neutrons by the protons and to the fact that the mean free path of slow neutrons in a hydrogenous material is considerably smaller than the mean free path of fast neutrons. Thus slow neutrons disappear within a rather short distance from the position where they attained thermal velocities, and neutrons of medium and high energies are therefore admixed with the slow neutrons.

The separation of fast and slow neutrons can be carried out more easily in other substances, for instance, graphite. Though more collisions with carbon nuclei are needed to slow the neutrons down to thermal energies, yet graphite has two decisive advantages. One is that slow neutrons are less readily captured by carbon than by hydrogen. The other is that the mean free path of the slow neutrons in graphite is not much shorter than the mean free path of the fast neutrons. It is, therefore, possible to separate in graphite the slow neutrons from the fast neutrons by a simple diffusion process.

It is of interest that we can obtain slow neutrons of sharply defined energies. This can be done in three different ways. One is to pass neutrons through rotating absorbers. Arrangements can be constructed which will allow only neutrons of certain velocities to pass. This method is based on the same principle on which the mechanical velocity selectors operate which have been used to prove the Maxwell velocity distribution in gases. The applicability of this method to neutrons depends on the existence of substances which absorb slow neutrons very efficiently.

The second method of producing slow monoenergetic neutrons is to derive these neutrons from a sharp pulse of fast neutrons and to observe the slow neutrons at a somewhat removed position after a given short delay. One produces the pulse of fast neutrons by allowing an accelerating equipment to operate for a very short interval. In the immediate neighborhood of the accelerating equipment the neutrons are slowed down by a paraffin block. The slow neutrons are then observed at a distance of several yards. The time of flight of the neutrons determines their velocity and energy.

Finally monoenergetic neutrons may be obtained by reflection from crystals. Reflections will occur only at definite angles, the Bragg angles of the neutrons so reflected have a definite de Broglie wavelength. In this way we obtain neutrons of sharply defined momenta and kinetic energies. This method is entirely similar to the production of monochromatic X rays by crystal reflection. Not only can we get in this manner neutrons of a given energy, but we can, conversely, use slow neutrons in exploring the properties and the structure of crystals.

12.19 FAST-NEUTRON REACTIONS When a fast neutron collides with a nucleus the ensuing reactions are in a general way similar to the reactions produced by other nuclear collisions. The only practical difference is that collisions with heavy nuclei are more easily produced with neutrons than with charged particles.

As an example we will consider the bombardment of zinc by fast neutrons which results in the attachment of the neutrons to the zinc and the emission of a proton. One obtains in this way a copper nucleus which is isobaric with the original zinc nucleus. The copper nucleus then can revert into the original zinc nucleus by beta emission, a process which takes a long enough time * to be observed after the neutron bombardment has been stopped. Processes of this kind can occur for any one of the several zinc isotopes so that a number of radioactive copper nuclei can be expected. These will have different decay periods, and indeed several beta periods have been observed (2.8 hr. and 5 min.).

Another fast-neutron reaction of the same type is

$$S^{32} + n^1 \rightarrow P^{32} + H^1 \qquad\qquad 12.19(1)$$

The resultant phosphorus nucleus is again beta-active and has the rather long period of two weeks. This makes it a convenient indicator in chemical or biological experiments.

A fast neutron can knock out an alpha particle from a nucleus. This happens, for instance, in the reaction,

$$Ne^{20} + n^1 \rightarrow O^{17} + He^4 \qquad\qquad 12.19(2)$$

In this case the products are stable nuclei, and the reaction is studied by observing the alpha particles emitted immediately rather than by finding the electrons emitted later.

If the neutron possesses a sufficiently high energy (about 8×10^6 volts), it may knock out a neutron from a nucleus without being itself attached. This happens for instance with antimony which under fast-neutron bombardment gives rise to a positron-emitting element with a period of 15.4 min. It seems that in the reaction a neutron is detached from Sb^{121} giving Sb^{120}, and the latter nucleus emits a positron and transforms into the stable nucleus Sn^{120}.

Examples of fast-neutron reactions of the types previously described could be very greatly extended. These reactions are in general endothermic and do not proceed if slow neutrons are used. The most typical

* Cu^{64} has a half life of 12.8 hr.

exothermic reactions will be discussed under slow neutrons. Of course, each of the endothermic reactions will require a certain amount of energy, and so some of them may not be observed if neutrons are produced by $Li^7 + H^1$ collisions using not too fast protons, whereas the neutron reaction proceeds readily if $He^4 + Be^9$ collisions are used as a neutron source. Because of the ease with which heavy nuclei react with neutrons, these reactions together with the slow-neutron reactions were the first to yield new beta-active elements in great numbers. Owing to the development of energy-producing piles and other artificial sources, the number of isotopes synthesized by man exceeds the number of nuclei occurring in nature.

12.20 RADIATIVE CAPTURE, SLOW-NEUTRON REACTIONS There is one nuclear transformation that may proceed, however small the energy of the neutron. The neutron may attach itself to the nucleus, and the binding energy may be emitted in the form of gamma radiation. This process occurs for fast neutrons and protons as well. Thus, when C^{12} is bombarded by protons having sufficient energy to penetrate a coulomb barrier, the proton may be captured with formation of the nucleus N^{13}. This nucleus is a positron emitter of the period 10 min. For neutrons, similar processes are very frequent and persist when the neutrons are slowed down. In this way for instance sodium, potassium, chlorine, bromine, iodine, phosphorus, arsenic, and very many other elements can be converted into radioactive isotopes. These can be used often as indicators in biological and chemical experiments.

The radioactive elements so produced all have an excess of neutrons and therefore transform by electron emission into elements having fewer neutrons and more protons. Neutron capture can proceed of course without being followed by radioactive disintegration. For instance Cd absorbs thermal neutrons very strongly and does not get radioactive.

The absorption of slow neutrons by various materials seems at first glance to follow rather complicated laws. For instance, silver absorbs slow neutrons apparently strongly since a thin sheet of silver placed in a neutron beam becomes very active while activity decreases rapidly in further sheets of silver placed behind the previous sheets. At the same time activity can be induced in iodine by neutrons which have passed through silver almost as easily as by neutrons that have not done so. But the effectiveness of neutrons on iodine is greatly reduced by previous filtration through iodine. It follows that different kinds of neutrons must be responsible for the activation of silver and of iodine.

Actually, practically all elements capture slow neutrons only within small energy ranges of the breadth of about 1/10 electron volt. The neutrons specifically affecting silver and iodine differ in their energy, the energy of the former being a few electron volts, that of the latter about 100 electron volts. Within the narrow energy range in which neutrons can be absorbed, the effective cross section for absorption is often surprisingly high and becomes sometimes 10,000 times greater than the geometrical cross section of the nucleus. This can be explained only by remembering that the neutrons as well as all other particles have wave properties. When the energy is appropriate for absorption, resonance phenomena occur, and absorption cross sections in these regions may be as great as the square of the neutron wavelength. For slow neutrons the neutron momentum is small, and, according to the de Broglie relation, the wavelength is great. This introduces the possibility of great cross sections. For fast neutrons the cross section could not become so great even though resonance occurs sometimes at higher energies as well.

The slow-neutron resonances just mentioned indicate the presence of compound nuclei possessing a rather long life, that is about 10^{-14} sec. Indeed a shorter lifetime τ of the compound nucleus would result according to the uncertainty relation,

$$\Delta E \tau \cong \frac{h}{2\pi} \qquad\qquad 12.20(1)$$

in a greater breadth ΔE of the energy of the compound nucleus. It is not surprising to find a long life whenever strong radiative capture is observed. Radiation is a slow process and could stabilize the nucleus only in very few cases if the neutron had a chance to escape within a time comparable to nuclear time units, 10^{-21} sec. Only if the compound nucleus has a life about a million times longer, does it become probable that energy loss by radiation occurs before the neutron has a chance to escape.

The reason why the neutron stays in the nucleus for such long times can be understood by considering the energies involved. The binding energy of a neutron to a nucleus is approximately 8×10^6 volts. The energy of a slow neutron outside a nucleus is a few volts in the later stages of the slowing down process and $\frac{1}{40}$ of a volt for the final stage of thermal energies. Therefore the neutron is very strongly accelerated when it enters the nucleus, and additional kinetic energy is distributed among the numerous particles within the nucleus. If the only chance for a nuclear disintegration is re-emission of the neutron, the lifetime may be very long indeed, because one will have to wait until by chance practically all the large binding energy is concentrated on a neutron near the surface enabling that neutron to escape. The process is very similar to the addition reaction of two big molecules where the reaction product though possessing sufficient energy to disintegrate still does stay together for a long time because the energy of dissociation is dispersed among the many degrees of freedom in the molecule. Such molecules may wait a long time for a stabilizing collision because it is unlikely that the required energy should be concentrated on one bond which is to be broken. In a similar manner the compound nucleus obtained by neutron addition can spend a long time waiting for emission of a gamma ray because concentration of all energy on one neutron is very improbable.

It is practically hopeless to understand quantitatively why the resonance energies for slow neutrons have particular values for various elements. These resonance energies lie several million volts above the ground state of the compound nucleus, and a relatively small change in total energy may cause the resonance level to be much closer to or much farther from the particular energy at which a neutron is just able to escape from the compound nucleus.

Although the radiative capture of slow neutrons occurs in various resonance regions for various elements, all elements show a general tendency to absorb slower neutrons more strongly. The simple reason for this tendency is that a slower neutron spends a longer time near any particular nucleus. Thus all elements capture neutrons at very low energies, the capture cross section in this region being inversely proportional to v, the velocity of the neutron $\left(\dfrac{1}{v} \text{ law} \right)$. There are some instances in which neutron capture is promptly followed by highly probable nuclear disintegrations. This is, for instance, the case in the reaction:

$$B^{10} + n^1 \rightarrow Li^7 + He^4 \qquad\qquad 12.20(2)$$

The lifetime of the compound nucleus is here so short that any trace of resonance is wiped out, and the neutron-capture cross section obeys the $\dfrac{1}{v}$ law up to rather high neutron energies.

Some nuclear species can undergo fission if bombarded by slow neutrons. This is the case for the light isotope of uranium, U^{235}. This property of U^{235} makes this nucleus particularly suitable as a nuclear energy source. The isotope U^{235} can also be used as a sensitive neutron detector.

12.21 NUCLEAR ISOMERS It sometimes happens, as, for instance, in the case of the bombardment of indium by neutrons, that a greater number of periods are observed than can be explained by different radioactive nuclei. It is then necessary to assign two periods to two different states of the same nucleus. This is possible only if one of these states is excited and has a lifetime long enough to be measured. Excited nuclear states of long life are called nuclear isomers. It requires careful analysis to decide whether a nuclear isomer is present, and, if so, which of the periods belongs to the excited state.

All nuclear isomers may transform into the ground state of the nucleus either by gamma-ray emission or by transferring their energy to an electron in the atomic shell and consequently ejecting this electron. The last process is called internal conversion and is observed frequently in isomers and also in excited nuclear states of shorter lives which are not called isomers.

It is also possible for the nuclear isomer to suffer a beta decay before a transition to the ground state occurs. From the mere presence of two beta-decay periods, it is not possible to conclude whether the isomer and the ground state disintegrate independently with two different periods or whether the ground state is the only one whose beta decay is observed and the second period is due to a gamma transition from the isomer to the ground state followed by a beta decay of the latter state. A decision between these two possibilities can be made by studying the presence and properties of gamma rays or by investigating the energies of the beta rays.

For all practical purposes isomers can be considered as additional nuclear species. Thus their number must be added to that of the active bodies produced in nuclear collisions.

12.22   CHEMICAL CHANGES DURING NUCLEAR REACTIONS

Artificially produced radioactive nuclei are becoming increasingly important as indicators in biology, chemistry, and physics. The usefulness of a substance as an indicator may be greatly influenced by the concentration in which it is available. If a radioactive element is produced from another atomic species such as the formation of P^{32} from S^{32}, then the radioactive element can be separated chemically from the mother substance. Chemical separation increases greatly the concentration of activity. Often the amount of P^{32} present after bombardment is so small that a trace of ordinary phosphorus must be added as a carrier for the separation to be effective.

If, on the other hand, a radioactive body is produced from its own isotope by neutron capture, concentration of the radioactive element might seem more difficult. Such concentration becomes possible if during the neutron capture the activated nucleus is knocked out from its original chemical surroundings. The radioactive species is then present in a chemical form different from the unaffected atoms and can therefore be separated by appropriate treatment.

The effect just discussed may be undesirable if a complicated molecule is being bombarded with the object of making it active without destroying it. Sometimes the chemical synthesis of a molecule cannot be carried out, and the only alternative to the direct activation of the molecule is introducing the radioactive matter into the plant or animal body and producing the desired active molecule "biologically." This procedure is possible only for isotopes of sufficiently long life, and even in the most favorable cases it involves considerable dilution of the activity. In view of these facts, it is of interest to find out whether the activated atom can be expected to stay in its original place in the molecule or whether it is more likely to be knocked out. Of course, even if the atom is knocked out from its original position, it still has a chance to replace another atom of the same kind. However, there are often many possibilities of forming other compounds as soon as an atom is liberated, and these possibilities may increase greatly when the atom is knocked out with a high velocity and if it has left a certain number of its original electrons behind.

Whenever a reaction is produced by fast particles, that is, by alpha particles, deuterons, protons, or fast neutrons, the reacting nucleus will with practical certainty be ejected from its surroundings. However, in most cases where a radioactive nucleus is produced from its stable isotope, the process consists in capturing a slow neutron. As a general rule, this slow neutron does not carry sufficient momentum to break the atomic bonds. Molecular breakup may occur, nevertheless, as a consequence of the emission of energy which follows neutron capture. This can happen in two ways: (1) High-energy gamma radiation may be emitted, the momentum of which is sufficient to hurl the atom out by the recoil. (2) Internal conversion may take place, the molecule may lose an electron, and the new electronic configuration might give rise to repulsion between atoms which have been previously chemically bonded.

Among the internal-conversion processes, ejection of a K electron is most likely. An atom with an electron missing from the K shell will act on a neighboring atom as though it carried one more nuclear charge, and the nucleus of the neighboring atom will be repelled. This repulsion may be sufficient to break the bond. It is also possible that a bonding electron will drop down and fill the hole in the K shell, and, since now there is one bonding electron less, dissociation may ensue.

A simple estimate would indicate that direct recoil is always sufficient to eject the atom from its molecular surroundings, provided that the capture energy of the neutron, which is several million volts, is carried away by a single gamma ray. Then the recoil momentum is sufficient to impart even to the heaviest atoms more than their binding energy. The recoil energy of lighter nuclei would be even greater. But it is probable that the binding energy of the neutron will be emitted in several gamma rays rather than in one step. It is unlikely that, with so many intermediate states available, direct transition into the lowest nuclear state should take place. The first gamma ray to be emitted is likely to lead to one of the extremely great number of excited nuclear levels. During the usual time required for gamma radiation, 10^{-14} sec., the nucleus remains in the neighborhood of its original position and will finally be affected only by the vector sum of momenta obtained in the individual recoils. As a general rule, there is at least a partial cancellation of these momenta, and, depending on the number of quanta emitted, there will be a higher or a lower probability for the nucleus to remain in its original surroundings. Great numbers of gamma rays and great nuclear mass are factors favoring such retention. Even in relatively unfavorable cases, it may be worth while to separate chemically the small fraction of radioactive atoms which remains in the original chemical combination from the radioactive atoms which have been knocked out from their positions. The radioactive atoms retained in their original positions will be of particular interest if the chemical compound in question is difficult or impossible to synthesize.

12.23 NUCLEAR FORCES In conclusion, we shall summarize our present knowledge concerning the forces which are responsible for the stability of nuclei. More properly, we should talk about our lack of knowledge. Yet a few general features are clear, and a few hypotheses are plausible. These we shall mention in the following paragraphs.

There exists at present no satisfactory theory which explains nuclear forces in terms of other known forces such as electromagnetic or gravitational forces. Our experience concerning nuclear forces is derived from simple experiments with nuclear particles, such as scattering of neutrons or protons by protons. In addition, valuable information is obtained from the properties of the simplest nucleus containing more than one particle: the deuteron. Some further conclusions may be drawn from the properties of complex nuclei. But in these the mathematical difficulties of an exact analysis are great, and we cannot expect that study of heavy nuclei will suffice to give us a clear-cut picture of nuclear forces.

From the previous evidence the following conclusions have been obtained. Nuclear forces seem to have an extremely short range of 3×10^{-13} cm. or perhaps less. It is even doubtful if the concept of length retains its usual significance when such small dimensions are considered. Within their range the nuclear forces are much more effective ($\sim$100 times more effective) than electrostatic forces. At least over a part of their range nuclear forces act as an attraction. This is shown by the fact that neutrons and protons are bound into stable nuclei.

Apart from the electrostatic repulsion of the proton, we find that the interactions between two protons, between two neutrons, and between a proton–neutron pair are the same. But, although the nuclear forces do not seem to depend on the charges of the particles, they do depend on the spins. The exact form and nature of this spin dependence is unknown.

Nuclear forces show a peculiar effect of saturation. Crowding of too many neutrons or protons into too small a space does not seem to lower the potential energy. Some theories of nuclear forces actually postulate that neutrons and protons attract each other strongly only if they occupy the same orbit.

Many of the hypotheses concerning the origin of nuclear forces have one common element. The existence of nuclear forces is assumed to be in close connection with the emission and absorption of a certain particle, the meson. Several kinds of mesons have been observed in cosmic rays. Recently artificial production of mesons by 4×10^8-volt alpha particles has been demonstrated. Their emission and absorption by protons and neutrons may be related to nuclear forces in a way similar to the relation of the emission and absorption of light quanta to the electric forces acting within atoms.

Study of meson emission by nuclei requires particles of very high energies. This is one of the main incentives for constructing high-voltage equipment capable of giving particles which carry energies of more than 10^8 or even 10^9 volts. These particles will also have exceedingly high momenta and short de Broglie wavelengths. Short wavelengths are necessary if the detailed behavior of nuclear forces is to be explored.

13. STATE OF MATTER IN STARS

13.1 COMPOSITION AND APPEARANCE OF STARS According-
ing to spectroscopic evidence, practically all elements are found in the
stars, and there is no reason to assume that the surfaces of the stars
have a composition greatly differing from each other or from that of the
earth. Of course, different spectral lines appear with greatly varying
intensities in different stars, but this may be explained by the different
temperatures and densities on the surfaces of different stars. Some
stars indeed show indications of a chemical composition differing from
others, but on the whole the stars can be considered as rather alike in
chemical composition.

In striking contrast to these statements is the great variety of physical
conditions and appearances of stars. The majority of the known stars,
the so-called main-sequence stars, have average densities not differing
greatly from the density of water. Their surface temperatures and
luminosities, however, differ widely, the most brilliant ones emitting more
than 1000 times the sun's radiation as contrasted with the faintest ones
radiating only $\frac{1}{100}$ that of the sun. The intensity shows a definite correlation with the stellar mass; heavier stars emit much more radiation
than light stars. The most luminous and heaviest stars have a very hot
surface and a white or even bluish color. They are called the blue giants.
The faintest stars have cooler surfaces and emit mostly red light and
are called red dwarfs. The sun is a star of the main sequence and lies
approximately in the middle of the main sequence.

If finer subdivisions are disregarded, there exist two other kinds of
stars in addition to the main-sequence stars. First, we have the red
giants with a luminosity greatly exceeding that of the sun. Their masses
are about the same as the masses of the main-sequence stars having a
comparable luminosity, but they differ from the main-sequence stars by
emitting their radiation from a much greater and rather cooler surface,
and therefore they appear red. Their mean density is often very low;
a density of 10^{-6} g. per cubic centimeter is not uncommon. Second, a
group of very faint stars called white dwarfs is known whose mass is
about equal to or smaller than the sun's mass. Their faintness is due

to their relatively small surface, but the surface temperature is rather high, and so they emit much radiation per unit surface. For this reason they appear white and are called white dwarfs. Their striking feature is their extremely high density exceeding in some cases 100,000 g. per cubic centimeter.

13.2 INTERIOR OF THE STARS Nothing is known by direct evidence about the interior of the stars, but the high average density of the white dwarfs shows that at least in these stars matter must exist in a state very different from that ordinarily observed.

Indirect evidence about the interior of the stars can be obtained by assuming that known physical laws operate inside the stars and by calculating what conditions in the interior will produce the known effects on the surface. Even though the conditions in the interior are far beyond conditions obtainable in the laboratory, the application of physical laws to this region is not so uncertain as it would appear. The main deviations from ordinary conditions are that the temperature always greatly exceeds those experimentally realizable and that densities are in some cases extremely high. Both these conditions tend to impart, as we shall see presently, high kinetic energies to electrons so that their orbits will not be influenced by the coulomb forces so strongly as the orbits of the outermost electrons in atoms or molecules. But it is just the complicated nature of these outermost orbits which makes the physical properties of chemical compounds so difficult to calculate. The great electronic velocities within the stars disrupt any chemical combination in the ordinary sense, and the equation of state and other characteristics of the resulting state of matter are relatively easy to treat.

The great temperatures just mentioned have to be assumed for the interior of the stars in order to produce a sufficient flow of energy from the interior to the surface. Such energy flow is necessary if it is assumed that the greatest part of the energy emitted by the stars is produced in a region not close to the surface. Since no physical process can be reasonably assumed which will localize the energy production on the surface, an energy flow from the interior must indeed occur. The most efficient method of energy transport at the temperatures involved is by radiation, but even this requires a high-temperature gradient for a sufficient energy flow. This leads to temperatures for the interior which are measured in millions of degrees. As we shall see, it is probable that in at least a great number of cases the energy is produced near the center of the star. If we integrate the equation of state and the equation for energy transport within a star with a central energy source, we obtain about $2 \times 10^{7 \circ}$ C. for the central temperature in the main sequence and about $5 \times 10^{6 \circ}$ for the red giants. The actual figures vary of course from star to star and depend to some extent on the detailed assumptions about stellar composition. At these high temperatures the kinetic energies of the electrons are such that all elements are almost completely ionized, and matter can be considered as a gas consisting of free electrons and nuclei. At high temperatures the picture is somewhat complicated by the influence of radiation pressure which at the highest temperatures outstrips the gas pressure. This radiation pressure can be visualized by the inclusion of light quanta among the particles of the gas.

According to the direct evidence of great densities, the volume available for one atom within a white dwarf is much smaller than the usual atomic volume. We have seen in discussing the repulsive van der Waals forces that one important reason why repulsion results if two closed shells are pushed too close to each other is that, as a result of operation of the Pauli principle, some electrons are shifted into states of higher momentum and higher kinetic energy. Indeed, if the probable distance of two neighboring electrons is denoted by Δr and the difference of probable momentum by Δp, the two electronic orbits become indistinguishable, according to the uncertainty principle when $\Delta r \, \Delta p$ becomes smaller than $h/2\pi$. If, therefore, the electron density increases and the average distance between electrons becomes small, electrons can continue to be in different orbits only if the differences of their momenta increase as $h/2\pi$ divided by their distance.

The high densities in white dwarfs make it necessary that the electrons have very high average momenta and that the kinetic energies greatly exceed the usual energies of ionization. Though in this condition the electrons are constantly closer to some nucleus than they usually are within atoms, yet owing to the high velocities their path is not greatly affected by coulomb forces, and the electrons may for many purposes be considered as free. The kinetic energy also exceeds the thermal energy corresponding to the calculated temperatures of the interior of the white dwarfs, even though these temperatures may be as high as or perhaps higher than those obtained for the main-sequence stars. Under these conditions the behavior of electrons within a white dwarf is similar to the behavior of electrons in metals. The electron gas is degenerate in the sense that practically all low electron orbits are filled, and temperature is insufficient to lift an appreciable fraction of the electrons to still higher orbits than required by the Pauli principle. Therefore, up to a certain kinetic energy practically all electron levels are filled, and practically all higher electron levels are empty. In such degenerate electron gas, the energy flow proceeds rather easily, since most transitions of the electrons are barred by the Pauli principle, and therefore the electrons are not effective in dissipating the energy flow whether this energy be carried by other electrons or by radiation. In fact, calculations about the interior of the white dwarfs show that the temperature throughout the interior is fairly constant owing to the high thermal conductivity. Whatever temperature difference exists between the approximately 10,000° surface and the undoubtedly much hotter interior must take place in the skin of the star. Detailed calculations have shown that temperature changes are small except in the outer 3 per cent of the radius.

The cause of the great difference between the white dwarfs and the less dense stars is this: In a normal star the two main forces balancing each other are the thermal pressure and the gravitational attraction. In a white dwarf the gravitational forces are much greater owing to the greater density. This gravitational force is balanced by the pressure of the high-velocity electrons in the degenerate gas, and temperature plays a very minor role in this equilibrium; thus from the point of view of stellar equilibrium a white dwarf may be called a "cold" star.

An interesting corollary of this picture is the absence of white dwarfs with masses greatly exceeding the mass of the sun. In normal stars the gravitation of greater masses may be balanced by higher temperatures. In white dwarfs the pressure of the degenerate electrons depends on the density of the electrons alone. For each mass and chemical composition of a white dwarf a definite equilibrium radius is prescribed, and this radius will be the smaller, the greater the mass is. Only through the greater density corresponding to this smaller radius can the greater gravitation be balanced. It is interesting to note in this connection that the greatest radius a "cold" star can have is about the radius of Jupiter. If more mass were piled on Jupiter, the shrinkage due to increasing pressure inside would exceed the increase of volume due to the additional mass. At a critical mass which depends somewhat on the composition but does not exceed greatly the mass of the sun, the equilibrium radius of a cold star goes to zero. It is entirely open to conjecture what would happen to one of the heavy stars if in the course of time it could get rid of its energy and contract. But at any rate the absence of heavy white dwarfs is in agreement with theory.

Ultimately the difference between white dwarfs and normal stars must be a difference in energy production. The normal stars produce at comparatively low densities enough heat to balance the gravitational pressure, whereas in the white dwarfs in spite of the higher density the degenerate gas pressure rather than the temperature stabilizes the star. We shall now proceed to discuss the energy production in stars.

13.3 ENERGY PRODUCTION IN THE STARS We know from geological evidence about life on earth that the earth's surface temperature did not differ very greatly from its present temperature in the last 500,000,000 years. Since our energy source is the sun, it is evident that the energy production in the sun must have been rather steady for this long period. Accepting the sun as a typical star, we shall have to account for a very great total energy output by the individual stars.

Ordinary chemical reactions are quite insufficient as an energy supply. Even in historic times a change in the reaction would have been noticed owing to the depletion of the reactants.

It has been suggested that the solar heat is derived from gravitational contraction. Even this would not cover the energy loss for a period longer than a few million years unless an extremely dense core is assumed within the sun in which gravitational effects are unusually high. But it is difficult to reconcile the equation of state within the stars with the existence of such very dense cores.

The most probable energy source is that provided by nuclear transformations. Nuclear reactions produce about a million times greater energy than ordinary chemical reactions, and transformation of about 10 per cent of the sun's material would keep the sun going at the present rate for the required time. The chief difficulty in liberating great amounts of nuclear energy is the strong repulsion between nuclei which does not allow them to get sufficiently close to each other for the purpose of reaction. Only for neutrons is this difficulty absent, but for this very reason neutrons are absorbed by other nuclei in a very short time, both in the laboratory and presumably in the stars, so that neutron reactions cannot be considered as the energy source.

The high temperatures in the stellar interior give nuclei sufficient velocities to penetrate in a few instances close enough to each other and therefore to react. Nuclear reactions can be considered as having not only a very high energy output but also very high activation energies. This is exactly what is needed for a reaction which apparently is far from being completed though it has been going on for 500,000,000 years. Though the exact nature of the nuclear reactions is still open to some modification, it is remarkable that the temperatures for the interior as derived from the equation of state is of the right order of magnitude to make the thermonuclear reactions proceed at the required rate. It may also be seen that the nuclear-energy sources are most efficient near the center where the temperature is highest. This localization of the energy production makes the problem of calculating the physical conditions within the star better defined.

The nuclear-reaction velocities are primarily regulated by the probability of two nuclei getting into actual contact with each other. The probability for such contact even in a head-on collision is as a rule small and is equal to a penetration probability of the same type as discussed in section 12.15. The collision cross section is given by equation 12.15(1). At velocities prevailing in the interior of a star, the first of the two terms in the exponential is much the more important, and the penetration probability is very small. It can be made greater by raising the temperature and thereby raising the velocity v of the nuclei, and it may also be seen that reaction probabilities are highest when the product of the colliding charges is smallest.

The nuclear collision most likely to occur is therefore a collision between two protons. This is all the more to be expected since, according to information about the equation of state in stars, hydrogen is rather plentiful in most of them. However, two protons cannot combine directly with each other since the resulting nucleus He^2 very probably dissociates at once back into $H^1 + H^1$. A combination is possible if during the short time of contact a positron–neutrino pair is emitted transforming the reaction complex into a stable deuteron nucleus. This transformation is, however, very improbable, because the beta process has a lifetime measured in seconds while the collision is measured in nuclear time units, 10^{-21} sec. Thus only a very small fraction of the contacts result in actual transformation. But even though this small reaction probability is somewhat further reduced by the penetration probability, the reaction may proceed sufficiently quickly to account for the energy production of the less luminous main-sequence stars. It should be emphasized that the reaction here described has not been observed in the laboratory, and it is indeed so improbable that we cannot expect to observe it. The very existence of the reaction is based on a somewhat dubious extrapolation of experimental data about beta-active nuclei.

The $H^1 + H^1 \rightarrow H^2 +$ positron $+$ neutrino reaction is promptly followed by further reactions, the probable course of which is:

$$H^2 + H^1 \rightarrow He^3 + \text{radiation}$$

$$He^3 + He^4 \rightarrow Be^7 + \text{radiation} \qquad 13.3(1)$$

$$Be^7 \rightarrow Li^7 + \text{positron} + \text{neutrino *}$$

$$Li^7 + H^1 \rightarrow He^4 + He^4$$

* Actually there is not enough energy for this positron activity to occur, and the equivalent reaction $Be^7 +$ electron $\rightarrow Li^7 +$ neutrino takes place (see section 12.7).

The net effect is that an alpha particle has been synthesized from four protons, the excess charge being carried away by two beta reactions. Under conditions prevailing in the stars, the first step which leads to the production of a deuteron is the slowest and therefore this is the rate-determining reaction. The intermediate reaction products will be present in small amounts; this holds particularly for deuterium which ought to occur in the center of the sun under present conditions in such small concentrations (about 10^{-18}) that the earth's deuterium content could not be derived from the sun if the part of the sun from which the earth was torn out was ever subject to conditions approaching those which obtain at present in the center of the sun. Among the intermediate products He^3 is probably the most abundant, owing to the relative slowness of the $He^3 + He^4 \rightarrow Be^7$ reaction in which the product of the charges of the colliding nuclei is 4.

A further building up of He^4 into heavier nuclei is not likely to occur. Collisions between He^4 and H^1 do not lead to a reaction since, according to laboratory evidence, the resulting nucleus Li^5 is unstable and decomposes back into He^4 and H^1. There are, however, a number of light nuclear reactions which could proceed in the center of the sun.

$$Li^6 + H^1 \rightarrow He^3 + He^4$$

$$Li^7 + H^1 \rightarrow He^4 + He^4$$

$$Be^9 + H^1 \rightarrow Li^6 + He^4 \qquad\qquad 13.3(2)$$

$$B^{10} + H^1 \rightarrow C^{11} + \text{radiation}$$

$$B^{11} + H^1 \rightarrow He^4 + He^4 + He^4$$

All these reactions utilize rather rare elements which are, however, present in the atmosphere of the sun. If the elements Li, Be, and B were present in the sun's interior in the same concentration as on the surface, they would produce far more energy at the temperatures prevailing there than the sun emits. On the other hand, they would be used up in a small fraction of the known age of the sun. It seems therefore probable that the elements lithium, beryllium, and boron have been used up in the interior and that at present they do not constitute the sun's fuel, having been reduced to negligible concentration. An interesting consequence of this is that mixing between the surface and deep interior of the sun does not take place or at best proceeds at a rate measured in hundreds of million years.

Among reactions with heavier nuclei, the following chain seems to satisfy all necessary conditions for the energy production in the sun and in the heavier stars of the main sequence:

$$C^{12} + H^1 \rightarrow N^{13} + \text{radiation}$$

$$N^{13} \rightarrow C^{13} + \text{positron} + \text{neutrino}$$

$$C^{13} + H^1 \rightarrow N^{14} + \text{radiation} \qquad 13.3(3)$$

$$N^{14} + H^1 \rightarrow O^{15} + \text{radiation}$$

$$O^{15} \rightarrow N^{15} + \text{positron} + \text{neutrino}$$

$$N^{15} + H^1 \rightarrow C^{12} + He^4$$

Thus the net result again is the synthesis of an alpha particle from four protons. Carbon enters into the reaction in the role of a catalyst, the fuel being the plentiful hydrogen. Reactions involving still heavier nuclei are probably too slow to be of importance in normal stars.

It is to be noted that the carbon cycle quoted here utilizes observed nuclear reactions. The observations have been made possible by the use of higher velocities than those occurring in the sun. Thus reactions which need millions of years on the sun proceed at observable rates in the laboratory. The observation of the reaction is of course aided by the fact that each individual reaction process can be recorded by amplifying the high reaction energy.

The carbon cycle and the $H^1 + H^1$ reaction seem to account reasonably for the energy production in the main-sequence stars, but these reactions do not seem to be sufficient to explain the great amounts of radiation emitted by red giants. Either another source of energy will have to be assumed, or else the distribution of density and temperature differs from the results yielded by a simple stellar model.

In the case of the white dwarfs, on the other hand, the problem is how to explain the absence of any appreciable nuclear reactions. In fact, the white dwarfs are the only stars which could easily run on their contraction energy alone. It would be tempting to assume that the white dwarfs have consumed all their hydrogen, but considerations of the equation of state indicates that at least one white dwarf (Sirius B) contains very much hydrogen. Either we must assume that some of our data on Sirius B are incorrect, or else we have to conclude that the $H^1 + H^1 \rightarrow H^2 + \text{positron} + \text{neutrino}$ reaction is exceedingly improbable.

13.4 INSTABILITY IN STARS We have described the stars as having a relatively cool surface of a few thousand degrees and an interior the temperature of which is more than a thousand times higher. We also have seen that the energy-producing mechanism in the stars is an essentially explosive one: its rate increases rapidly with increasing temperature. It is conceivable that the analogue of a heat explosion can take place in a star. If the temperature rises, the energy production is greatly increased; this in turn produces a rise in temperature, and an explosion occurs unless expansion, adiabatic cooling, and dissipation of energy interrupt the cumulative process.

Actually strong changes in stellar luminosities are commonly observed phenomena. There are typical variable stars which change their luminosity by a considerable fraction in a regular periodic way. The period may be as short as a few hours or as long as a few months, according to the size of the star, the larger stars having slower periods. There are also some stars, the novae, which flare up within a short time to an enormous brilliancy of perhaps 100,000 times their usual value and fade away again in the period of about a year. Still others, the supernovae, increase their light to thousands of million times that of an ordinary star and fade then like the novae do.

As already indicated, there is no scarcity of reasons why a star undergoes large changes in luminosity. If anything is surprising, it is that no explosions occurred in the sun for the last 500,000,000 years, for which period we know of life on earth, or even for the last 2,000,000,000 years, which is the approximate age of the oldest rocks. Calculations have shown, of course, that, despite the possibility of a nuclear heat explosion, the sun should be stable with regard to heat explosions if its energy is produced near the center. The reason for this in greatly simplified language is that, even if a small explosion should get under way, it would be promptly stopped by adiabatic expansion, merely giving rise to a slight disturbance being propagated towards the outside of the sun, and this disturbance would be dissipated before it could give rise to further effects. But the fact remains that stars are composed of explosive material which might actually cause periodic small explosions as in the variable star or single immense flares as in the novae, if the conditions are appropriate. To mention only two of such possible conditions, the energy production may take place close to the surface, and the possible explosion waves may be damped less efficiently than in the sun, or "combustible" nuclei may be transported by convection into a hot region and cause the explosion.

But novae may be explained even without utilizing processes analogous to a chemical explosion. It is quite sufficient for the explanation of ordinary novae to assume that, through the operation of hydrodynamics within the star, the hot interior gets exposed; in fact, stellar statistics show that the average star may have been a nova several times in its long life of a few thousand million years. But more drastic explanations are needed to explain the much rarer and much more spectacular phenomena of supernovae. One might think of great thermonuclear explosions or perhaps of stellar collapse in which great amounts of gravitational energy are liberated by producing matter much denser even than that observed in the white dwarfs. But it is too soon to say which of these explanations should be used or whether there are still further reasons for stellar vibrations and explosions.

13.5 THE EXPANDING UNIVERSE Our knowledge of the distribution of matter in space is increasing. We know that our sun is one of many stars which are spaced at a few light-years from each other. There are altogether a few thousand million stars spaced at such distances which occupy a region in space almost 1000 light-years across and extending for over 10,000 light-years in two other directions. When looking along the most extended direction of this region, we see on the night sky the white haze of the Milky Way which is made up of these extremely numerous stars most of them too far away to be seen individually by the naked eye.

In the Milky Way system stars move very much like atoms in an ideal gas, in fact, a very ideal gas. Stellar distances and sizes are such that collisions are all but excluded, and stars move in the concerted gravitational field of the other stars; this concerted gravitational field keeps the system together. By very distant collisions small exchanges of kinetic energy between stars occur which occasionally give the star enough energy to escape. The lenslike shape of the system is apparently due to rotation. The interstellar space within the Milky Way is empty except for some dust and extremely dilute gases. Condensation of such matter might give rise to formation of new stars. The total amount of interstellar matter within the galaxy is not known, but its mass cannot exceed very greatly the total amount of matter in visible stars. Beyond the galactic system, both stars and other forms of matter thin out. At a very much greater distance of about 1,000,000 light-years, we find another galaxy which appears as a milky haze and in which even the most powerful telescope can distinguish only the brightest stars individually. This is the Andromeda nebula. Further galactic systems are found at distances of a few million light-years apart, each of them consisting of a few thousand million stars. Some of them are spherical, others elongated, still others have spiraling arms. Our own system is probably of the last type, though being inside it we know less about its shape than about the shape of neighboring nebulae. The nebulae are interspersed fairly uniformly in space although clusters do appear. The nebulae do not become sparser even at the greatest distances where they can be observed with the equipment available at present. The farthest observable nebulae are about 400,000,000 light-years away and appear even in the greatest reflectors as faint disks of luminosity. Their light reaching us at present has left them at about the time when the oldest-known fossils populated the earth. But, according to the theory of relativity, simultaneity over such great distances does not have much significance.

The distant galaxies have been observed to recede from us. Evidence for their recession is obtained from their spectra. Their lines are the familiar lines of the elements but they are shifted towards the red which appears to be due to the Doppler effect. A proportionality is found between this velocity and the distance of the nebulae from us. The farthest nebulae move with about one-fifth the velocity of light. This creates the impression in the observer that he is at rest at the center of an expanding universe. In reality the only conclusion one is justified in drawing is that we are within a system all dimensions of which are uniformly increasing with time. This explains proportionality between distance and observed velocities, and the question which part of the system is at rest is completely idle. Extrapolating back in time we find that about 2×10^9 years ago all nebulae were very much nearer to each other than they are now. It is interesting to note that the observed age of the earth has the same order of magnitude as the time at which all galaxies happened to be close, if indeed they did not actually form a single dense stellar system.

13.6 ORIGIN OF ELEMENTS Since the energy radiated by the stars is due to nuclear transformations, the hope may seem to be justified that atomic transformations within the stars explain the abundance with which elements occur. However, transformations which seem to go on at present within the stars affect only the lighter elements up to oxygen, and even for these lighter elements the reactions, as postulated for the stars, fail to give the proper distribution. In fact, it has been mentioned that at the present stage elements between helium and carbon can be present only in quite negligible amounts in the interior of the sun. Though these elements are not very abundant on the earth, they would be hardly obtainable at all if they were derived from matter such as is postulated at present in the center of the sun.

It is entirely possible that the elements have originated in some state of matter in which nuclear reactions go on even more readily than in the interior of the more common stars. It may be that even at present some stars contain cores with temperatures and densities exceeding the highest that have been discussed in the previous sections. Again unusually efficient transformations of matter may occur during some stellar explosions. At any rate, the present distribution of elements might give us some indication about the conditions which produced that distribution. Actually it is difficult to determine the distribution of elements at present. The earth's crust is a poor sample for at least two reasons: (1) The gravity of the earth is insufficient to hold hydrogen and most probably helium, and therefore these two elements, which we believe were originally very abundant, have escaped to a great extent. (2) Abundant elements and combinations such as iron and magnesium oxides and silicates have condensed and later at least partly solidified in the interior of the earth. The elements and combinations which are not soluble or do not form solid solutions with the great masses forming the earth's interior got crowded out and seem to form now a slag which we know as the earth's crust. Thus the abundance of the elements in the earth's crust is misleading in that it gives improperly high weights to comparatively rare elements.

A more representative distribution of elements may be guessed at by considering other sources of information. Such a source is found in the study of meteorites which probably originate from broken-up planets and whose composition gives information about the interiors of the planets. Stellar atmospheres, the composition of which is derived from the spectra, is another valuable means of obtaining the distribution of elements. Finally, gross considerations of matter in planets and stars give further help. Thus we can conclude from the average density and moment of inertia of the earth that its inner half is composed mainly of iron. Similarly we find for the heavy planets (Jupiter, Neptune) that they are thickly covered by light materials such as hydrogen or possibly helium, and it has already been mentioned that, according to considerations of the equation of state, hydrogen is a very abundant element in the interior of stars. Table 13.6(1) gives an estimated distribution of elements in which the factors mentioned above have been taken into account.

We have more exact information about the distribution of isotopes than we have about the distribution of elements. In fact, the relative abundance of isotopes is very greatly independent of the source of material as should indeed be expected considering the similarity of their behavior. Table 13.6(2) contains these data. The ratio of abundances of hydrogen and deuterium and probably He^3 and He^4 may have been considerably affected by their different rates of escape from the earth's gravitational field. The present abundance of A^{40} is almost certainly due to decay from K^{40}. But otherwise we have no strong reason to

TABLE 13.6(1)
ESTIMATED DISTRIBUTION OF THE ELEMENTS
Atoms per 10,000 Atoms of Si

Z	Element	Abundance	Z	Element	Abundance
1	H	1.25×10^8	44	Ru	0.15
2	He	2.78×10^7	45	Rh	0.057
3	Li	1	46	Pd	0.12
4	Be	0.2	47	Ag	0.043
5	B	0.2	48	Cd	0.10
6	C	30,000	49	In	0.011
7	N	80,000	50	Sn	0.96
8	O	160,000	51	Sb	0.021
9	F	10	52	Te	?
10	Ne	10,000	53	I	0.021
11	Na	462	54	Xe	?
12	Mg	8,870	55	Cs	0.010
13	Al	882	56	Ba	0.25
14	Si	10,000	57	La	0.021
15	P	170	58	Ce	0.023
16	S	3,300	59	Pr	0.0096
17	Cl	250	60	Nd	0.033
18	A	190	61	Unstable	
19	K	69.3	62	Sm	0.012
20	Ca	670	63	Eu	0.0028
21	Sc	0.18	64	Gd	0.017
22	Ti	26.0	65	Tb	0.0052
23	V	3	66	Dy	0.02
24	Cr	93	67	Ho	0.0057
25	Mn	81	68	Er	0.016
26	Fe	26,200	69	Tm	0.0029
27	Co	157	70	Yb	0.015
28	Ni	2,130	71	Lu	0.0048
29	Cu	6.9	72	Hf	0.007
30	Zn	2.6	73	Ta	0.0032
31	Ga	0.54	74	W	0.19
32	Ge	0.39	75	Re	6.8×10^{-5}(?)
33	As	0.73	76	Os	0.057
34	Se	0.026	77	Ir	0.022
35	Br	0.042	78	Pt	0.14
36	Kr	?	79	Au	0.016
37	Rb	0.068	80	Hg	?
38	Sr	0.13	81	Tl	?
39	Y	0.097	82	Pb	0.43
40	Zr	1.42	83	Bi	0.0037
41	Cb	0.010	90	Th	0.011
42	Mo	0.28	92	U	0.0027
43	Tc	Unstable			

The abundances of some of the elements given here are known only very crudely. Most of the data are of recent work and compilation by Dr. Harrison Brown, based largely on earlier work by V. M. Goldschmidt, A. Unsold, and others.

TABLE 13.6(2)
DISTRIBUTION OF ISOTOPES

Nuclear Charge	Atom	Abundance, Mole %	Nuclear Charge	Atom	Abundance, Mole %
1	H^1	99.98	20	Ca^{40}	96.92
	H^2	0.02		Ca^{42}	0.64
2	He^3	$\sim 10^{-4}$		Ca^{43}	0.132
	He^4	~ 100		Ca^{44}	2.13
3	Li^6	7.3		Ca^{46}	0.0032
	Li^7	92.7		Ca^{48}	0.179
4	Be^9	100	21	Sc^{45}	100
5	B^{10}	18.83	22	Ti^{46}	7.95
	B^{11}	81.17		Ti^{47}	7.75
6	C^{12}	98.9		Ti^{48}	73.45
	C^{13}	1.1		Ti^{49}	5.51
7	N^{14}	99.62		Ti^{50}	5.34
	N^{15}	0.38	23	V^{51}	100
8	O^{16}	99.757	24	Cr^{50}	4.31
	O^{17}	0.039		Cr^{52}	83.75
	O^{18}	0.204		Cr^{53}	9.55
9	F^{19}	100		Cr^{54}	2.38
10	Ne^{20}	90.00	25	Mn^{55}	100
	Ne^{21}	0.27	26	Fe^{54}	5.81
	Ne^{22}	9.73		Fe^{56}	91.66
11	Na^{23}	100		Fe^{57}	2.20
12	Mg^{24}	78.41		Fe^{58}	0.33
	Mg^{25}	10.18	27	Co^{59}	100
	Mg^{26}	11.41	28	Ni^{58}	67.76
13	Al^{27}	100		Ni^{60}	26.16
14	Si^{28}	92.27		Ni^{61}	1.25
	Si^{29}	4.63		Ni^{62}	3.66
	Si^{30}	3.05		Ni^{64}	1.16
15	P^{31}	100	29	Cu^{63}	68.94
16	S^{32}	95.1		Cu^{65}	31.06
	S^{33}	0.74	30	Zn^{64}	50.9
	S^{34}	4.2		Zn^{66}	27.3
	S^{36}	0.016		Zn^{67}	3.9
17	Cl^{35}	75.4		Zn^{68}	17.4
	Cl^{37}	24.6		Zn^{70}	0.5
18	A^{36}	0.307	31	Ga^{69}	61.2
	A^{38}	0.061		Ga^{71}	38.8
	A^{40}	99.632	32	Ge^{70}	21.2
19	K^{39}	93.38		Ge^{72}	27.3
	K^{40}	0.012		Ge^{73}	7.9
	K^{41}	6.61		Ge^{74}	37.1

TABLE 13.6(2).—(*Continued*)

DISTRIBUTION OF ISOTOPES

Nuclear Charge	Atom	Abundance, Mole %	Nuclear Charge	Atom	Abundance, Mole %
32	Ge^{76}	6.5	44	Ru^{101}	16.98
33	As^{75}	100		Ru^{102}	31.34
34	Se^{74}	0.87		Ru^{104}	18.27
	Se^{76}	9.02	45	Rh^{103}	100
	Se^{77}	7.58	46	Pd^{102}	0.8
	Se^{78}	23.52		Pd^{104}	12.25
	Se^{80}	49.82		Pd^{105}	22.2
	Se^{82}	9.19		Pd^{106}	30.7
35	Br^{79}	50.53		Pd^{108}	26.7
	Br^{81}	49.47		Pd^{110}	7.35
36	Kr^{78}	0.35	47	Ag^{107}	51.35
	Kr^{80}	2.01		Ag^{109}	48.65
	Kr^{82}	11.53	48	Cd^{106}	1.22
	Kr^{83}	11.53		Cd^{108}	0.98
	Kr^{84}	57.11		Cd^{110}	12.35
	Kr^{86}	17.47		Cd^{111}	12.76
37	Rb^{85}	72.8		Cd^{112}	24.00
	Rb^{87}	27.2		Cd^{113}	12.30
38	Sr^{84}	0.55		Cd^{114}	28.75
	Sr^{86}	9.75		Cd^{116}	7.63
	Sr^{87}	6.96	49	In^{113}	4.23
	Sr^{88}	82.74		In^{115}	95.77
39	Y^{89}	100	50	Sn^{112}	0.90
40	Zr^{90}	51.51		Sn^{114}	0.61
	Zr^{91}	11.27		Sn^{115}	0.35
	Zr^{92}	17.14		Sn^{116}	14.07
	Zr^{94}	17.30		Sn^{117}	7.54
	Zr^{96}	2.78		Sn^{118}	23.98
41	Cb^{93}	100		Sn^{119}	8.62
42	Mo^{92}	15.86		Sn^{120}	33.03
	Mo^{94}	9.12		Sn^{122}	4.78
	Mo^{95}	15.70		Sn^{124}	6.11
	Mo^{96}	16.50	51	Sb^{121}	57.25
	Mo^{97}	9.45		Sb^{123}	42.75
	Mo^{98}	23.75	52	Te^{120}	0.091
	Mo^{100}	9.62		Te^{122}	2.49
43	Tc	Unstable		Te^{123}	0.89
44	Ru^{96}	5.68		Te^{124}	4.63
	Ru^{98}	2.22		Te^{125}	7.01
	Ru^{99}	12.81		Te^{126}	18.72
	Ru^{100}	12.70		Te^{128}	31.72

TABLE 13.6(2).—(Continued)

DISTRIBUTION OF ISOTOPES

Nuclear Charge	Atom	Abundance, Mole	Nuclear Charge	Atom	Abundance, Mole %
52	Te^{130}	34.46	63	Eu^{153}	50.9
53	I^{127}	100	64	Gd^{152}	0.2
54	Xe^{124}	0.094		Gd^{154}	1.5
	Xe^{126}	0.088		Gd^{155}	18.4
	Xe^{128}	1.90		Gd^{156}	19.9
	Xe^{129}	26.23		Gd^{157}	18.9
	Xe^{130}	4.07		Gd^{158}	20.9
	Xe^{131}	21.17		Gd^{160}	20.2
	Xe^{132}	26.96	65	Tb^{159}	100
	Xe^{134}	10.54	66	Dy^{158}	>0.1
	Xe^{136}	8.95		Dy^{160}	0.1
55	Cs^{133}	100		Dy^{161}	21.1
56	Ba^{130}	0.101		Dy^{162}	26.6
	Ba^{132}	0.097		Dy^{163}	24.8
	Ba^{134}	2.42		Dy^{164}	27.3
	Ba^{135}	6.59	67	Ho^{165}	100
	Ba^{136}	7.81	68	Er^{162}	0.1
	Ba^{137}	11.32		Er^{164}	1.5
	Ba^{138}	71.66		Er^{166}	32.9
57	La^{139}	100		Er^{167}	24.4
58	Ce^{136}	<1		Er^{168}	26.9
	Ce^{138}	<1		Er^{170}	14.2
	Ce^{140}	89	69	Tm^{169}	100
	Ce^{142}	11	70	Yb^{168}	0.06
59	Pr^{141}	100		Yb^{170}	4.21
60	Nd^{142}	25.95		Yb^{171}	14.26
	Nd^{143}	13.0		Yb^{172}	21.49
	Nd^{144}	22.6		Yb^{173}	17.02
	Nd^{145}	9.2		Yb^{174}	29.58
	Nd^{146}	16.5		Yb^{176}	13.38
	Nd^{148}	6.8	71	Lu^{175}	97.5
	Nd^{150}	5.95		Lu^{176}	2.5
61	61	Unstable	72	Hf^{174}	0.18
62	Sm^{144}	3		Hf^{176}	5.30
	Sm^{147}	15.2		Hf^{177}	18.47
	Sm^{148}	10.8		Hf^{178}	27.10
	Sm^{149}	14.1		Hf^{179}	13.84
	Sm^{150}	7.7		Hf^{180}	35.11
	Sm^{152}	27.1	73	Ta^{181}	100
	Sm^{154}	22.4	74	W^{180}	0.135
63	Eu^{151}	49.1		W^{182}	26.41

TABLE 13.6(2).—(*Continued*)

DISTRIBUTION OF ISOTOPES

Nuclear Charge	Atom	Abundance, Mole %	Nuclear Charge	Atom	Abundance, Mole %
74	W^{183}	14.40	80	Hg^{200}	23.3
	W^{184}	30.64		Hg^{201}	13.2
	W^{186}	28.41		Hg^{202}	29.6
75	$Re^{180-184}$	$<10^{-2}$		Hg^{204}	6.7
	Re^{185}	37.07	81	Tl^{203}	29.46
	Re^{186}	$<10^{-2}$		Tl^{205}	70.54
	Re^{187}	62.93	82	Pb^{204}	1.37
	$Re^{188-190}$	$<10^{-2}$		Pb^{206}	25.15
76	Os^{184}	0.018		Pb^{207}	21.11
	Os^{186}	1.59		Pb^{208}	52.38
	Os^{187}	1.64	83	Bi^{209}	100
	Os^{188}	13.3	84	Po	Unstable
	Os^{189}	16.1	85	At	Unstable
	Os^{190}	26.4	86	Rn	Unstable
	Os^{192}	41.0	87	Fa	Unstable
77	Ir^{191}	38.5	88	Ra	Unstable
	Ir^{193}	61.5	89	Ac	Unstable
78	Pt^{192}	0.8	90	Th^{232}	100
	Pt^{194}	30.2	91	Pa	Unstable
	Pt^{195}	35.3	92	U^{234}	0.00518
	Pt^{196}	26.6		AcU^{235}	0.719
	Pt^{198}	7.2		U^{238}	99.274
79	Au^{197}	100	93	Np	Unstable
80	Hg^{196}	0.15	94	Pu	Unstable
	Hg^{198}	10.1	95	Am	Unstable
	Hg^{199}	17.0	96	Cm	Unstable

For radioactive elements whose lifetimes are of the order of geological times, the natural abundances have been given. Radioactive elements of shorter lifetimes do not occur in nature except sometimes in combinations with their mother substances. In these cases no abundances have been given, but the notation "unstable" has been used.

assume that the observed ratios differ from the ratios in which the elements were produced.

There are three rough regularities observable in the abundance of elements and of isotopes: (1) Nuclei containing an even number of protons and an even number of neutrons tend to be more abundant. (2) Elements beyond $Z \approx 30$ have a small and roughly constant abundance. (3) Considering the isotopes of heavy elements, we find that the isotope containing fewest neutrons has often a quite small abundance. The first of these regularities is undoubtedly connected with the greater stability of nuclei in which an even number of each kind of particle is present. The greater stability connected with the presence of even numbers of particles is analogous to the fact known in chemistry that stable molecules carry, with very few exceptions, an even number of electrons. The reason for this rule is, as has been pointed out before, the exclusion principle which will permit the presence of no more than two particles in any orbit. The third rule, the small abundance of light isotopes among the heavy elements, seems to indicate that, at the time of formation of the heavy elements, great quantities of neutrons have been available in or around the nuclei.

Two of the most frequently discussed mechanisms for building up elements are thermodynamic equilibria at extremely high temperatures and progressing nuclear reactions with definite rates which had no time to reach equilibrium but did settle down to a steady-state distribution of elements and gave rise to definite ratios of nuclear species. According to both of these explanations it is plausible to expect that more stable nuclei will be more abundant, and, if pressures are not too high and temperatures not too low (that is, considerably higher than 10^9 degrees), the presence of great amounts of hydrogen can be understood. The puzzling fact which cannot be explained by any of the foregoing considerations is the presence of uranium. Uranium is both energetically and, except under extremely high pressures, thermodynamically unstable. Such extremely high pressures, however, would be in contradiction with great abundance of light elements, particularly hydrogen. The building up of uranium in a steady process is also difficult to understand. Such a building-up process would require nuclear collisions in which some of the colliding particles stick and lead to heavier nuclei. But, if such collisions are to be effective, we must expect that uranium itself will be hit quite frequently, and under the effect of nuclear collisions uranium suffers fission rather easily. It seems that, in a steady-state equilibrium in which nuclei collide and react with each other, uranium is much more easily destroyed than produced.

We may argue that elements are transformed into each other in different regions of the universe under different conditions. In some equilibria, for instance, enormous pressures stabilize uranium, whereas in other regions somewhat lesser pressures allow the formation of hydrogen. Of course, the pressure necessary to stabilize uranium is such that even heavier nuclei may be formed. In fact, there is no known reason why matter could not form macroscopic aggregates with densities equaling that of nuclei. Uranium could then be formed if such dense material should break up. It is interesting to speculate about such a superdense state of matter and its possible subdivision into nuclei. Here we shall merely state that in this superdense state all electrons are probably pressed into the nuclei, transforming the protons into neutrons, so that the actual aggregate consists of neutrons only. Whenever superdense matter breaks up, beta processes would occur and, together with the emission of electrons, protons would be formed within the nuclei.

It would seem reasonable to assume that all of the heavier elements have been formed from a superdense state by fission processes. The breaking up into drops and the further subdivision could have gone on so rapidly as not to allow the formation of any equilibria or steady states. It would not be unreasonable to assume that more stably bound fragments are more often produced. During such a decomposition fission would take place first, evaporation of neutrons might follow, and beta decays would occur last. The lightest isotopes are formed if the number of evaporated neutrons exceeds the average. These isotopes may thus be formed in smaller numbers. The fission of a droplet is, however, such a complicated process that, if the picture presented here is correct, we might never be able to get a complete explanation of the abundance of elements and isotopes.

It is perhaps interesting to note that a few thousand million years ago the universe must have been denser than it is now. If we want to hazard a very great extrapolation, we might assume that "originally" all matter was in a superdense state from which the elements have been formed by a universal breakup.

ὥστε εἰς τὸ τέλος τῆς ἀταξίας αὕτη ἡ
παραίνεσις εἰς τὸ τέλος ἀφικέσθω.

INDEX

For reasons explained in the Preface, no author index is included